Methods for Teratological Studies in Experimental Animals and Man

Edited by

HIDEO NISHIMURA, M. D.
Department of Anatomy, Faculty of Medicine, Kyoto University

JAMES R. MILLER, Ph. D.
Division of Medical Genetics, Department of Pediatrics, Faculty of Medicine, University of British Columbia

with the assistance of

MINEO YASUDA, M. D.
Department of Anatomy, Faculty of Medicine, Kyoto University

METHODS FOR TERATOLOGICAL EXPERIMENTAL

Proceedings of The Second

STUDIES IN ANIMALS AND MAN

International Workshop in Teratology, Kyoto, 1968.

IGAKU SHOIN LTD.

MEDICAL EXAMINATION PUBLISHING CO., INC.

PUBLISHERS
© First Edition, March 1969, by IGAKU SHOIN Ltd., 5-29-11 Hongo, Bunkyo-ku, Tokyo, Japan
Sole distribution rights in the United States of America and Canada granted to
MEDICAL EXAMINATION PUBLISHING CO., INC., Flushing, N.Y., 11365, U.S.A.

Printed and Bound in Japan

FOREWORD

In the summer of 1966, the First International Workshop in Teratology was held in Copenhagen, Denmark, and was very successful with participants from 24 countries, mostly European. As a sequel to that Workshop, a Second International Workshop in Teratology was planned to encourage scientists in the countries of Asia and Australasia to increase their efforts in this important field as well as to stimulate international cooperation. Dr. C.A. SWINYARD, Staff Associate of the Association for the Aid of Crippled Children, New York, U.S.A. played a key role in encouraging the development of this plan. This Workshop was held in Kyoto, April 1–5, 1968 with Professor HIDEO NISHIMURA as Director with the attendance of 40 participants and 48 observers from 21 countries. These Proceedings are a record of the Workshop.

Several volumes on the subject of teratology have been published recently and there may be questions raised regarding the justification of having another appear. However, to our knowledge this is the first in which anomalies in human beings have been discussed in detail and from a comparative viewpoint, and this seemed justification enough. After all, the ultimate aim of the increased interest in teratological methodology is to improve techniques of drug screening, and to search for etiological clues and developmental mechanisms in experimental animals which might be relevant for the understanding and prevention of congenital defects in man. We hope this justification is warranted and that the reader will benefit from the material presented.

The Proceedings record the complete Workshop with five exceptions. Professor M.N. RUNNER, Boulder, U.S.A. read a paper, " The Nature and Causal Mechanisms of Developmental Variability " and presented a demonstration on " The Explanted Chick Embryo as an Experimental System for Teratogenesis: Effect of Teratogens on the Rate of DNA, RNA and Protein Synthesis " which were identical in content with presentations in *" Embryology and Teratology "* edited by M.N. RUNNER and published by University of Chicago Press. The reader is referred to this volume for these presentations. Dr. STEVENSON, Oxford, England was not able to attend the Workshop to present his paper, " Findings and Lessons for the Future from a Comparative Study of Congenital Malformations at 24 Centres in 16 Countries " but kindly granted permission for it to appear in these Proceedings. Dr. J. WARKANY conducted a demonstration " Histological Analysis of Malformations Produced by Various Agents " which does not appear in these Proceedings. In addition, Dr. J.G. WILSON presented a demonstration " Detection of Malformation in Rat and Monkey Fetuses " which does not appear in the Proceedings. Much of the material on the monkey has been incorporated into Dr. WILSON's lecture " Teratological and Reproductive Studies in Non-Human Primates " while the material on the rat can be found in his paper " Methods for Administering Agents and Detecting Malformations in Experimental Animals " in *Teratology: Principles and Techniques,* edited by J.G. WILSON and J. WARKANY and published by the University of Chicago Press.

In addition to the many agencies which helped to sponsor and finance the

Workshop we should like to acknowledge the support and assistance of the members of the many committees who helped in the organization and the staff, students, secretaries and volunteers who worked so earnestly before and during the Workshop to make it a success. A grant from the Medical Research Council of Canada made it possible for Professor J. R. MILLER to be a Visiting Research Associate in Kyoto University for 1967–68, and thus to participate in the Workshop and act as co-editor of these Proceedings. Finally, we are indebted to the Association for the Aid of Crippled Children, New York, U.S.A. and National Institute of General Medical Sciences-NIH, Bethesda, U.S.A. for their generous aid which made possible the publication of these Proceedings.

HIDEO NISHIMURA
JAMES R. MILLER
Kyoto, June 1968

THE WORKSHOP WAS MADE POSSIBLE BY THE SPONSORSHIP
AND AID OF THE FOLLOWING BODIES.

Association for the Aid of Crippled Children, U.S.A.
Center for Southeast Asian Studies, Kyoto University, Japan
Committee on Safety of New Drugs of the Japan Pharmaceutical Manufacturer's
    Association
Congenital Anomalies Research Association of Japan
Fujiwara Memorial Foundation of Kyoto University, Japan
Institute of Child Health and Human Development, NIH, U.S.A.
Institute of General Medical Sciences, NIH, U.S.A.
Japan Science Council
National Academy of Science-National Research Council, U.S.A.
National Foundation, U.S.A.
Overseas Technical Cooperation Agency of the Japanese Foreign Ministry
Teratology Society, U.S.A.

CONTENTS

2   Contents

PART I. LECTURES

MANAGEMENT OF ANIMALS FOR USE IN TERATOLOGICAL EXPERIMENTS

Tatsuji Nomura

Director, Central Institute for Experimental Animals,
Tokyo Japan.

In order to obtain reliable and reproducible results in animal experiments, it is necessary to understand the principles behind animal management. For this paper, animal management will be considered as the defining and controlling as precisely as possible the factors which affect the results of animal experiments.

In teratological research, the factors which affect animal experiments can be divided into four groups as follows:

I. Genetic factors
    1) Genotype of mother 2) Genotype of fetuses

II. Environmental factors
    1) Food 2) Housing   3) Climatic (Physical and Chemical)
    4) Biological

III. Interaction of genetic and environmental factors
    1) Phenotypes of mothers 2) Dramatypes of mothers

IV. Experimental procedure
    1) Nature of teratogen 2) Administration of teratogen 3) Stage of fetuses on administration

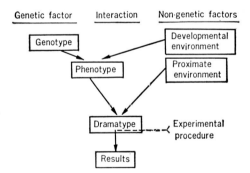

Fig. 1 The "dramatype" in relation to the phenotype and proximate environment

A better understanding of what part the genetic and non-genetic factors play in general animal experiments can be seen from Figure 1. It is generally considered that the results of animal experiments are the response of the phenotype only, but the phenotype is determined by the interaction of the environment with the genotype during development from conception to sexual maturity. Therefore it represents, relatively stable morphological and physiological characteristics. However, there is considerable evidence that the proximate environment, i.e. the environment to which the mice are exposed during the experimental procedure, affects the experimental results[11,12]. For this reason, the phenotype is not applicable in terms of relatively short physiological changes caused by this proximate environment. A new concept must be introduced, the dramatype, which results from the interaction of the phenotype and the proximate environment[15]. The dramatype therefore represents the physiological status of the animals during the experiments. The results of the experiments can then be considered as the response of the dramatype to the experimental procedure.

In teratological experiments the relation among these factors became as shown in Figure 2. In the first place, it is necessary to choose genetically defined parent animals since these parents will determine the genotype of the fetuses. After mating, the phenotype of the mother will interact with the proximate environment to determine the dramatype of the pregnant mother. The dramatype, i.e. the physiological status of the pregnant mother, will in turn become the

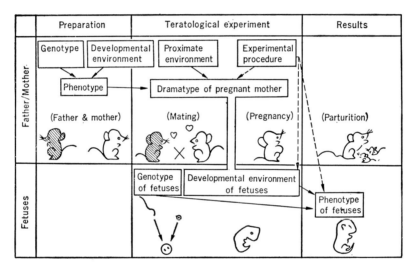

Fig. 2 Effect of proximate environment on result of teratological experiments

developmental environment, i.e. maternal environment of fetuses. This developmental environment, along with the genotype of the fetuses will determine the phenotype of the fetuses. This phenotype is, in effect, the result of the teratological experiment. It is therefore evident from the figure that the control of the proximate environment to stabilize the physiological status of the pregnant mother plays a very important role in the results of teratological experiments.

In this paper, I will point out the importance of controlling environmental factors in the management of laboratory animals, especially mice, by introducing data showing the influence of environmental factors on teratological experiments, drug toxicity and anaphylaxis as well as the physiological status of animals. In these experiments we used only mice because mice are the most controlled and defined of all laboratory animals but the results can be applied to other animals as well.

INFLUENCE OF ENVIRONMENTAL FACTORS
ON EXPERIMENTAL RESULTS AND PHYSIOLOGY OF MICE

First let us consider a breakdown of the environmental factors which can affect laboratory animals. They can be divided into four groups as follows:

Food: diet, water

Housing: cage, bedding

Climatic (physical and chemical): temperature, relative humidity, barometric pressure, light, sound, odor, draught, etc.

Biological: no. per cage, socio-psychological effect, contact with man and other animals, presence of microorganisms and parasites

The importance of nutrition has been well discussed by Dr. ASLING and Dr. FRASER in this workshop[2,8], and climatic factors can be easily understood. Housing deals with design and materials of cages, and bedding materials. Biological factors include the number of animals per cage, effects of crowding, socio-psychological effects, contact with human beings and other animals, and the presence of microorganisms and parasites. Many workers have shown how these factors affect experimental results[11] and all of these factors have some degree of psychological and somatic effect on laboratory animals[1]. Defining and controlling the environmental factors is essential in management of laboratory animals to insure reliable and reproducible results. First, however, in order to define and control these factors, we must know how these factors influence the animals. These environmental factors never act independently, but are always interrelated, which makes them very difficult to study. The only means of approach is to select one or two factors and define the others. Therefore, for this paper temperature was chosen as a representative factor since there is already extensive literature concerning its effects on experimental results[3,5]. Similar experimental results could also be obtained using other environmental factors.

A series of experiments concerned with teratology, drug toxicity and anaphylaxis were conducted in our institute to show the effects of temperature on experimental results and also on the physiology of the animals themselves.

Influence of Temperature

Teratological experiments

The experiments were carried out to investigate the effects of changing the environmental temperature on the incidence of malformations induced by hypervitaminosis A and ethyl-urethane.

In the first experiment with vitamin A, four groups of pregnant ICR-JCL mice were prepared; (1) the VA+Hi-T group of mice was exposed to a temperature of $34\pm1°C$ for 16 hours after intraperitoneal administration of 5,000 I.U./head of vitamin A on the 10th day of gestation; (2) VA group of mice was intraperitoneally administered with only 5,000 I.U./head of vitamin A; (3) the Hi-T group of mice was exposed to a temperature of $34\pm1°C$ for 16 hours for the same time as the VA+Hi-T group without administration of vitamin A; and (4) a control group of mice was kept at normal temperature without administration of

Table 1 Effect of high temperature on incidence of malformations
by hypervitaminosis A

Group		VA+Hi-T	VA	Hi-T	Control
No. of live fetuses		263	206	289	235
Malformed fetuses		174**	99	7	2
	(%)	(66.2)	(48.1)	(2.4)	(0.9)
Cleft palate	(%)	40.3**	27.2	0.3	0.4
Micromeli					
fore-limbs	(%)	22.8**	9.2	0	0
hind-limbs	(%)	26.2**	18.9	0	0
Micro- or oligodactylism					
fingers	(%)	52.5**	35.4	0	0
toes	(%)	26.2*	17.0	0	0
Abnormal tail		2.3	2.4	0	0.4
Exencephalia		0	0.5	0.3	0
Subcutaneous bleeding		0.8	0	1.7	0
Opened eyelids		0	0	0.3	0

* $P < 0.05$
** $P < 0.01$

vitamin A. All mice were sacrificed on the 18th day of pregnancy, and the mortality of embryos and fetuses, and external malformations in living fetuses were observed. The mortality of embryos and fetuses in VA+Hi-T group (22.4 %) was higher than that of the other groups (10–11%). As shown in Table 1 the occurence of malformation of live fetuses in VA+Hi-T group (66.2%) was higher than that of the VA group (48.1%). Cleft palate was observed in 40.3 % and 27.2% of live fetuses in the VA+Hi-T and the VA groups, respectively, but there was no difference in the occurrence of cleft palate in the Hi-T and control groups (0.3 and 0.4%). Anomalies of the limbs, fingers and toes were also higher in the VA+Hi-T group than in the VA group[6].

In the second experiment with ethyl-urethane, four groups of pregnant ICR-JCL mice were prepared; (1) the EU+Hi-T group of mice was exposed to a temperature of $31\pm2°C$ for 13 hours after intraperitoneal administration of 1,500 mg/kg of ethyl-urethane on the 10th day of gestation; (2) the EU group of mice was intraperitoneally administered with the same dose of ethyl-urethane at normal temperature; (3) the Hi-T group of mice was exposed to a temperature of 31 $\pm2°C$ for 13 hours at the same time as the EU+Hi-T group without administration of ethyl-urethane; and (4) a control group of mice was kept at normal temperature without administration of ethyl-urethane. As in the vitamin A experiments, all mice were sacrificed on the 18th day of pregnancy, and the mortality of embryos and fetuses, and external malformations in live fetuses were observed.

There was little difference between the EU+Hi-T and EU groups concerning

Table 2 Effect of high temperature on incidence of malformations by ethyl-urethane

Group	EU+Hi-T	EU	Hi-T	Control
No. of live fetuses	244	283	309	249
Malformed fetuses	204**	184	2	1
(%)	(83.6)	(65.0)	(0.7)	(0.4)
Cleft palate (%)	47.5	44.5	0.7	0
Micromelia				
fore-limbs (%)	0	0.7	0	0
hind-limbs (%)	10.0	5.9	0	0
Micro-, oligo, syn- or polydactylism				
fingers (%)	62.3**	43.1	0	0
toes (%)	13.1	15.9	0	0
Abnormal tail (%)	12.7**	2.8	0	0
Cephalocele	4.5	3.2	0	0
Back edema	0	0	0	0.4
Anomalies of external genitalia	0	0.4	0	0
Atresia ani	1.6	3.2	0	0

** $P < 0.01$

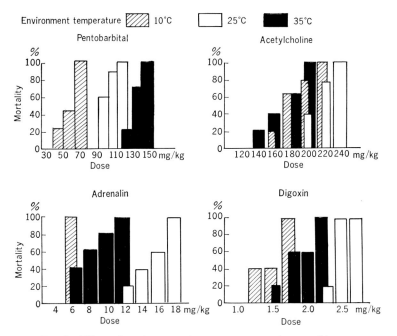

Fig. 3 Effect of environmental temperature on drug toxicity

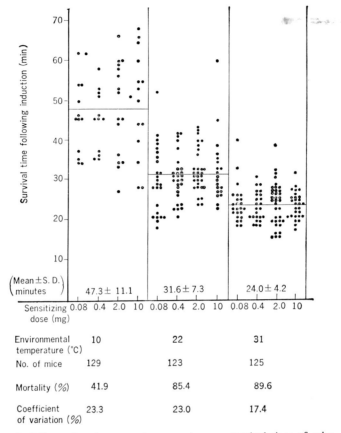

Fig. 4 Effects of environmental temperature on survival time of mice
following anaphylactic shock

the mortality of embryos and fetuses (17.5 and 14.5%), but as shown in Table 2 the occurrence of malformation of living fetuses in the EU+Hi-T group (83.6 %) was higher than that of the EU group (65.0%). The anomalies on fingers and tails occurred more frequently in the EU+Hi-T group than in the EU group[7].

Drug toxicity

Since drugs are used as teratogens, the influence of temperature on drugs is applicable to teratological experiments.

Many studies have been done concerning the influence of temperature on drugs[5,9].

The results of our work done on the influence of environmental temperature on acute drug toxicity are shown in Figure 3. ICR-JCL mice were exposed to three environmental temperatures of 10, 25 and 35°C for 24 hours before and after an intraperitoneal injection of various doses of pentobarbital, acetylcholine, adrenalin and digoxin. The susceptibility of mice to the toxicity of pentobarbital in terms of mortality was highest in the group of mice exposed at 10°C

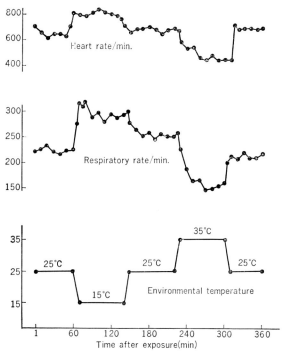

Fig. 5 Changes in vital functions of unrestrained mice during
exposure to various environmental temperature

and lowest at 35°C. The susceptibility of mice to adrenalin was highest at 10
°C and lowest at 25°C. The same hold true for digoxin. For acetylcholine, the
mortality rate of the mice was highest at 35°C but slightly higher at 10°C than
at 25 °C[17].

Anaphylaxis

In the anaphylaxis experiments crystalline egg albumin was used for both
sensitization and challenge. Mice were sensitized subcutaneously with 0.08–10
mg/head of egg albumin (this differences in sensitizing dose had negligible effects
on the result) at 5 and also 6 weeks of age under normal temperature (22°C),
and challenged subcutaneously with 2 mg/head of egg albumin, under three different environmental temperatures (10, 22 and 31°C) at 7 weeks of age[16].

The survival times at different temperatures following a challenge injection
are shown in Figure 4. The survival time becomes shorter at high temperatures
and longer at low temperatures.

Since all of these experimental results are affected by environmental temperature, this suggests that the physiological constitution of mice might be affected by low or high environmental temperatures. Therefore, the next group
of experiments was carried out to find out how physiological functions are affected by environmental temperature.

Physiological status

CHEVILLARD et al.[4] reviewed extensively the influence of temperature on the
physiology of rats. Physiological studies were carried out in our institute using

mice. Figure 5 shows the changes of heart rate and respiratory rate according to hourly changes in environmental temperature (15, 25 or 35°C), under unrestrained conditions in the cage. At this time, heart rate was assessed by counting the number of R-spikes on the ECG which was recorded by means of a small flexible wire with electorodes at the dorsal cervic area and the ventral breast area. Respiration was recorded by attaching a small tambour to the lateral breast area, and air was led out through a small tube to the transducer. Both the heart rate and the respiratory rate increased as soon as the temperature fell and decreased when the temperature rose.

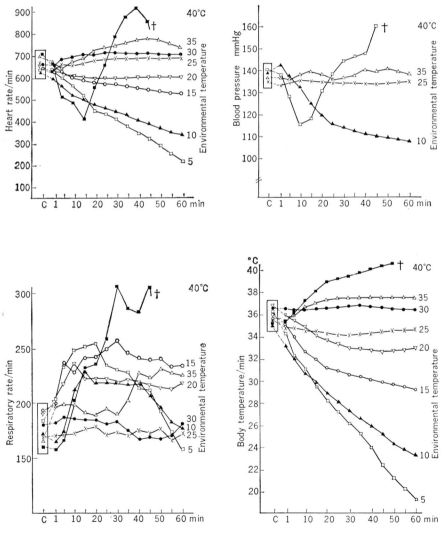

Fig. 6 Changes in heart rate, respiratory rate, blood pressure and body temperature in restrained mice at various environmental temperatures

To obtain more details concerning the influence of environmental temperature on vital functions, mice were examined under restrained conditions for 60 min. without anesthesia. Figure 6 shows the results of these experiments. All functions were examined simultaneously. Observation methods have been given elswhere[13,14].

a) The heart rate decreased gradually at and below 20°C, while it was generally stable at 25°C and 30°C. At or above 35°C, the heart rate decreased immediately after exposure, and then increased.

b) The respiratory rate was stable at 25°C and 30°C. At low temperature, the rate increased at first, then decreased rapidly especially at 10°C and 5°C. At high temperature (35 and 40°C), the rate increased remarkably.

c) The body temperature was stable at 25°C or 30°C, decreased at 20°C or below, but increased at 35°C and above.

d) The blood pressure did not drop at 25°C and 35°C but it did drop at 10°C. At 40°C it dropped in accordance with the appearance of the arrhythmia. but it rose as the heart rate increased.

Since the above experiments dealt only with short exposure, the next experiments were conducted over a longer period of time by observing changes in the heart rate, respiratory rate and body temperature of mice reared at 15, 25 and 35°C. As shown in Table 3, the body temperature remained

Table 3 Changes in vital functions of mice exposed to 15, 25 or 35°C for 48 hours. ICR-JCL, ♂, 8 w.

	Env. temp.	No. of mice	Mean ± S.D.	t-test
	15°C	11	746. 4 ± 31. 0	] **
Heart rate/min.	25	16	681. 8 ± 51. 6	
	35	10	667. 4 ± 77. 3	]
	15	11	217. 5 ± 35. 0	]
Respiratory rate/min.	25	16	202. 7 ± 29. 6	
	35	10	170. 5 ± 24. 6	] *
	15	11	36. 5 ± 0. 5	]
Body temperature °C	25	16	36. 5 ± 0. 7	
	35	10	36. 6 ± 0. 9	]

* $0.01 < p < 0.05$
** $p < 0.01$

essentially unchanged in all three groups, but the heart rate of mice exposed to 15°C increased more than at 25°C or 35°C. However, the respiratory rate in the 35°C group is much lower than in the other groups. These results seem to be caused by heat regulation in order to maintain a constant body temperature. In animals exposed to low environmental temperatures, circulatory functions increased in order to prevent a decrease in the body temperature. When these animals are exposed to high temperature for the same period, the respiratory rate decreased. These changes in respect to the normal rates can be thought of as adaptation syndromes.

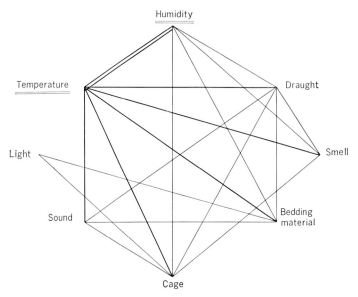

Fig. 7 Web of the physical components[11]

Influence of Relative Humidity

It must be noted that environmental factors do not act independently of one another. They act in the form of a complex web as Figure 7 shows[11]; temperature is connected with sound, cages, bedding materials, humidity, draught and smell.

The next experiment will show the effect of relative humidity in combination with temperature on anaphylaxis and physiological status.

Anaphylaxis

Table 4 shows the effects of relative humidity on the mortality rate of mice following anaphylactic shock at 25 and 35°C. The method was the same as in the previous anaphylaxis experiments except that the sensitizing dose was 1 mg/

Table 4 Effects of relative humidity on mice following anaphylactic shock

Temp.	Relative humidity	No. of experiment	No. of death	Mortality %	X²-test
25°C	40%	30	5	16.7	⏋
	55	30	5	16.7	
	94	30	4	13.3	⏌
35°C	40	30	5	16.7	⏋ *
	55	30	14	46.7	
	94	30	20	66.7	⏋ **

* $0.01 < p < 0.05$
** $p < 0.01$

head of egg albumin.   The relative humidity was varied among 40%, 55% and 94% (range±5%).   From the table it can be seen that there was no significant difference in mortality at 25°C, but there was considerable difference for each relative humidity at 35°C.

Physiological status

Figure 8 shows the heart rate, respiratory rate, body temperature of mice at 60 minutes after exposure to various relative humidities at 25 and 35°C. Within the same 3 humidity ranges, no significant changes were observed in heart rate, respiratory rate and body temperature at 25°C, but at 35°C there were significant differences between heart rate at low and high humidities and also between body temperature at low and high, and medium and high relative humidities after 60 minutes of exposure.

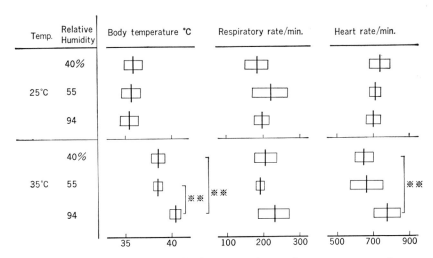

Fig. 8   The vital functions of mice at 60 minutes after exposure to various relative humidities   ** p<0.01

In the above experiments, the mortality rate of anaphylactic shock is affected only when the environmental humidity and temperature have some influence on the physiological status of the animals.   When the environmental factors do not change the physiological status, then they have no effect on the experimental results.

Although observation of physiological changes was limited to vital functions, it can be assumed that environmental factors are simultaneously affecting the autonomic nerve system and endocrine system via central nervous system[10]. These physiological changes seem to shift the response threshold to various treatment.

CONCLUSIONS

Let us now go back to some of the basic concepts discussed in the introduction. From Figure 9, it can be seen that the dramatype can be actually changed

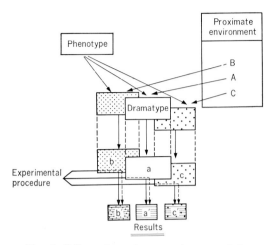

Fig. 9 Effect of proximate environmental factors

by varying factors in the proximate environment. This was shown by the results of temperature and experiments given previously. Even though the experimental procedure may be the same, these variation in the dramatype will cause differences in the experimental results. Therefore it is essential to control the proximate environment in order to stabilize the dramatype and thus assure reproducibility of experimental results.

Applying these conclusions to teratological experiments (Fig. 2), the dramatype of the pregnant mother must be stabilized by strict control of the proximate environment. However, the dramatype of the pregnant mother is identical with the developmental environment of the fetuses. This developmental environment, along with the genotype of the fetuses determines the phenotype of the fetuses, which is the result of the teratological experiment.

Therefore, defining and controlling the proximate environment, that is strict management of the pregnant mother, is as important as well-defined experimental procedure in obtaining reliable and reproducible results in teratological experiments.

REFERENCES

1. ADLER, J.H.: Aspects of Stress in Animals. In: Husbandry of Laboratory Animals, edited by M.L. CONALTY. pp. 239-252. Academic Press, Inc., London and New York, 1967.
2. ASLING, C.W.: Nutrition and Teratogenesis. In: Methods for Teratological Studies in Experimental Animals and Man, edited by H. NISHIMURA and J.R. MILLER. pp. 76-91. Igaku Shoin Ltd., Tokyo, 1969.
3. CHANCE, M.R.A.: The contribution of environment to uniformity. Lab. Anim. Bur.. Collected Papers 6: 59-72, 1967.
4. CHEVILLARD, L., BERTIN, R. and CABOT, M.: The Influence of Rearing Temperature on Some Physiological Characteristics of Small Laboratory Animals. In: Husbandry of Laboratory Animals, edited by M.L. CONALTY. pp. 395-445. Academic Press, Inc.,

London and New York, 1967.

5. ELLIS, T.M.: Environmental Influences on Drug Responses in Laboratory Animals. In: Husbandry of Laboratory Animals, edited by M.L. CONALTY. pp. 569–587. Academic Press, Inc., London and New York. 1967.

6. ESAKI, K., TANIOKA, Y. and NOMURA, T.: Effect of changing the environmental temperature on the incidence of cleft palate in the mouse fetuses induced by hypervitaminosis A. Cong. Anom. 8: 13–17, 1968.

7. ESAKI, K., TANIOKA, Y., NOMURA, T. and YAMAUCHI, C.: Effect of changing the environmental temperature on the incidence of malformation in the mouse fetuses induced by treatment with ethylurethane. Cong. Anom. 8: 96–97, 1968.

8. FRASER, F.C.: Gene-environmental Interactions in the Production of Cleft Palate. In: Methods for Teratological Studies in Experimental Animals and Man, edited by H. NISHIMURA and J.R. MILLER, pp. 34–49. Igaku Shoin Ltd., Tokyo, 1969.

9. FUHRMAN, G.J. and FUHRMAN, F.A.: Effects of temperature on the action of durgs. Ann. Rev. Pharmacol. 1: 65–78, 1961.

10. HARDY, J.D.: Physiology of temperature regulation. Physiol. Rev. 41: 521–606, 1961.

11. KALLAI, L.: Pharmaco-ecology and Some Nutritional Paradoxes. In: Husbandry of Laboratory Animals, edited by M.L. CONALTY. pp. 589–613. Academic Press, Inc., London and New York, 1967.

12. KALTER, H.: Interplay of Intrinsic and Extrinsic Factors. In: Teratology: Principles and Techniques, edited by J.G. WILSON and J. WARKANY. pp. 57–80. The University of Chicago Press, Chicago, 1967.

13. NOMURA, T., YAMAUCHI, C. and TAKAHASHI, H.: Influence of Environmental Temperature on Physiological Function of Laboratory Mouse. In: Husbandry of Laboratory Animals, edited by M.L. CONALTY. pp. 459–470. Academic Press, Inc., London and New York, 1967.

14. NOMURA, T. and YAMAUCHI, C.: Environments and physiological status of experimental animals. In: Gann Monograph No. 5. Experimental Animals in Cancer Research. pp. 14–31. Maruzen Co., Ltd., Tokyo, 1968.

15. RUSSELL, W.M.S. and BURCH, R.L.: The Principle of Human Experimental Technique. Methuen & Co., Ltd., London, 1959.

16. TANIOKA, Y., ESAKI, K., YAMAUCHI, C. and NOMURA, T.: Influence of the environmental temperature on the mortality of anaphylactic shock in mice. Exp. Anim. 17: 7–10, 1968.

17. YAMAUCHI, C., TAKAHASHI, H., ANDO, A., IMAISHI, N. and NOMURA, T.: Influence of environmental temperature on acute toxicity. Bull. Exp. Anim. 16: 31–38, 1967.

TERATOLOGICAL AND REPRODUCTIVE STUDIES
IN NON-HUMAN PRIMATES

James G. Wilson

*Professor, Departments of Research Pediatrics and Anatomy, University of
Cincinnati and Children's Hospital Research Foundation,
Cincinnati, U.S.A.*

The need for a teratological test animal intermediate between the laboratory
rodents used in screening and the clinical trial of new drugs in man may soon
be met. Several recent studies have dealt with the teratological susceptibility of
macaque monkeys and baboons to agents of known or potential teratological
significance in man. Before discussing the experimental studies in primate
teratology, however, it is important to consider the matter of spontaneous
occurrence of malformations in these animals. To obtain such information, I
undertook a survey on the subject several months ago by sending a questionnaire
to a number of persons over the world who were thought to have bred primates
under laboratory or other conditions that would permit close observation of the
outcome of all pregnancies.

SPONTANEOUS OCCURRENCE OF MALFORMATION
IN NON-HUMAN PRIMATES

Thirty-nine persons responded to the questionnaire but, as might be expected,
some were not able to supply useful information. Several replies were not used
because the respondents admitted to having no particular interest in malformations and, consequently, they had not looked for them by examining abortuses
or performing autopsy or x-ray studies on stillborn infants or those animals
dying in the neonatal period. Table 1 summarizes the observations judged to
have been collected under conditions that made likely the detection of at least
external malformations in all deliveries, including abortions, stillbirths and neonatal deaths. The estimated rate of spontaneous malformations for the ten
species and two generic groups represented was 0.44%, which compares closely
with the rate of 0.48% given for macaques and baboons at the Sukhumi Primate
Institute in the Soviet Union[23]. Furuya[12] has reported a much higher rate of
malformations, 16.8%, among the total births in the Gagyusan Troop of free-
ranging Japanese monkeys; but for several reasons this figure is not comparable
to those cited above. Although information is still too limited to warrant a
conclusion about the overall rate of spontaneous malformations, much less a
rate for any one species, there is little evidence to date to suggest that non-
human forms are any more prone to abnormal development than is man.

The types of defects shown by the animals in Table 1 include three cases
of anencephaly, two of diaphragmatic hernia and one each of hydrocephaly,

Table 1 Primates bred under conditions permitting detection of external malformations*

Common name	Specific name	Number of deliveries	Number malformed
Rhesus	Macaca mulatta	1567	6
Cynomolgus	Macaca irus	579	2
Baboon	Papio, sp.	382	2
Chimpanzee	Pan troglodytes	172	1
Squirrel	Saimiri sciurea	77	1
Pinche	Oedipomidus oedipus	75	0
Pig tailed	Macaca nemestrina	40	0
Marmoset	Callitrix jacchus	26	0
Stump tail	Macaca speciosa	17	0
Shrew	Tupaia chemenisis	8	0
Pata	Erythrocebus patas	4	0
Orangutan	Pango pygmaeus	3	1
	totals Estimated incidence 0.44%	2950	13

* These data have been published previously[44].

anophthalmia, cutaneous angioma of the face, patent ductus arteriosus, pigmented nevus, subdural hygroma, and congenital blindness of unknown type.   Little significance can be placed on the fact that the brain was involved in five of these instances because of the small number of total cases.   The predominant type of malformation among the young born in the Sukhumi colony in Russia was reported to affect the cardiovascular system[23].   Dr. MASAO KAWAI, Research Director of the Japan Monkey Center at Inuyama has informed me (personal communication) that most of the anomalies seen in natural troops of Japanese monkeys are limb defects.   SCHULTZ[33] also mentioned frequent limb defects in discussing teratological conditions in primates taken in the wild.   The latter two reports would seem to suggest that survival of free-ranging or wild primates is not severely impaired by limb abnormalities, but they give little indication of the prevailing types at birth.

Births of primates not under close scrutiny in zoos, laboratory colonies and in the wild have yielded a wide variety of types of malformations[2–4,6,10–13,15, 17–22,25,29–36,38,39].   Little can be gained by reviewing these here but it is noteworthy that, when allowance is made for possible destruction by the mother or other animals of malformed dead and moribund fetuses, and those with open lesions (eg. anencephaly), the types of anomalies reported seem to cover the same range as those described in human beings.

EXPERIMENTAL PRODUCTION OF MALFORMATIONS IN NON-HUMAN PRIMATES

Earlier reports[44,45] have summarized the relatively few studies in which experimental production of congenital defects has been attempted in non-human primates.   It was emphasized that three agents known to be teratogenic in man,

Table 2 Experimental production of malformations in monkeys and baboons

Agent (Species)	Treatment		Outcome	References
	Dose (mg)	Days		
Thalidomide (*M. irus*)	10/kg × 10	22–32 50–60	4 severe limb defects 2 teratomas aborted 1 normal	9
Thalidomide (*M. mulatta*)	12–19/kg × 1 18/kg/d × 1 16–19/kg × 1	23, 24 *or* 32 24–26 27 *or* 30	3 normal 1 severe limb defects 2 typical limb defects	44
Thalidomide (*Papio, sp.*)	5/kg/d	various, 0–44	2 aborted, 1 resorbed 3 limb defects 1 edema, single umb. a. 3 normal	14
Rubella virus (*M. irus*)		20 *or* later	9 aborted, 2 cataracts 3 normal	9
Testosterone (*M. mulatta*)	25/monk./d	various, 24–124	10 ♀ some degree of masculinization	40, 42
Norethindrone (*M. mulatta*)	125/monk./wk.	27–term	9 ♀ some degree of masculinization	43
Vincristine (*M. mulatta*)	0.15–0.20/kg × 1	various, 25–36	1 syndact., 1 encephalocele, 3 normal	5

namely, thalidomide, rubella virus and steroid hormones with androgenic activity, are also teratogenic in macaque monkeys and/or baboons at comparable doses and stages of development (Table 2).   In addition it has recently been shown by COURTNEY and VALIERIO[5] that vincristine, a promising cancer chemo-therapeutic alkaloid, sometimes causes maldevelopment in the rhesus monkey.   The latter drug has not been shown to be teratogenic in man, but it is representative of a large and steadily increasing group of growth suppressing substances which may be used in the treatment of cancer.   Precautions must be taken to avoid the use of such drugs in early unsuspected human pregnancy.

Several other drugs have not been found to be teratogenic when tested under what are regarded as realistic conditions of dosage and times of treatment (Table 3).   In addition to those shown, a series of synthetic estrogens and antiestrogens given at various dosages and times were reported by MORRIS et al.[27] to be non-teratogenic in the rhesus monkey.   In the author's laboratory an effort has been made to test certain drugs with particular emphasis on large doses given at early gestational ages.   Among those currently under investigation are acetylsalicylic acid (aspirin), methotrexate (amethopterin), hydroxyurea, LSD, 5-fluorouracil and retinoic acid.   All are well known teratogens in the rat except LSD which has recently been found by WARKANY and TAKACS[41] to have no such effect in carefully controlled studies in one strain of this species.   In the monkey LSD is not teratogenic at doses greatly in excess of the hallucinogenic level in man (Table 4).   Aspirin is highly teratogenic in rats at the dose rate of 250 mg/kg but comparable total amounts had little effect on the monkey fetus until several times this dosage was used (Table 5).   At the rate of 400–500 mg/kg/day between the 18th and 21st day of gestation, however, aspirin is abortifacient and teratogenic in the rhesus monkey.   One female so treated (♯31, Table 5) produced a

Table 3 Drugs not shown to be teratogenic in monkeys (*M. mulatta* and *irus*)

Agent*	Treatment*		Outcome	Reference
	Dose (mg)	Day (s)		
Progesterone	250/monk./wk.	24–term	6 normal	43
Aspirin	20–40/kg/d	25–term	2 normal	28
Meclizine	5–22/kg/d	16–29	5 normal 2 aborted	24
Chlorcyclizine	12.5–25/kg/d	various, 19–43	4 normal 4 aborted	24
Meclizine	10/kg × 5	various, 24–44	7 normal	5
Methamphetamine	5/kg/d	11–term	5 normal	5
Aminopterin	1.0/kg/d 0.1–0.2/kg/d	38–39 21–33	1 normal 2 aborted	8
Colcemide	2/kg × 1	24, 45, 66, 84	4 normal	26
BW (S7–323H) (mercaptopurine)	7.5/kg × 3	28–30	1 normal	26

* Many treatments at non-relevant times (after 50th d.) not included.

Table 4 Teratogenicity of LSD in rhesus monkeys (by gavage in CMC)

Animal number	Total dose	Day(s) of gestation	Outcome
22	75 μg total	22	normal
35	75	25	normal
2	100	29	mild polyhydramnios
11b	200	27	mild polyhydramnios
16	200 × 3	24, 26, 28	normal
10	200 × 3	22, 24, 26	mother severely anemic, fetus retarded but grossly normal

Table 5 Teratogenicity of acetylsalicylic acid (aspirin) in rhesus monkeys (by gavage in CMC)

Animal number	Dose (mg/kg)	Day(s) of gestation	Outcome
12	100	23	normal
10	100 × 3	24–26	normal
14	200 × 3	23–25	normal
26	200 × 6	22–24	reverse rotation of gut
31	250 × 6*	18–21	microcephaly, micrognathia, syndactyly, hind 5th digits short and crooked, esophageal stenosis, ventricular septal defect, polyhydramnios
13	250 × 6	18–21	aborted day 32
1	200 × 6	18–21	aborted day 45

* Dosage @ 3.35 gm. per day in this 6.7 kg. monkey

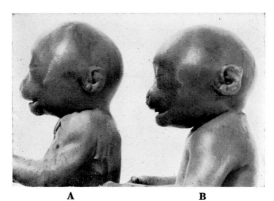

A   B

Fig. 1   A. Abnormal fetus showing microcephaly and micrognathia, removed by hysterotomy at 100 days gestation from a female monkey that received aspirin at the rate of 500 mg/kg/day between days 18 and 21 of gestation.   **B.** Normal fetus of the same age and weight.

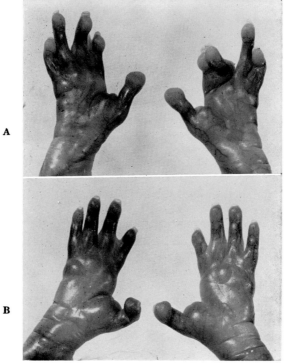

Fig. 2   A. Syndactyly of hindlimb digits 2 and 3 and shortening of digits 5 on the fetus shown in Figure 1 A.   **B.** Normal hindlimb digits of the fetus shown in Figure 1 B.

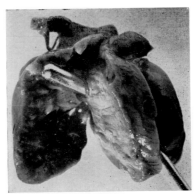

Fig. 3 Heart with ventricular septal defect
(note probe) from the fetus shown in Figure 1 A.

severely malformed fetus with microcephaly associated with agyria, micrognathia
(Fig. 1), syndactyly of hindlimb digits 2 and 3 and brachydactyly of digits 5
(Fig. 2), esophageal stenosis and ventricular septal defect (Fig. 3). Moderate
polyhydramnios was present at the 100th day of gestation when pregnancy was
interrupted by hysterotomy. Another female (♯13, Table 5) similarly treated
aborted approximately 10 days after the last dosage and another which received
400 mg/kg/day aborted on the 45th day of gestation. The doses indicated in
Table 5, particularly at the higher levels, must be regarded as approximations
because of the tendency of the females to regurgitate some of each dosage after
about the third treatment.

The folic acid antagonist methotrexate (amethopterin) seems to be abortifacient at 4.0 mg/kg/day prior to the 19th day of gestation but no malformations
have yet been produced in monkeys with this agent (Table 6). Methotrexate is
highly teratogenic in rats (a) 0.2 mg/kg in a single dose. Hydroxyurea, 5-fluoro-
uracil and retinoic acid have also proven to be non-teratogenic in the rhesus
monkey at doses in excess of the teratogenic level for rats (Table 7). Thus,
there is some evidence indicating that the rhesus monkey may be teratologically
less susceptible than the rat. A striking exception to this generalization, however,
is thalidomide which is highly teratogenic in monkeys and scarcely at all in rats.

Table 6 Teratogenicity of methotrexate (amethopterin) in rhesus monkeys
(intravenously)

Animal number	Dose (mg/kg)	Day(s) of gestation	Outcome
17a	0.5	24	? small brain
13	1.0	21	? polyhydramnios
16	2.0	22	normal
25	3.0	21	normal
27	2.5×2	18, 19	threatened abortion days 20–22 normal fetus day 100
1	4.0	17	aborted day 27
6	4.0	19	normal

Table 7 Teratogenicity of other compounds in rhesus monkeys

Animal number	Agent	Dose (mg/kg)	Day(s) of gestation	Outcome
4	Hydroxyurea	250	21	normal
9	//	250	18	intestinal diverticulum
18	//	250 × 2	18, 19	normal
30	//	500	18	small
29	5-Fluorouracil	20	20	normal
20	//	40	20	normal
19	Retinoic acid	20	20	normal
34	//	40	22	small accessory thymus

THALIDOMIDE TERATOGENESIS IN MONKEYS

This drug, despite its dramatic and tragic entry into the field of teratology, has now become a useful tool as a standard for comparison in primate studies. The embryos of two species of macaque monkeys and of the baboon have been shown to be approximately as sensitive to this compound as the human embryo and to display a very similar pattern of limb defects (Fig. 4 and Table 8). In fact, enough data have accumulated that it would be possible to construct a crude dose-response curve. The original report of DELAHUNT and LASSEN[9] indicated that a total dose of 100 mg/kg over a period of 10 days is overwhelming and likely to preclude survival of the fetus to term in most cases. Recent tests in my laboratory suggest that the non-effective single dose lies between 8 and 16 mg/kg, probably varying somewhat with the embryo's age at the time of treatment. It was emphasized previously[44,45] that the rhesus embryo is most susceptible to this drug from the 25th through the 30th days of gestation, in other words, that at this time there is a typical teratological response to moderate dosage (16–19 mg/kg). Dosage at this level given either before or after the susceptible period is without effect (Table 8). If dosage is increased appreciably above this level, however, it is possible to produce abnormalities. A monkey given 50 mg/kg on the 22nd day produced a fetus with minor abnormalities of forelimbs, preaxial hemimelia and ectrodactyly of digit I, which were unmistakably of the thalidomide type. No treatment after the 30th day produced typical defects. A fetus from a female treated with 40 mg/kg on the 32nd had an extra thoracic vertebra and an extra pair of ribs, but these are not attributed to the action of thalidomide, because a female treated with 100 mg/kg on the 32nd day produced a normal fetus (Table 8).

The results in Table 8 clearly demonstrate the existence of a cephalocaudal development gradient. It is a well-known fact that the forelimbs of the higher vertebrates develop a few hours or a few days earlier than the hindlimbs. Accordingly, it was observed that treatment on the 22nd day caused only forelimb defects, whereas treatment on the 30th day caused only hindlimb defects (Fig. 5). Furthermore, the animal treated on the 24th, 25th, and 26th days, near the beginning of the susceptible period, had abnormalities of all extremities but the

Fig. 4   A. Term fetus from a female monkey treated with 16 mg/kg of thalidomide on the 30th day of gestation. Malformation is limited to the hindlimbs which are phocomelic and have preaxial ectrodactyly (1t. digit 1) and brachydactyly (rt. digits 1 and 2). **B.** Term fetus from a female monkey treated with 19 mg/kg of thalidomide on the 27th day of gestation. All limbs are phocomelic and have digital anomalies and, in addition, the ears are mildly abnormal and the tail short.

Table 8   Sensitive period of rhesus monkey to thalidomide

Day(s) of treatment (gest. age*)	Total dose (mg/kg)	Condition of offspring
20	50	no fetus—only chorion at 100 ds.
22	50	preaxial forelimb defects only
23	12	normal
24	19	normal
24, 25, 26	18 × 3	extreme defects of all limbs, ears abnormal, tail missing
25	8	normal
26	8	normal
27	19	phocomelia of all limbs, ears mildly abn., tail short
28	8	normal
30	16	phocomelia hindlimbs only
30	50	phocomelia hindlimbs only
32	17	normal
32	40	extra T. vertebra & pr. of ribs
32	100	normal

sensitive period for moderate dosage

* Stated age is ±1 day—all females with male for 48 hours.

forelimbs were more severely affected than the hindlimbs.

All published studies on experimental teratology in primates have dealt with the higher or simian forms. The search for a suitable animal model for the preclinical testing of drugs need not necessarily be limited to the higher primates if a prosimian form can be found that parallels human teratological sensitivity in a way comparable to that already shown in macaques and baboons. The ideal animal would be a small primate that is easy to maintain, has a short

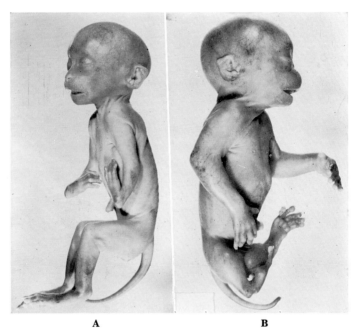

A   **B**

Fig. 5 A. Monkey fetus showing only preaxial forelimb malformations, removed on the 100 th day of gestation from a female treated on the 22nd day of gestation with 50 mg/kg of thalidomide. **B.** Monkey fetus showing only hindlimb defects, removed on the 100 th day from a female treated on the 30th day with 50 mg/kg of thalidomide.

gestation period and produces more than one offspring per year. With these thoughts in mind, a collaborative study was undertaken with Dr. ROBERT W. COOPER, Director of the Primate Research Colony at the Zoological Society of San Diego, to investigate the sensitivity of the bushbaby, *Galago crassicaudatus,* to thalidomide teratogenesis. Nine pregnant females were treated orally with a single dose of 20 mg/kg on day 16, 18, 20, 22, 24, 25, 26, 28 or 30 of gestation. This dosage exceeds that found effective in the rhesus monkey and it was given over a broad range of times including the period previously found to be that of greatest sensitivity in the monkey. No abnormalities of any sort resulted from this treatment. The total dosage was then tripled by treating nine additional pregnant Galagos on three successive days with 20 mg/kg per day (60 mg/kg total) between the 16th and 30th days of gestation. No malformations were observed at this dosage which would be highly teratogenic to rhesus embryos.

It must be concluded that this prosimian species is much less sensitive to thalidomide than the higher primates.

IMPROVED BREEDING METHODS IN THE RHESUS MONKEY

In the absence of a primate better suited to breeding in the laboratory than *Macaca mulatta*, considerable effort has been directed toward improving the breeding efficiency of this animal. Possibilities for achieving this lie mainly in three areas of reproduction: 1) a more precise method for anticipating ovulation, 2) earlier and more accurate diagnosis of pregnancy, and 3) increased fecundity, i. e., more pregnancies per year.

Various attempts to predict more accurately the time of ovulation have been unsuccessful. As did HARTMAN[14] a number of years ago, we also have failed to find a useful correlation between the cellular content of the vaginal smear and the maturation of the ovarian follicle. Rectal palpation of the ovaries for preovulatory follicles, also described by HARTMAN, has not proven practicable or reliable. At present we rely on the calendar and the statistical probability that ovulation in young adult rhesus monkeys is most likely to occur on the 11th or 12th days of the menstrual cycle. Females are routinely placed with a male for 48 hours, from noon on the 11th until noon on the 13th day after the beginning of menstruation.

Considerable success has been met in developing a method for early and accurate diagnosis of pregnancy. Quantitative assays for chorionic gonadotropin in the blood and urine of pregnant rhesus monkeys have recently been described by TULLNER and HERTZ[31] and by ARSLAN et al.[1]. Both of these groups demonstrated significant amounts of gonadotropin between the 18th and 35th days postconception, but in both instances the assay required $3^1/_2$ to 4 days to learn the outcome. For use in teratological studies such a delay is a serious drawback because it would mean that a monkey would not be diagnosed as pregnant and could not be treated with a test substance until about the 22nd day of gestation. Treatment at this time would fall within the teratologically susceptible period for many substances, but it almost certainly would not fall at or near the beginning of the susceptible period, if the latter can be extrapolated on the basis of comparable developmental stages in rats or mice. Data from teratological studies at known stages in rodents suggest that monkeys, and probably man as well, may become susceptible to teratogenic influences as early as the 15th day postconception. Embryos of many species are known to show maximal sensitivity to teratogenic influences early in the susceptible period, hence if testing is to be reliable, it must be done early.

The procedure described below has diagnosed pregnancy with unfailing accuracy within 24 hours after the collection of a 6 ml blood sample, if blood were taken between the 18th and 30th days after mating. Five immature Swiss mice (10±2 gm) are injected subcutaneously with 0.4 ml of monkey serum at noon of the day on which it is collected and prepared. Four hours later a second injection of 0.2 ml of the same serum is given to the same mice. Twenty four hours after the first injection the mice are sacrificed and the uteri weighed on a ROLLER-SMITH balance. Uterine weights are converted to a factor reflecting

relative body weight by the formula $\dfrac{\text{uterine wt. in mg.}}{\text{body wt. in gm.}} \times 1000$.   Five additional
immature mice injected with saline by the same schedule serve as controls. The
mean factor for saline treated mice, as well as for mice given serum from
nonpregnant monkeys, approximates unity (1.0), whereas the mean factor for
mice receiving serum from monkeys 18 to 30 days pregnant has always exceeded
1.36 and often exceeds 2.0. Thus, although statistical analysis has not been
undertaken, an increase of 33 % or more in uterine weight of serum-treated
mice over that of control mice has always been indicative of pregnancy. Figure

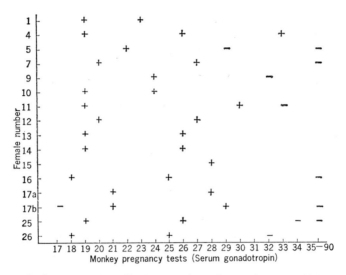

Fig. 6 Scatter graph indicating the days of gestation on which 16
monkeys of proven pregnancy showed positive tests (see text for test
procedure). No false positive responses have been obtained with this
test using more than 100 serum samples from non-pregnant animals or in
more than 60 control tests in which saline was used instead of serum.

6 presents the results of one or more such tests performed on 16 pregnant
rhesus monkeys, and shows that blood taken between the 18th and 28th days
always gives a positive test. Thereafter negative results are obtained with
increasing frequency in pregnant animals, as might be anticipated, in view of
the rapid fall in serum gonadotropin level known to occur after the 30th day[1,37].
No false positives have occurred either in more than 100 tests using serum
from non-pregnant females or in more than 60 tests using saline.

A useful procedure for confirmation of the gonadotropin pregnancy test has
been bimanual palpation of the uterus by way of the rectum. The anatomical
and positional relationships of the palpation are shown in Figure 7. The size
of the uterus can be estimated readily by this means, but to minimize the
subjective factor and achieve greater consistency in recording observations, I
have devised a set of gauges (Fig. 8) representing uterine size and shape at
various stages in the animals' reproductive life. When palpation is done with

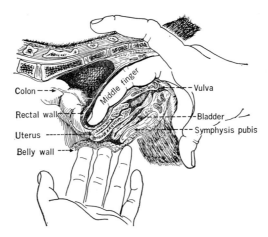

Fig. 7 Drawing illustrating anatomical and positional relationships in bimanual palpation of the uterus in the rhesus monkey.

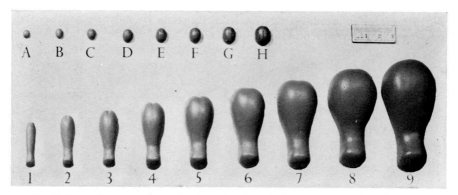

Fig. 8 Set of gauges for estimating the size of the uterus as palpated via the rectum. Pregnancy is suspected in any uterus achieving a size of 4 if the female was bred approximately 20 days earlier, and any larger size is almost always indicative of pregnancy. The smaller, hemispherical models above represent the ranges of size of the ovary as palpating the ovary to anticipate ovulation with a useful degree of accuracy.

the uterine size gauge in view and avaliable for tactile reference, if needed, the examiner quickly learns to associate the size of the uterus with one of the numbered on models the gauge with a high degree of reproducibility. Table 9 indicates the correlation of functional state with size of the uterus. Pregnancy can be diagnosed by this means, often as early as the 20th day postconception, but not with sufficient precision to give the accurate timing needed in teratological investigation. It not only serves as a useful confirmation of the chorionic gonadotropin test described above, but also is of value in determining that early abortion has or has not occurred following teratological treatment (Tables 5 and 6).

The remaining direction in which it was hoped more efficient breeding procedures might be developed, namely, the production of more pregnancies per

Table 9 Rectal palpation of the uterus in *Macaca mulatta*

size gauge*	reproductive state
1	immature
1–2	adolescent
2–3	young nuliparous
3	young parous or older nuliparous
3–4	older parous, possible early pregnancy
4	suspect 18–21 day pregnancy
5	pregnancy 20–25 days
6	// 23–28 //
7	// 26–32 //
8	// 30–36 //
9	// 33–45 //

* The numbers refer to the models in Figure 8.

female per year, has not progressed far enough to allow evaluation of its success. Pregnancies have been routinely interrupted by cesarean section on the 100th day, in hope of re-breeding the female earlier than would be possible if pregnancy went to term on the 167th, particularly if parturition were followed by lactation. This procedure has already proven useful in one regard: it provides faster results about the outcome of a teratological test than if pregnancy went to term. A 100-day fetus can be fully evaluated as far as structural development is concerned and some functional parameters, such as heart rate and certain reflexes, can also be observed. Since the procedure was instituted, however, only a relatively few of the females re-bred one or more times following cesarean section have become pregnant a second time. If this procedure is to be useful in producing more pregnancies per year per female, the majority of animals must again become pregnant within a few months after cesarean section, and in any event, sooner than would be required for term delivery followed by lactation.

SUMMARY

A survey of malformations among almost 3000 non-human primates delivered under conditions that would permit observation of defects in all animals delivered yielded a spontaneous malformation rate of 0.44 %. The types of malformations do not appear to differ from those occurring spontaneously in man.

Macaque monkeys and/or baboons have been shown to be susceptible to three known human teratogens, thalidomide, rubella virus and steroid hormones with androgenic activity, with similar defects and at times of gestation and levels of dosage comparable to those known to be teratogenic in man. The rhesus monkey has also been shown to be teratogenically susceptible to vincristine. Several additional drugs have been realistically tested, and at this time only aspirin in large doses at early gestational ages seems to be teratogenic, as well as abortifacient.

Further studies on thalidomide teratogenesis in the rhesus monkey indicate that the minimally effective dose is between 8 and 16 mg/kg and that increased dosage of 40 or 50 mg/kg before but not after the usual susceptible period may produce mild abnormality. The prosimian primate, *Galago crassicaudatus*, failed to respond to doses in excess of those causing teratogenesis in higher primates and, consequently, is regarded as less sensitive to thalidomide than higher primates.

Efforts to improve the breeding efficiency of *Macaca mulatta* are described. The most noteworthy to date is a pregnancy test based on serum chorionic gonadotropin assay which gives reliable diagnosis of pregnancy within 24 hours after collection of serum at any time between the 18th and 30th days postconception. This pregnancy test should prove of great value in primate teratological studies in which it is desirable to treat animals of known pregnancy status as early as possible in the susceptible period of the embryo.

ACKNOWLEDGEMENT

Some of the results reported herein were published previously with Dr. JAMES A. GAVAN (reference[44]) and with Miss ROCHELLE FRADKIN (reference[45]). Thanks are due these collaborators as well as to Miss JOAN SHIELDS, Mrs. VIRGINIA RINGENBERG and Mr. ROBERT JORDAN.

The original works of the author were supported in part by NIH research grants HD–00607, HD–02553, HD–02792 and by FDA contract 67–14.

Thalidomide was supplied through the courtesy of Dr. F. JOSEPH MURRAY of the WILLIAM S. MERRILL Company, Cincinnati, Ohio.

REFERENCES

1. ARSLAN, M., MEYER, R.K. and WOLF, R.C.: Chorionic gonadotropin in the blood and urine of pregnant rhesus monkeys (*Macaca mulatta*). Proc. Soc. Exp. Biol. & Med. 125: 349–352, 1967.
2. BOLK, L.: Die Doppelbildung eines Affen. Beitr. Path. Anat. 76: 238–253, 1926.
3. CAMERON, A.H. and HILL, W.C.O.: The Arnold-Chiari malformation in a sacred baboon (Papio hamadryas). J. Path. Bact. 70: 552–554, 1955.
4. CHASE, R.E. and DE GARIS, C.F.: Anomalies of venae cavae superiores in an orang. Amer. J. phys. Anthropol. 24: 61–65, 1938.
5. COURTNEY, K.D., VALERIO, D.A. and STAFF, B.R.L.: Experimental teratology in *Macaca mulatta*. Proc. of 7th Annual Meeting, Teratology Society, Estes Park, Col., May 1967.
6. DE GARIS, C.F.: Pericardial patency and partial ectocardia in a newborn orangutan. Anat. Rec. 59: 69–82, 1934.
7. DELAHUNT, C.S.: Rubella-induced cataracts in monkeys. Lancet 7441: 825, 1966.
8. DELAHUNT, C.S.: Discussion of a paper by J.G. WILSON. Food and Drug Administration Conference of Nonhuman Primate Toxicology, Arilie House, Va., 1966.
9. DELAHUNT, C.S. and LASSEN, L.J.: Thalidomide syndrome in monkeys. Science 146: 1300–1305, 1964.
10. FERREIRA, A.L.: Un cas de lésions deformantes polyarticulaires chez un "Gorilla Gina" d'Angola. Anais da Faculdade Ciênciàs do Porto 23: 3–22, 1938.
11. FRIEDLOWSKY, A.: Über eine missbildete Affenhand. Verh. k.k. Zool. -bot. Ges.

Wien 20: 1017–1026, 1807.

12. FURUYA, Y.: On the malformation occurred in the Gagyusan troop of wild Japanese monkeys. Primate 7: 488–492, 1966.
13. GARY, J.: Oral abnormalities in laboratory chimpanzees. Lab. Primate Newlett. 6: 11–12, 1967.
14. HARTMAN, C.G.: Studies in the reproduction of the monkey *Macacas* (Pithecus) *rhesus,* with special reference to menstruation and pregnancy. Carnegie Contrib. Embryol. 23: 1–161, 1932.
15. HARTMAN, C.G.: Birth of a two headed monster in the rhesus monkey. Science 98: 449, 1943.
16. HENDRICKX, A.G., AXELROD, L.R. and CLAYBORN, L.D.: Thalidomide syndrome in baboons. Nature 210: 958–959, 1966.
17. HILL, W.C.O.: Spina bifida in a sacred baboon (Papio hamadryas). Ceylon J. Sci. 5: 9–15, 1939.
18. HILL, W.C.O.: Lobster-claw deformity in a Drill (Mandrillus leucophaeus). Bibl. primat. 1: 239. 1962.
19. HILL, W.C.O.: Congenital abnormalities of the urinary tract in primates. Folia primat. 2: 111–118, 1964.
20. HODOW, C.J.: Field and laboratory studies on an African monkey, *Cercopithecus asconius schmidti Malschie.* Proc. Zoll. Soc. London 122: 297–394, 1952.
21. ITANI, J., TOKUDA, K., FURUYA, Y. and KANO, K.: The social construction of natural troops of Japanese monkeys in Takasakiyama. Primates 4: 2–42, 1963.
22. KOFORD, C.B., FARBER, P.A. and WINDLE, F.: Twins and teratisms in rhesus monkeys. Folia primat. 4: 221–226, 1966.
23. LAPIN, B.A.: Defects in development and malformation. The monkey–subject of medical and biological experiments. Akademia Meditsinskich Nauk SSSR, Sukhumi, 1963.
24. LITTLE, W.A.: Personal communication, 1966.
25. MARUFFO, C.A. and CRAMER, D.L.: Congenital renal malformations in monkeys. Folia primat. 5: 305–311, 1967.
26. MORRIS, J.M., VAN WAGENEN, G., HURTEAU, G.D., JOHNSTON, D.W. and CARLSEN, R.A.: Compounds interfering with ovum implantation and development. I. Alkaloids and antimetabolites. Fertil. & Steril. 18: 7–17, 1967.
27. MORRIS, J. M., VAN WAGENEN, G., MC CANN, T. and JACOB, D.: Compound interfering with ovum implantation and development. II. Synthetic estrogens and antiestrogens. Fertil. & Steril. 18: 18–34, 1967.
28. PALLOTTA, A.H.: Personal communication, 1966.
29. PEARSON, K.: On the existence of the digital deformity, so-called "lobster claw", in the apes. Ann. Eugen. 4: 339–340, 1931.
30. PRAG, J.J.: An abnormal baboon sacrum found at Lindeques Drift. *South African J. Science* 32: 356–359, 1935.
31. SCHULTZ, A.H.: Zygodactyly and its inheritance. *J. Hered.* 13: 113–117, 1922.
32. SCHULTZ, A.H.: Studies on the variability of platyrrhine monkeys. J. Mammalogy 7: 286–305, 1926.
33. SCHULTZ, A.H.: The occurrence and frequency of pathological and teratological conditions and of twinning among non-human primates. Primatologia 1: 965–1014, 1956.
34. SCOTT, H.H. and COMB, H.: Congenital malformations in the kidney. Proc. Zool. Soc. London 2: 1259–1270, 1925.
35. SENSENIG, E.C.: Unilateral vertebral arch duplication in the slow lemur, Perodicticus.

Anat. Rec. 101: 275–280, 1948.

36. SULLIVAN, D.J. and DROBECK, H.P.: True hermaphrodism in a rhesus monkey. Folia primat. 4: 309–317, 1966.

37. TULLNER, W. W. and HERTZ, R.: Chorionic gonadotropin levels in the rhesus monkey during early pregnancy. Endocrinol. 78: 204–207, 1966.

38. TUTTLE, R.H. and ROGERS, C.M.: Reduced first digits in Pongo pygmaeus. Amer. J. phys. Anthrop. 25: 211, 1966.

39. TUMBELAKA, R.: Das Gehirn eines Affen worin der interhemisphariäle Balkenverbindung fehlt. Folia neuro-biol. 9: 1–64, 1915.

40. VAN WAGENEN, G. and HAMILTON, J.B.: The experimental production of pseudohermaphroditism in the monkey. Essays in Biology pp. 583–607, University of Chicago Press, 1943.

41. WARKANY, J. and TAKACS, E.: Lysergic acid diethylamide (LSD): no teratogenicity in rats. Science 159: 731–732, 1968.

42. WELLS, L.J. and VAN WAGENEN, G.: Androgen-induced female pseudohermaphrodism in the monkey (*Macaca mulatta*): anatomy of the reproductive organs. Carnegie Contrib. Embryol. 35: 93–106, 1954.

43. WHARTON, R. and SCOTT, R.B.: Experimental production of genital lesions with norethindrone. Amer. J. Obst. & Gyn. 89: 701–715, 1964.

44. WILSON, J.G. and GAVAN, J.A.: Congenital malformations in nonhuman primates: Spontaneous and experimentally induced. Anat. Rec. 158: 99–110, 1967.

45. WILSON, J.G. and FRADKIN, R.: Teratogenicity in non-human primates, with notes on breeding procedures in *Macaca mulatta*. Ann. N.Y. Acad. Sci. (in press).

DISCUSSION

ISHAQ (Pakistan)

I am not very clear in my mind about the definition of the term "critical period". This period, as I understand, corresponds to that period of "rapid development" which is susceptible to the effects of a teratogenic agent.

Taking a specific example (a hypothetical one though), the time of most rapid development would be the time of, and immediately following, the appearance of a primordium. Extending this concept to the bronchial tree, I would imagine that each time a new branch buds off, this time, then, would correspond to the time of "rapid development" for that particular branch, and therefore each successively appearing generation along the growing bronchial stem would have successive and corresponding critical periods.

Would you kindly give your comments?

WILSON

I agree with you that the concept of

critical period or susceptible period should be thought of as extending throughout the organogenesis of an organ such as the lung. In fact it has been demonstrated that most organs and systems have more than one period when they are susceptible to the action of teratogenic agents. As Dr. RUNNER has pointed out such organs may respond to the same agent in different ways at different times or to different agents in the same way. I regard the response of any organ at any time as a product of the way in which the agent interferes with the metabolic or homeostatic needs of that organ at that moment.

GREEN (Australia)

To what extent do you think that women of reproductive age have been and will be exposed to vincristine?

WILSON

It is my impression that vincristine has to date been used largely in leukemic children. A related compound, vinblastine, is more likely to be used in adults, and consequently during pregnancy. For that reason we are now planning teratogenicity studies using vinblastine in pregnant monkeys. My knowledge of the subject of human drug usage, however, is very limited.

SISODIA (India)

For purposes of comparative pharmacology and teratology it will be desirable to have data on blood levels of drug administered at various dosages to experimental animals and to compare the same with human blood levels after giving therapeutic dose of the same drug.

WILSON

Information on comparative pharmacology as related to teratogenicity is at present very limited. I agree that complete studies on teratogenic hazard of drugs studied in monkeys should be accompanied by metabolic and excretion rate data for comparison with such data in man. We hope to include this in some of our future studies and hope that others, testing drugs for teratogenicity in monkeys, will do likewise.

FUENTES (Philippines)

I do not know about the menstrual cycle of the monkey but in human beings we have had positive pregnancy tests 24 days after conception with the use of frogs and more recently several commercial tests. Have you tried such tests in your laboratory?

WILSON

The menstrual cycle of rhesus monkey is very similar to that in the human female, both in total duration of cycle as well as in the period of bleeding. The main difference may be the time of ovulation. In the woman this is thought to occur on the average about the middle of the cycle, that is on about the 14th day. The regularly cyclic female monkey probably ovulates a bit earlier in the cycle, perhaps most often on the 12th day of the cycle.

We have tried some of the commercially available pregnancy tests such as those you mentioned. The monkey does not react to some, to others it reacts much as does the human subject, that is, a positive test may be obtained as early as the 25th day postconception. This is

several days later than the serum gonadotrophin assay which we have used, and therefore less useful in teratological work.

LOO (Malaysia)

It may be useful to use the concentrated early morning urine specimen to produce increased sensitivity for the chorionic gonadotrophic test in the diagnosis of pregnancy in monkeys, instead of using serum levels.

WILSON

I am very much interested in your suggestion. We have not tried our test for pregnancy using each morning urine specimens. If it contains more gonadotrophin than blood serum or urine collected at other times of the day, urine collected early in the morning might increase the sensitivity of our test. We shall be glad to try it, thank you.

ETO (Japan)

1. Methotrexate is quite effective for the treatment of chorionic tumors. Is the teratogenicity of methotrexate mainly due to its effects on the trophoblast or can its effects reach the embryoblast?

2. In order to establish useful correlations between the ovary and the cellular contents of vaginal smear, the utilization of laparoscopy in stead of trying to palpate the preovulatory follicle seems to be quite effective. What do you think of this?

3. What would be the chief cause of the teratogenicity of the steroid hormone with androgenic action? Why is it that the steroid hormone with androgenic action alone can manifest teratogenicity?

WILSON

1. In the first place, I should like to stress that methotrexate is not a very effective teratogen in the monkey. Its effect on the trophoblast in a teratological situation is unknown to me. It is known to suppress mitosis and consequently selectively to modify localized growth. At least some of any teratogenicity this drug has might be related to such thing as growth suppression within the embryo.

2. Laparoscopy would certainly permit recognition of any correlation that may exist between the appearance of the ovary and the cellular content of the vaginal

smear. We have not performed laparoscopy but are contemplating combining culdoscopy with palpation of the ovary.

3. The steroid hormones with androgenic activity are able to direct the course of embryonic differentiation of the genital ducts and external genitalia of genetic females, transforming these individuals into female pseudohermaphrodites. Experience in human subjects indicates that exposure around the 12th week of gestation is most likely to cause hermaphroditism because it is at this time that the genital organs other than gonads are actively undergoing sexual differentiation.

TAKANO (Japan)

You hesitated to make a definite conclusion about the usefulness of the primate as an experimental animals in testing for the teratogenicity of new drugs. I would like to hear your definite opinion in this regard, because your hesitation might cause some confusion among the audience.

WILSON

I hesitated to make definite recommendations about the use of primates in teratological testing for several reasons. One of the principal ones is that this is, and should remain, the responsibility of the governmental regulating agencies. Furthermore, the amount of available information is too limited to serve as the basis of definitive recommendations. My private opinion, however, is that the rhesus monkey is well on the way toward proving its worth as a valid and reliable test object for preclinical trial of new drugs of medicinal importance particularly if these are likely to be used in women of reproductive age.

GENE-ENVIRONMENT INTERACTIONS IN THE PRODUCTION OF CLEFT PALATE

F. CLARKE FRASER

Professor, Human Genetics Sector, Department of Genetics,
McGill University, Montreal, Canada.

Every developmental process is, of course, an example of gene-environment interactions. Cleft palate is an abnormal developmental process in which some of the contributing genetic and environmental factors, and their interactions, can be recognized. This paper will (1) review the process of palate closure, (2) point out various steps in the process at which the influence of genetic or environmental factors can lead to cleft palate, and (3) present several examples of the ways in which genetic differences can result in differences in response of embryos to teratogens.

FORMATION OF THE SECONDARY PALATE

The palatal shelves first appear as downgrowths from the inferior surface of the maxilla, posterior to the primary palate, on either side of the tongue. In order to close, the shelves must change their position from the vertical to the horizontal plane. This requires displacement of the intervening tongue. The process involves a complicated interaction of shelf movement, tongue resistance, mandible growth and head growth, all of which need to be co-ordinated with one another, and probably with many other factors, to achieve successful closure[5].

At the beginning of closure the shelves are lying parallel to one another, with the tongue between them (Fig. 1). In the mouse, at least, palatal movement seems to begin posteriorly, and proceed anteriorly[33]. A finger-like projection extends backward at the posterior end of the shelf; this is the first part to move in medially, above the tongue. (It is difficult to see from the usual, ventral, viewpoint). If the tongue is experimentally displaced from between the shelves in the living embryo, just before closure normally begins, the shelves rapidly move upwards and medially towards the horizontal[33], even against gravity[26]. Thus there is a force in the shelves that causes them to move towards each other, against the resistance of the intervening tongue. VERRUSIO (cited by FRASER[5]) has presented an interesting model that may explain the nature of this force.

At the beginning of closure, the tip of the tongue is lying behind the primary palate[30]. It then moves forward, sliding down the sloping posterior surface of the primary palate, and coming to lie under its inferior surface (Figs. 2 and 3). Medial movement of the posterior tip of the shelf begins before forward displacement of the tongue, since in embryos fixed at this stage, some are observed with the posterior end of the shelf deviated medially and the tongue

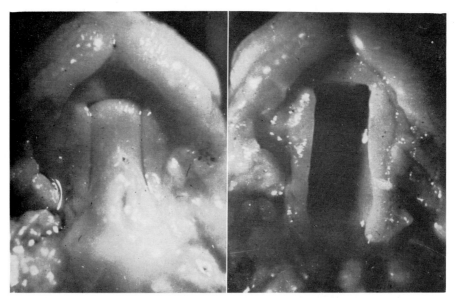

Fig. 1 A day 14 mouse embryo before closure of the secondary palate begins (stage 0)[30]. Tongue in place (left) and removed (right).

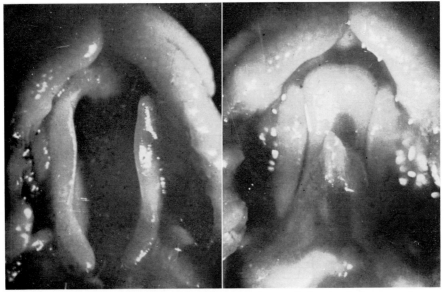

Fig. 2 The shelves have moved towards each other, and the tip of the tongue has moved forward (stage 1)[30]

still behind the primary palate, but none are seen with the tongue tip advanced and no evidence of shelf movement[30]. Possibly the primary palate may act as an inclined plane, displacing the whole tongue downward as it moves forward, and thus creating a space above the tongue into which the more anterior parts of the shelves can move. Forward and downward movement of the tongue may

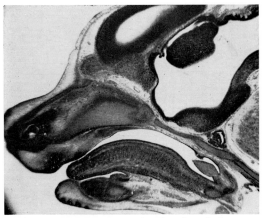

Fig. 3 Sagittal section of stage 1: the tip of the tongue has moved forward and downward, and there is a space above the tongue into which the shelves will move.

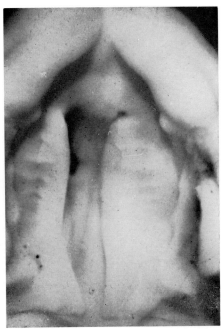

Fig. 4 The left shelf is now horizontal; the right shelf is still vertical anteriorly.

also be aided by forward growth of the mandible. In the rabbit, according to WALKER[38], the tongue may be displaced by sudden extension of the neck.

Reorientation of the shelf from vertical to horizontal proceeds forward until the whole shelf is horizontal (Fig. 4). Both shelves then become progressively flattened, and their free edges approach one another, to meet at a point about one-third of the length of the shelf from the front. The flattening process may be aided by the presence of the underlying tongue[26]. Epithelial contact then spreads anteriorly and posteriorly, the epithelia break down, and fusion is complete.

MECHANISMS OF CLEFT PALATE

Cleft palate will result from any process that prevents the free edge of the shelf reaching the midline, or fusing with its partner when it gets there.

Let us now consider, briefly, the possible ways in which this could happen.

1. The *palate shelves may develop abnormally* and
   (a) be unable to move to the horizontal or extend to the midline in time, as in the case of the recessive " phocomelia " gene in the mouse[2]
   (b) be too narrow to meet, if they do become horizontal and flatten, as in the case of the recessive " urogenital " gene in the mouse[2], or following X-radiation[20].
   Hypervitaminosis A in the rat may act through both these mechanisms[15].

2. The *shelf force may be reduced*, so that movement of the shelf to the midline is delayed.
   There is probably a genetically determined difference between the A/J and C 57 BL strains in strength of shelf force[38], underlying the observed tendency of the shelves in the A/J strain to close later than those of the C 57 BL strain[33]. Reduction of shelf force by teratogens has been demonstrated in organ culture for cortisone, x-rays, and hypervitaminosis A in the mouse[38]. So far there is no proof of the mechanism by which any teratogen reduces shelf force, although a number of possibilities have been suggested — e.g., reduction of acid-mucopolysaccharide synthesis by cortisone and salicylates[17,18,35], mitotic inhibition, changes in hydration, or changes in the lysosomal enzymes. Even when such changes are observed in the shelves, following treatment, it is difficult to prove that the changes are the cause of the cleft, rather than coincidental effects of the teratogen, or a result of the induced palatal abnormality.

3. The *tongue may obstruct shelf movement*. Anything that interferes with displacement of the tongue from between the shelves could cause cleft palate by delaying shelf movement. This could happen in a number of ways.
   (a) Forward movement of the tongue under the primary palate can be obstructed by the *large median process* present in an animal with cleft lip. The tongue may remain arched between the shelves and impede movement of the shelves over it[30].

(b) Acute *flexion of the head,* as in oligohydramnios, may press the jaw on the chest and push the tongue up between the shelves, impeding their movement[28]. Oligohydramnios does not, however, seem to be the factor that causes the cleft palate caused by cortisone or 6-aminonicotinamide[9].

(c) If displacement of the tongue from between the shelves depends on sudden extension of the head, as suggested by WALKER for the rabbit and possibly other species, anything that caused *interference with extension,* such as anomalies of the cervical vertebrae or oligohydramnios, could secondarily interfere with shelf movement[38].

(d) If displacement of the tongue depends to some degree on forward growth of the mandible, *interference with mandibular growth* could delay shelf movement. This might be a cause of the cleft palates that frequently occur in association with micrognathia, as in the PIERRE ROBIN syndrome[19].

(e) If successful closure is aided by the flattening of the shelves by the underlying tongue[26], a *small tongue* could predispose to cleft palate since in this case the flattening action of the tongue would be less.

(f) Furthermore, a *small tongue* may get wedged between the shelves, which appear to press in under it instead of over it, so the tongue cannot get out of the way This is seen in the recessive " shorthead " mutant in the mouse[3]. We have observed several C57BL/6 embryos with severe microglossia in which the tongue extends upwards through a cleft in the palate[23].

4. Presumably an abnormally wide head would make it more difficult for the shelves to meet, even if they became horizontal, flattened at the right time, and were the normal width.

5. Cleft palate would result if the shelves met but the epithelia did not fuse and break down. In culture, vitamin A and cortisone interfere with this process in the rat[24]. In the mouse, however, cortisone in the culture medium delays movement but does not prevent eventual fusion[16].

6. Finally, it is theoretically possible that the shelves would break down and reopen after closure.

Doubtless other possible mechanisms exist as well. It should be clear from all this that cleft palate can result from a great many factors and combinations of factors, be they fetal genetic, maternal genetic or environmental. It is often difficult to tell, by the appearance of the palate at term, how the defect originated.

CLEFT PALATE AS A THRESHOLD CHARACTER

In considering the various interactions of factors it may be useful to think of cleft palate as a *threshold character.*

In a population of normal embryos there will be a certain amount of variation in the time in development at which the shelves become horizontal, and flatten. In a non-inbred population some of the variation will be genetic, and some environmental.   Some embryos will be relatively young when the shelves reach the horizontal (the early ones), and some relatively old (the late ones). During this stage the embryo is continually growing.   A small delay in shelf movement, relative to the growth of the embryo as a whole, may not produce a cleft palate, because the shelves can still reach each other in time, and fuse.   With a greater delay some embryos (the late ones) will have cleft palates, because by the time the shelves reach the horizontal position the head is so wide that the shelves are too far apart to meet (Fig. 5).   The stage of development

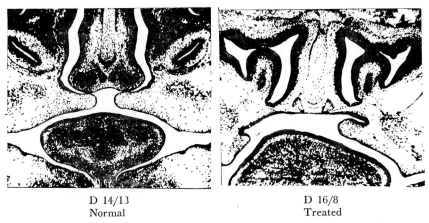

D 14/13
Normal

D 16/8
Treated

Fig. 5 Cross section of a normal embryo just before fusion of the palatal shelves (left) and a cortisone-treated embryo 1 days, 14 hours older.   Shelf movement has been delayed; the shelves will reach the horizontal, but the head is now so large they will be unable to meet. (Courtesy of B.E. Walker).

at which it is no longer possible for the shelves to meet constitutes a *threshold*, which separates those embryos which will be born with normal palates from those with cleft palates.   We may think of the population of embryos as a frequency distribution, with the X axis representing the stage in development of the embryo as a whole at the point when the shelves become horizontal, and the Y axis the number of embryos at the given stage (Fig. 6).   Thus the left tail of the distribution represents the few embryos in which shelf movement occurs relatively early in development, and the right tail of the distribution the few embryos in which shelf movement occurs relatively late, with most embryos falling in between.   The vertical line, T, represents the threshold; after this point the head is so wide that the shelves cannot meet when they become horizontal[8].

The dotted line represents a similar population of embryos exposed to a factor that delays shelf movement, relative to the developmental age of the embryo.   The embryos in which shelf movement occurs relatively late now fall beyond the threshold, and will have cleft palate.   Thus the combination of genetic and environmental factors that make the embryo late make it susceptible to cleft palate production.

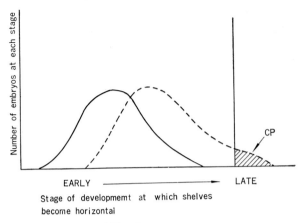

Stage of developmemt at which shelves
become horizontal

Fig. 6

THE BASIS FOR A STRAIN DIFFERENCE IN RESPONSE

Some years ago we found that maternal treatment with cortisone during pregnancy caused a higher frequency of cleft palate in the A/J strain than the C57BL strain[6,7]. The difference appears to be multigenic, involving both embryonic and maternal genes[8,12]. Cortisone causes the cleft palate by delaying shelf closure[34](Fig.7). This difference in susceptibility is related to the fact that C57BL embryos close their palates earlier in development than A/J embryos do (Fig. 8), that is, in our diagram the C57BL distribution is farther to the left of the distribution than is the A/J distribution[4,29,33]. Thus even if treatment delayed shelf closure in the two strains *by the same amount,* the A/J would have cleft palate more often than the C57BL (Fig. 9). The A/J embryo is more susceptible because its genotype places its palate nearer the threshold.

Notice that this strain difference in cortisone-induced cleft palate frequency depends on the normal developmental pattern of the mouse, not on how it handles the teratogen. One might therefore call it an *intrinsic* strain difference. This difference in susceptibility to cleft palate production between the two strains *should exist for any teratogen that acts by delaying shelf movement,* no matter what the mechanism. In addition to cortisone, the A/J is more susceptible than the C57BL strain with respect to 6-aminonicotinamide[11] (Table 1), hypervitaminosis A[35], X-radiation[1], 5-chlorodeoxyuridine[22], mitomycin C and chromomycin A[21]. The difference does not exist for galactoflavin[14], which could mean either that galactoflavin does not act by delaying palate closure (but in fact it does cause a delay[36]), or that there is another genetic difference tending to make A/J animals insensitive to this teratogen.

DIFFERENCES IN METABOLISM OF TERATOGEN

Another class of gene-environment interactions is that in which genetically different animals metabolize the teratogen differently, which may lead to differences

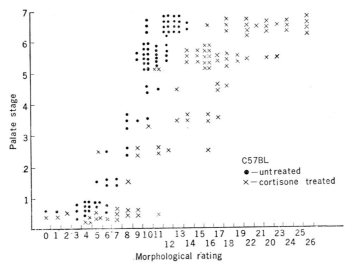

Fig. 7 Relation of palate stage to developmental age (morphological rating) of embryo. Stage 1 is beginning closure, 7 is closed (after WALKER and FRASER[34]).

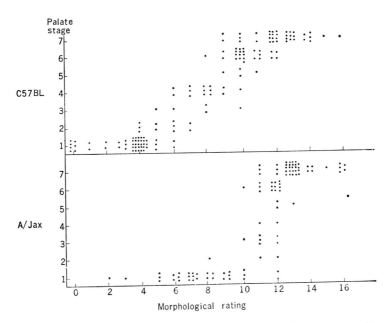

Fig. 8 Diagram showing palate closure begins at an earlier developmental age in C57BL than in A/J embryos (after WALKER and FRASER[33]).

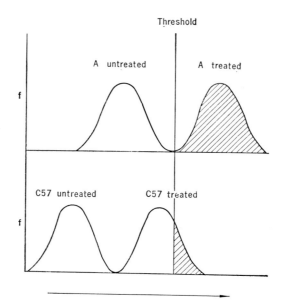

Fig. 9 For explanation see text

Table 1 Frequencies of cleft palate produced by maternal treatment with 6–aminonicotinamide (6 AN), followed two hours later by nicotinamide (NIC) on day $13\frac{1}{2}$ of pregnancy; the mothers were maintained on Purina Lab Chow (L.C.) or Breeder Chow (B.C.).

	Cross	Diet	Dose 6AN mg/kg	Dose NIC mg/kg	Number females	Number offspring	Number CP	% CP	P
1.	A × A	L.C.	14. 25	5. 48	14	82	53	64. 6	0. 001
2.	C × C	L.C.	19	7. 3	15	108	12	11. 1	
3.	A × A	B.C.	14. 25	5. 48	14	102	57	55. 9	
4.	C × C	B.C.	19	7. 3	18	117	79	67. 5	
5.	A × C	L.C.	19	7. 3	12	80	29	36. 3	0. 001
6.	C × A	L.C.	19	7. 3	10	56	2	3. 6	
7.	AC × A	L.C.	19	7. 3	23	200	89	44. 5	0. 01
8.	CA × A	L.C.	19	7. 3	30	295	76	25. 8	
9.	AC × A	B.C.	19	7. 3	16	133	57	42. 9	
10.	CA × A	B.C.	19	7. 3	18	157	72	45. 9	
11.	ACA × A	L.C.	14. 25	5. 48	33	243	105	43. 2	
12.	CAA × A	L.C.	14. 25	5. 48	33	263	134	50. 9	

ın frequency of malformation.   Such a case has been shown for 6-aminonicotin-amide by VERRUSIO in our laboratory[31].   This teratogen causes cleft palate when given to the pregnant mouse.   When nicotinamide ıs given concurrently, no cleft palates are produced.   Thus nicotinamide protects the embryo against the teratogen.   As mentioned above, the A/J strain is more susceptible to the teratogen than the C57BL/6 strain (Table 1, lines 1 and 2).   It takes less nicotin-amide to protect a C57 embryo against a given amount of 6AN than it does to protect an A/J embryo[31].   Furthermore, as the nicotinamide is given at progressively longer intervals after the 6-aminonicotinamide, the protective effect diminishes and eventually disappears.   In the A/J strain when the nicotinamide is given two hours after the 6AN the cleft palate frequency is the same as that produced by 6 AN alone.   In the C57BL/6 strain, however, there is still a significant amount of protection at 2 hours, and the protective effect does not disappear completely until 6 hours after the 6AN is given[31].   Thus there is a genetically determined difference in the rate at which the animal handles the teratogen — the " turnover " appears faster in the A/J strain.   A similar difference has been shown for the turnover of nicotinamide.   It must be added, however, that we do not know how much of the observed difference in cleft palate frequency between the two strains is due to this difference in rate of turnover; the greater susceptibility of the A/J strain could depend entirely on the " intrinsic " difference in developmental pattern referred to above.

INTERACTION OF GENETIC FACTORS AND DIET

Another complexity was added to the analysis of gene-environment interac-tions by the discovery of a cytoplasmic factor conferring resistance to the cleft-palate-producing effect of 6AN in the C57BL strain, which is manifested on one diet, but not another.

When A/J females were crossed to C57BL/6 males and treated with 6AN (always followed two hours later by nicotinamide) the frequency of cleft palate in the F1 offspring (called AC) was higher than in the reciprocal cross — C57BL/6 females by A/J males (called CA) (Table 1, lines 5 and 6).   When the two types of F1 females were crossed to A/J males, and treated with 6AN the off-spring of AC females had more cleft palates than the offspring of CA females (Table 1, lines 7 and 8)[11].   Since the two types of female have identical nuclear genes, the difference between them must have been transmitted to them through the cytoplasm.   This would suggest that the C57BL/6 strain carries a cytoplasmically transmitted difference that makes it more resistant to the 6AN. It seems likely that the difference in this case lies in the mitochondria, although conceivably it could involve a virus.   The difference disappears in the second back-cross (Table 1, lines 11 and 12)[23].

To add to the complexity, this cytoplasmically transmitted difference, which is present when the F1 mothers are maintained on Lab Chow, is not expressed when the mothers are on Breeder Chow (Table 1, lines 9 and 10)[32].   Preliminary results indicate that the difference is related to the fact that Lab Chow has more nicotinic acid than Breeder Chow.   Finally, if the difference resides in a cytoplasmic factor, the effect of diet should occur in the inbred strain as well,

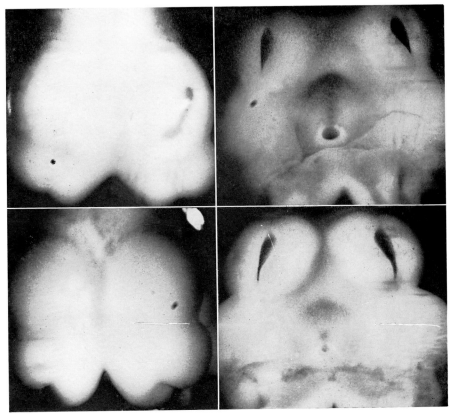

Fig. 10 Front (left) and ventral (right) views of C57 (top) and A/J (bottom) embryos on day 11, showing differences in shape of early face[27].

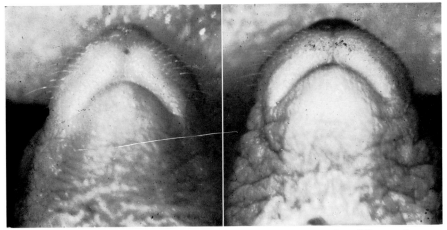

Fig. 11 Newborn A/J (left) and C 57 (right) embryos, showing difference in face shape.

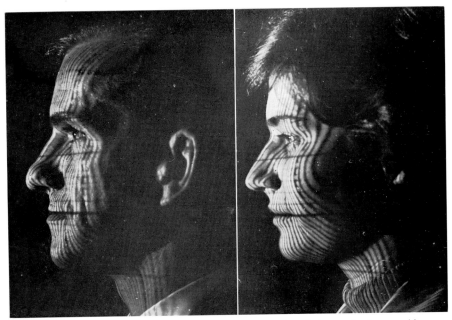

Fig. 12   Topographical patterns of face shape, produced by projecting a grid on the face[25].

and it does. The C57BL strain is more resistant to 6AN when maintained on Lab Chow than on Breeder Chow (Table 1, lines 2 and 4), whereas no such difference has been demonstrated in the A/J strain (Table 1, lines 1 and 3)[32].

To summarize thus far, we have presented three examples of interactions between genetic and environmental factors. Strain A/J is more susceptible to the teratogenic action of 6–aminonicotinamide (as measured by cleft palate frequency) than strain C57BL/6. This differences involves a difference in the normal rate of palate closure between the strains, quite independent of the teratogen, and we have therefore termed this an " intrinsic " difference. It is multifactorially inherited, and involves a developmental threshold, thus resembling many common congenital malformations.

The second example involves a difference between the two strains in the rate at which they metabolize the teratogen. It may contribute to the difference in cleft palate frequency, and could have a simple mode of inheritance, though this has not yet been demonstrated.

Third, when the animals are maintained on Lab Chow, a cytoplasmically transmitted factor increases the resistance of the C57BL/6 strain to 6-aminonicotinamide, but not that of the A/J strain. This effect is not present when the animals are raised on Breeder Chow. This example may teach us something new about mammalian mitochondria. It also adds a new complexity to the question of drug-induced malformations in particular and of gene-environment interactions in general.

. What relevance do such teratological considerations have to the problem in man? I would like to conclude by discussing another threshold character, cleft lip, in which our experimental studies led to a hypothesis which we are testing in man. The A/J strain has a 15% frequency of lateral cleft lip. The frequency can be increased by maternal treatment with aspirin. Treatment of C57BL mothers with aspirin causes median cleft lip. This difference in response seems to depend on a difference in shape of the face[27]. The medial nasal processes are farther apart and diverge more sharply in C57BL than in A/J embryos (Figs. 10 and 11).

It is reasonable to suppose that susceptibility to cleft lip in man may be related to face shape. If so, certain characteristics of face shape may occur more often in parents of cleft lip children than in other parents. To test this hypothesis, parents of children with cleft lip were compared with controls in photographs taken with a grid pattern projected on to the face by the method of Sassouni[25] (Fig. 12). Certain features of face shape appear more often in parents of cleft lip children than controls. For example the "vertical" pattern of lines, and a thin upper lip seem to occur more frequently in parents of children with cleft lip than in control individuals[10]. If these tentative findings are confirmed by further studies, they may help us to understand better the causes of congenital cleft lip.

REFERENCES

1. Callas, G. and Walker, B.E.: Palate morphogenesis in mouse embryos after X-irradiation. Anat. Rec. 145: 61–71, 1963.
2. Fitch, N.: An embryological analysis of two mutants in the house mouse both producing cleft palate. J. Exp. Zool. 136: 329–361, 1957.
3. Fitch, N.: Development of cleft palate in mice homozygous for the shorthead mutation. J. Morph. 109: 151–157, 1961.
4. Fraser, F.C.: The Use of Teratogens in the Analysis of Abnormal Developmental Mechanisms. In: First Intern. Conf. on Congenital Malformations. pp. 179–186. J.B. Lippincott Co., Philadelphia, 1961.
5. Fraser, F.C.: Cleft lip and cleft palate. Science, 158: 1603–1616, 1967.
6. Fraser, F.C. and Fainstat, T.D.: The production of congenital defects in the offspring of pregnant mice treated with cortisone. A progress report. Pediatrics 8: 527–533, 1951.
7. Fraser, F.C., Fainstat, T.D. and Kalter, H.: The experimental production of congenital defects with particular reference to cleft palate. Etudes Neo–Natales 2: 43–58, 1953.
8. Fraser, F.C., Walker, B.E. and Trasler, D.G.: Experimental production of congenital cleft palate: genetic and environmental factors. Pediatrics 19: 782–787, 1957.
9. Fraser, F.C., Chew, D. and Verrusio, A.C.: Oligohydramnios and cortisone-induced cleft palate in the mouse. Nature 214: 417–418, 1967.
10. Fraser, F.C. and Pashayan, H.: Unpublished observations.
11. Goldstein, M.B., Pinsky, M.F. and Fraser, F.C.: Genetically determined organ specific responses to the teratogenic action of 6–aminonicotinamide in the mouse. Genet. Res. Camb. 4: 258–265, 1963.
12. Jacobs, R.M.: Effects of cortisone acetate upon hydration of embryonic palate in two inbred strains of mice. Anat. Rec. 156: 1–4, 1966.
13. Kalter, H.: The inheritance of susceptibility to the teratogenic action of cortisone

in mice. Genetics 39: 185–196, 1954.

14. KALTER, H. and WARKANY, J.: Congenital malformations in inbred strains of mice induced by riboflavin–deficient, galactoflavin-containing diets. J. Exp. Zool. 136: 531–566, 1957.

15. KOCHAR, D.M. and JHONSON, E.M.: Morphological and autoradiographic studies of cleft palate induced in rat embryos by maternal hypervitaminosis A. J. Embryol. Exp. Morph. 14: 223–238, 1965.

16. LAHTI, A. and SAXEN, L.: Effect of hydrocortisone on the closure of palatal shelves *in vivo* and *in vitro*. Nature 216: 1217–1218, 1967.

17. LARSSON, K.S.: Studies on the closure of the secondary palate. II. Occurrence of sulpho–mucopolysaccharides in the palatine processes of the normal mouse embryo. Exp. Cell Res. 21: 498–503, 1960.

18. LARSSON, K.S.: Studies on the closure of the secondary palate. IV. Autoradiographic and histochemical studies of mouse embryos from cortisone-treated mothers. Acta Morph. Neerl.-Scand. 4: 369–375, 1962.

19. LATHAM, R.A.: The pathogenesis of cleft palate associated with the Pierre Robin syndrome. An analysis of seventeen–week human fetus. Brit. J. Plast. Surg. June, pp. 205–214, 1965.

20. MASUYAMA, Y.: Experimental studies on the genesis of cleft palate due to X–ray irradiation. Univ. Osaka J. Dent. 4: 847–870, 1959.

21. NISHIMURA, H.: Susceptibility to and modification of the teratogenic effects of antibiotics in mice. 34 th Ann. Report of the Jackson Laboratory, 1963.

22. NISHIMURA, H.: Chemistry and Prevention of Congenital Anomalies. Chas. C. Thomas, Springfield, 1964.

23. POLLARD, D.R. and FRASER, F.C.: Further studies on a cytoplasmically transmitted difference in response to the teratogen 6-aminonicotinamide. Teratology 1: 335–338, 1968.

24. POURTOIS, M.: In press. Cited by FRASER[5].

25. SASSOUNI, V.: Palatoprint, physioprint and roentgenographic cephalometry, as new methods in human identification. J. Forensic Sci. 2: 429–443, 1957.

26. TRASLER, D.G.: Unpublished observations.

27. TRASLER, D.G.: Pathogenesis of cleft lip and its relation to embryonic face shape in A/J and C57BL mice. Teratology 1: 33–49, 1968.

28. TRASLER, D.G., WALKER, B.E. and FRASER, F.C.: Congenital malformations produced by amniotic-sac puncture. Science 124: 439, 1956.

29. TRASLER, D.G. and FRASER, F.C.: Factors underlying strain, reciprocal cross and maternal weight differences in embryo susceptibility to cortisone-induced cleft palate in mice. Proc. X Intern. Cong. Genet. 2: 296–297, 1958.

30. TRASLER, D.G. and FRASER, F.C.: Role of the tongue in producing cleft palate in mice with spontaneous cleft lip. Devel. Biol. 6: 45–60, 1963.

31. VERRUSIO, A.C.: Biochemical Basis for a Genetically Determined Difference in Response to the Teratogenic Effects of 6–Aminonicotinamide. Ph.D. Thesis, McGill University.

32. VERRUSIO, A.C., POLLARD, D.R. and FRASER, F.C.: A cytoplasmically transmitted, diet-dependant difference in response to the teratogenic effects of 6–aminonicotinamide. Science 160: 206–207, 1968.

33. WALKER, B.E. and FRASER, F.C.: Closure of the secondary palate in three strains of mice. J. Embryol. Exp. Morph. 4: 176–189, 1956.

34. WALKER, B.E. and FRASER, F.C.: The embryology of cortisone–induced cleft palate. J. Embryol. Exp. Morph. 5: 201–209, 1957.

35. WALKER, B.E.: The association of mucopolysaccharides with morphogenesis of the

palate and other structures in mouse embryos. J. Embryol. Exp. Morph. 9: 22–31, 1961.

36. WALKER, B.E. and CRAIN, B.: Effects of hypervitaminosis A. On palate development in two strains of mice. Amer. J. Anat. 107: 49–58. 1960.
37. WALKER, B.E. and CRAIN, B. JR.: Abnormal palate morphogenesis in mouse embryos induced by riboflavin deficiency. Proc. Soc. Exper. Biol. Med. 107: 404–406, 1961.
38. WALKER, B.E.: Unpublished observations. Cited by FRASER[5].

DISCUSSION

GREEN (Australia)

1. Do you know of any significant geographical, racial, or nutritional difference in the incidence of cleft palate and or lip in man ?

2. What degrees of cleft palate occur and how do you regard high-arched (as opposed to horizontal) palate in relation to these ?

FRASER

1. There are certainly geographic differences, at least partly on a racial basis. Japanese have a higher frequency than Caucasians, and Negroes a lower one. Dr. J.R. MILLER will discuss differences in the Canadian Indians later in this workshop. I do not know of any evidence relating geographic differences to nutrition.

2. There are certainly degrees of severity in both cleft lip and cleft palate. I have not been able to make up my mind about the high arched palate. In many cases I think it may result from abnormal growth rates in the bones of the head rather than near-failure of the palate to close.

BAYANI-SIOSON (Philippines)

What is the basis for invoking the mitochondria as the cell organelle involved in the strain difference between A/J and C57 in their reaction to teratogens ? Could it be due to active metabolic activity of the mitochondria ?

FRASER

Mitochondria are a likely candidate for the site of the cytoplasmically transmitted difference in response to 6AN because they are transmitted by the egg cytoplasm, have a genetic system independant of the nuclear DNA, and are the site of the relevant biochemical reaction involving 6 ANAD.

MILLER, R.W. (U.S.A.)

What studies can be made in Asia, in man or in the laboratory, to elucidate the etiology or mechanism of cleft lip/palate ?

FRASER

Studies of the embryology of the face would be valuable, with comparison between facial development in races with high and low frequencies of cleft lip. Availability of embryos may make this a problem in some countries, however, and assuming there is a relation between embryonic and postnatal face shape, comparative studies of face shape in various races might be informative.

TAKANO (Japan)

Will you explain a little more about the mechanism or reason for the fact that, if nicotinamide is given a little later than the administration of 6-aminonicotinamide, it can prevent the teratogenic action of 6-aminonicotinamide.

FRASER

As I understand it, the 6 AN forms an inactive NAD analogue. Since it is a competitive reaction, flooding the system with nicotinamide prevents the formation of significant amounts of 6 ANAD.

SISODIA (India)

Is there any experimental evidence for the effects of isonicotinic acid hydrazide (NH) in producing or not producing cleft palate ?

FRASER

That is a very good point. I can't recall any experimental evidence on this possibility, but it would be interesting to try out.

DENIZ (Turkey)

Can stress factors play a role in producing cleft palates in animals kept in captivity in zoos ?

FRASER

It is very difficult to produce cleft palates by non-specific stress experimentally. Large doses of ACTH can produce cleft palate in the mouse, but it is doubtful if the pituitary could produce equivalent amounts of ACTH under stress. Incidentally, there is no valid evidence, that I know of, that stress can cause cleft palates in man.

CHROMOSOME ABERRATIONS IN CONGENITAL DISORDERS AND DEVELOPMENTAL ANOMALIES, BASED ON A CHROMOSOME SURVEY IN A JAPANESE POPULATION

Sajiro Makino

Professor, Zoological Institute, Faculty of Science,
Hokkaido University, Sapporo, Japan.

Within the past decade, rapid advances in cytogenetic techniques involving the use of tissue or blood cultures, colchicine and hypotonic solution pretreatments, have resulted in more precise and reliable analyses of chromosomes in man than were possible with the older direct squash or testis-section methods. With the discovery of a "new" chromosome number in man in 1956 by Tjio and Levan[13], and the findings of chromosome abnormality in Down's syndrome patients by Lejeune et al.[4], and by Ford et al.[1] and Jacobs and Strong[3] in sexually abnormal patients, a door was opened to modern human cytogenetics. Subsequent to these outstanding contributions, a number of investigators in the world have expended enthusiastic effort to define the morphology of the normal karyotype in various human races, as well as to screen congenital syndromes and/or clinical disorders for chromosomal abnormalities in man. Critical information has now been available on significant associations of chromosomal aberrations to disease states, and much evidence has lately been collected for differential diagnosis, or for critical understanding of the etiological cause, of these diseases. Thus, current progress in human cytogenetics with a surprising expansion of knowledge, has influenced many fields of clinical medicine, and has provided essential criteria for differential diagnosis of various congenital disorders. Present-day cytogenetics is contributing greatly to the elucidation of the etiology and morphogenesis of normal and abnormal physical traits in human beings. To date, cytogenetic studies in clinical settings are greatly valued, and this has led to the development of a new branch, "clinical cytogenetics", with a close association with many medical fields. Chromosomal analyses of somatic cells in man are now indispensable tools for diagnosis in various fields of clinical medicine.

Further, a recent association between virology and human cytogenetics has provided information on the role of viruses in the etiology of chromosome disturbances. In addition, there is now evidence that certain chromosome abnormalities are incompatible with live birth and associated with intrauterine death and abortion, on the basis of the discovery of a high incidence of chromosome abnormalities in spontaneous abortions (approximately 20%). Evidently most embryos with abnormal chromosome constitutions abort in early pregnancy.

Beginning in 1959, and continuing to date, a rather broad survey of chromosomes has been going on in my laboratory. This has involved normal individuals as well as patients with congenital and pathological conditions, with special emphasis on etiological problems and differential diagnosis of diseases, and also on the etiology of chromosome anomalies in the general population in relation to spontaneous abortions and congenital malformations.

During a period from September 1959 to November 1967, over 580 cases with diseases or syndromes usually diagnosed as congenital were screened for chromosomal abnormalities to obtain basic information on their etiological factors. These studies have been carried out in conjunction with clinicians in pediatrics, urology, obstetrics and gynecology, psychiatry, surgery, internal medicine, dermatology and others, with the intention of collecting data on a large scale from as many subjects as possible. On this occasion, I would like to present the chromosomal features from these 580 cases with congenital diseases with some appropriate comment on reported cases in the literature, with the intention of outlining recent advances in human cytogenetics on the one hand, and on the other hand, to encourage your interest in, or to complement your understanding of, the relationship or significance of chromosome abnormalities to certain congenital disorders, clinical defects and irregularities of sexual development[6-10,12].

CHROMOSOMAL FEATURES IN CONGENITAL SYNDROMES AND CLINICAL DISORDERS: A SUMMARY OF A SURVEY WORK IN THE MAKINO LABORATORY

Chromosome abnormalities which occur in relation to congenital diseases or disorders may involve both gene differences and changes in number and structure of the chromosomal elements. The recent advances in technical competence has facilitated to a considerable extent the analysis of some of these numerical and structural changes of chromosomes. Generally, reported instances of chromosome abnormalities in congenital diseases seem to involve either changes in autosomes or in sex chromosomes, but seldom both. Generally, numerical abnormalities of the chromosomes common in man involves polysomy (trisomy in many cases), monosomy, mosaicism and polyploidy (triploidy in most cases). Structural abnormalities generally occurring in human chromosomes are represented by translocation, deletion, inversion and some others such as enlarged satellites and isochromosomes. The most plausible mechanism leading to polysomy and monosomy, common abnormalities in human chromosomes, is nondisjunction in either autosomes or sex chromosomes. For instance, meiotic nondisjunction of the sex chromosomes in the course of both spermatogenesis and oogenesis in the parents may result in abnormal sex-chromosome combinations in the progeny as seen in Klinefelter's (XXY) or Turner's (XO) syndromes. Mitotic nondisjunction of the sex chromosomes in early stages of cleaving eggs may cause both mosaic and simple polysomic individuals, for example, XO/XXX, XY/XXY, XXYY, etc. Polyploidy may be ascribed in most cases to the union of non-reduced (diploid) gametes.

Many cases have been reported in which certain definite chromosome aberrations of sex chromosomes are possible causes usually recognized. Further, in many cases of congenital disorders or developmental anomalies, no definite correlation has been detected between the chromosome abnormalities and the clinical manifestations. But, it can be assumed that certain chromosome abnormalities are probably instrumental in the etiology of these disorders. In contrast, many cases of congenital and clinical defects have been reported which show no identifiable change or variation from a normal complement of chromosomes. A minute loss or rearrangement of chromosomal materials is, of course, far more difficult to demonstrate than gross chromosomal changes which can be detected with current techniques. A normal chromosome complement in a given patient with certain clinical defects is not always, therefore, an indication that chromosome aberrations have not occurred: a superficially normal complement does not always imply a normal genetic pattern. We must grant the possibility that a variety of chromosome abnormalities, not detectable by current technical methods, may be masked by a superficially normal karyotype.

Whether identifiable chromosomal aberrations or changes alone are the sole etiological cause of congenital disorders is uncertain. Congenital syndromes may be associated with certain environmental or physiological factors other than chromosome changes. Very probably, certain abnormal sex differentiation may result from some factor which causes endocrine imbalance and affects the course of sexual differentiation in some critical stage after it has been genetically determined. Mention should be made of the fact that most chromosome analyses are made on a limited number of tissues, so a theoretical possibility exists that the use of other types of tissue material would produce different results. The question of cell mosaicism may arise in relation to the etiology of congenital diseases.

In the following, I wish to present results of our chromosomal survey carried out during a period from September 1959 to November 1967 in my laboratory. The principal aim is to provide information useful for understanding the relationship of clinical conditions to cytogenetic features, as well as for indicating clues for better criteria for clinical consideration of those diseases.

1) A chromosomal survey was made on a total of 558 induced abortuses and on testicular specimens from 16 adults. It was shown that, regardless of sex, age, tissue, organ or technical methods, the vast majority of cells studied had 46 chromosomes, with an XX sex mechanism in females and an XY in males. The same result was obtained in some isolated races. AINU (13 ♀♀, 12 ♂♂), OROKS (1 ♀, 2 ♂♂) and GILYAKS (1 ♀). No evidence was obtained for chromosomal polymorphism in Japanese and other populations. Out of 558 induced abortuses, 19, or 3.4%, were chromosomally abnormal. These comprised 6 mosaic cases (XO/XY, XY/XXY, XO/XX and 3 OY (?)/XY cases), 1 case of X-trisomy (47, XXX), 2 cases of X-monosomy (45, XO), 1 case of D-trisomy (47, XX), 1 case of D/D translocation, 1 case with an unusually elongated long arm of A_1 chromosome (46, XY), 1 case with enlarged satellite of a D chromosome (46, XX) and 6 cases with an unusually long Y chromosome. It is evident that chromosome abnormalities occur much more frequently in spontaneous than in induced abortions. The prenatal sex-ratio in these induced abortuses was 100 ♀ : 83 ♂.

2) 118 case of *Down's syndrome* including 4 suspected ones were

chromosomally studied with marrow and blood cultures. With the following three exceptions, the majority of the cases had 47 chromosomes associated with the standard G group (21) trisomy. One of the exceptional cases (a girl) showed 46 chromosomes with a reciprocal translocation between chromosomes 21 and 14. A female infant with Down's syndrome with a heart defect of an unknown type was heterologous for chromosome 16 and trisomic for chromosome 21. A girl with typical Down's syndrome showed trisomy for one of the G group chromosomes which was characterized by a deletion of the short arm. A suggestion is possible that a trisomic condition for the long arm of one of the G group chromosomes is probably associated with the cause of this syndrome.

There are reported cases which showed certain karyotypic variants characterized by the translocation of the extra 21 chromosome. Many cases have been reported in which the extra chromosome is translocated onto another chromosome: the translocations between chromosome 21 and one of the 13–15 chromosomes, or between 21 and another 21 or 22 chromosome have been reported rather frequently. Cell-mosaicism is a less common occurrence in Down's syndrome.

3) It has been considered that *congenital heart defects* are caused by genetical abnormalities. The chromosomes of 24 patients with congenital heart defect were studied, and 9 of them showed certain chromosome abnormalities. The heart anomalies involved were 3 cases with atrial septal defect of unknown type, 2 cases involving both atrial septal defect and ventricular septal defect, 2 cases of heart defect of unknown nature, 1 case with heart defect with suspicion of ventricular septal defect, macropenis, coccigeal fovea and some other anomalies. Of special interest cytogenetically was a heterologous condition of chromosome No. 16 found in 8 cases: in all of them, members of the 16th pair were not homologous in the great majority of cells observed. The heterologous condtion of the 16th pair varies in degree even from cell to cell in the same individual. The remaining chromosomes did not show any morphological or numerical abnormality. Of interest was a girl with Down's syndrome and a heart defect of unknown nature: she showed 47 chromosomes involving no.21 trisomy and the odd manifestation of No. 16 chromosome. Similar types of chromosomal anomaly associated with congenital diseases are referred to in the literature. The most plausible interpretation for the heterologous manifestation of No. 16 is a partial deletion of a small segment in the long arm of one member of the 16 th pair, or alternatively, certain irregular condensation of chromosome material in the long arm. It is uncertain that this abnormality is an essential etiological cause of heart defects. In addition to the 8 cases, one patient, a member of male twin infants, who suffered from heart defect with suspicion of ventricular septal defect, macropenis and other anomalies, showed 46 chromosomes of a normal complement, but the Y chromosome was unusually long, corresponding in length to chromosomes 16–18. In the remaining 15 patients with a diagnosis of congenital heart defects, we have failed to detect any morphological chromosome anomaly.

4) Four cases of *"cri du chat" syndrome* including 2 suspected cases were investigated for chromosome abnormality. The two suspected cases, both males, were found to be chromosomally normal, while one case showed a standard

abnormality characterized by the short arm deletion of a B group chromosome. The remaining case, a 6–month female infant, was outstanding in having 45 chromosomes, with an absent G group chromosome, i.e., being monosomic for one of the G chromosomes. As a tentative interpretation for this anomaly, it is suggested that a masked translocation involving a B and a G chromosome exists. This is based on the assumption involving the possible formation of a zygote partially monosomic for the short arm of the no. 5 chromosome.

In the recent literature there are reports of several karyotypic variants involving mosaicism, translocation and ring chromosomes associated with the "cri du chat" syndrome.

5) Chromosomal data on *malformations* were derived from 16 cases of *multiple malformations,* 3 cases of *thalidomide-embryopathy,* 2 cases of *Pierre-Robin syndrome,* 14 cases of *cleft lip and cleft palate* 3 cases of *polycystic kidney,* and 4 cases of *Laurence-Moon-Biedl syndrome* including 2 incomplete ones. Out of 16 cases with multiple malformations of varying types and degrees dealt with here, a chromosome abnormality occurred in 2 cases. One of these a 3–year-boy with a number of abnormalities, was remarkable by having a Y chromosome of unusual length, while the other chromosomes were apparently normal. Another case, a stillborn female, showed 47 chromosomes associated with trisomy for the G group chromosome. The remaining 14 cases had 46 chromosomes of a morphologically normal complement, XX in females and XY in males.

The three cases of *thalidomide-embryopathy,* 2 cases of *Pierre-Robin syndrome* 14 cases of *cleft lip and cleft palate,* 3 cases of *polycystic kidney* and 4 cases of *Laurence-Moon-Biedl syndrome,* had a normal complement of 46 chromosomes. The two cases with incomplete manifestations of Laurence-Moon-Biedl syndrome were noted by an unusually long Y chromosome in each.

There are reports in the literature of a variety of chromosome abnormalities associated with malformation syndromes. They involve triploidy, trisomy for the chromosomes of the D, E, and G group, an extra chromosome of small size, enlarged satellites in certain chromosomes, and others.

6) Chromosomes were studied in 43 cases with *congenital ophthalmologic diseases.* The occurrence of a normal chromosome complement was shown in all of them. There were 9 male patients who had a Y chromosome of unusual length. One case with suspected *retinal angiogliosis* showed an anomalous chromosome of group 6–X–12, which was evident by an elongated and weakly stained structure near the centromeric region of the long arm. Recently LELE et al. studied the chromosome of five cases of coloboma iridis with some other anomalies and found in 2 of them a pericentric inversion in no.1 chromosome. No such abnormality was noted in our study.

7) Twenty eight cases of *mental deficiency* studied showed consistent counts of 46 chromosomes in all cases. With three exceptions, two of the three showed a Y chromosome of unusual length, one with a long Y and the other having a minute Y, while the remaining one case was remarkable by the presence of an enlarged short arm of one of the G group chromosomes. Various types of chromosome abnormality have been reported in patients with mental deficiency associated with some other clinical defects. These have included extra chromosomes with an increase of the chromosome number, translocation, dele-

tion, and so on.

8) Six patients with *microcephaly* studied had 46 chromosomes of a normal karyotype.

9) The chromosomes were studied in patients with *hydrocephaly* (1 case)., *anencephaly* (1 case), *Bourneville-Pringle disease* (1 case), *syringomyelia* (2 cases), *cerebral palsy* (2 cases), *postpartum psychosis* (1 case), *Recklinghausen's disease* (5 cases including a suspected one), *cerebral edema-spinal hernia* (1 case), *tuberous sclerosis* (2 cases), *choreoathetosis* (2 cases), *schizophrenia* (2 cases), *De Lange's syndrome* (1 case), *infantile nephrosis* (1 case), *diabetes insipidus renalis* (2 cases), *osteogenesis imperfecta* (1 case), *chondrodystrophy* (2 cases), *craniostenosis* (2 cases), *hereditary ataxia* (1 case), *dysphasia epiphysialis multiplex congenita* (1 case), *multiple exostosis* (1 case), *progressive muscular dystrophy* (2 cases), *myogenic myopathy* (1 case), *myasthenia myoclonus epilepsy* (1 case), *hypofunction of adrenals* (1 case), *hypothyroidism* (1 case), *Marfan's syndrome* (5 cases), *Hurler's syndrome* (2 cases), *ectodermal dysplasia* (2 cases), *naevus fuscocaeruleus ophthalmomaxillaris* (1 case), *poikiloderma congenitale* (1 case), *megaloblastic anemia* (1 case), *spherocytic anemia* (1 case), *Sturge-Weber syndrome* (1 case), *Kasabach-Merritt syndrome* (1 case), *Banti's syndrome* (2 cases), *Hippel-Lindau disease* (1 case), *sepsis with leukemoid reaction* (1 case), *brain arterio-venous malformation* (1 case), *von Willebrand's disease* (6 cases), and *congenital pulmonary stenosis* (1 case). Almost all the patients mentioned above showed in their cells 46 chromosomes of a normal complement. Exceptions are 1 case each of brain arterio-venous malformation and schizophrenia, and 2 cases of choreoathetosis: all of which possessed an unusual length of the Y chromosome.

In the literature there is reference to certain abnormalities such as enlarged satellites in certain acrocentric chromosomes, or abnormal length of the G group chromosomes in a few cases of Marfan's syndrome.

10) Patients with *metabolic disorders*, including 1 case of *hypercalcemia*, 2 cases of *phenylketonuria*, 1 case of *congenital cataract*, 3 cases of *albinism*, 1 case of *glycogen storage disease* of liver, 1 case of *progeria*, 5 cases of *Wilson's disease* 1 case each of *cystinuria, amaurotic family idiocy* and *hyperammonemia*, were subjected to chromosome study. All cases studied possessed 46 chromosomes of a normal karyotype. Two patients, one with hyperammonemia and the other with cystinuria, had an abnormally long Y chromosome.

11) In *growth disorders*, the chromosomes of 3 cases of *dwarfism*, 1 case each of *malnutrition* and *failure to thrive*, and 3 cases of *obesity* were studied and all showed 46 chromosomes with a normal complement.

12) Some 230 patients with diagnoses of *sex abnormalities* were screened for chromosome abnormality. In organizing data relevant to the chromosome abnormalities and their relationship to phenotypic manifestation, the cases were tentatively arranged into *phenotypic males, phenotypic females, hermaphroditism* and *agonadism*. Generally, numerical abnormalities of sex chromosomes in man are associated with a single loss or gain of either the X or Y chromosome, or of both, that is XO, XXX, XXXX, XXY, XYY, XXXY, XXYY, XXXXX, XXXXY and XXXYY constitutions.

Phenotypic males: Infertile males generally referred to by the term of *Klinefelter's syndrome* are generally characterized by azoospermia, gynecomastia, elevated urinary gonadotropin excretion and atrophic testes with degeneration and hyalinization of seminiferous tubules and hyperplasia of Leydig cells. Klinefelter patients are commonly sex-chromatin positive, and show mental retardation of varying degrees. The chromosomes of 46 patients with this syndrome including 4 suspected cases were studied, and we found among them 43 cases with chromosome anomalies. The remaining 3 cases were chromatin negative and had a normal male karyotype of 46,XY. Out of 43 abnormal cases, 35 showed a 47,XXY chromosome constitution, a standard cytogenetic pattern of this syndrome. Of interest are the following 7 cases: one case associated with a 48,XXXY constitution, one case with a 49,XXXXY, 3 cases with a 48,XXYY, one case with a 46,XX/47,XXY mosaicism, and one suspected case with a 46, XY/47,XXY. One of the XXY cases had an unusually long Y chromosome.

Though the chromatin-positive Klinefelter patients show in the majority of cases, an XXY constitution, many other variants of abnormal sex-chromosomes have been recorded in the literature. The major categories of abnormal sex-chromosome conditions so far recorded are: 1) simple aneuploidies such as XXY, XXXY, XXXXY, XXYY and XXXYY, 2) a variety of mosaicism including XY/XXY, XX/XXY, XY/XXXY, XXY/XXYY, XXXY/XXXXY, XO/XY/XXY, XY/XX/XXY, XX/XXY/XXXY, XY/XXY/XXYY, XXXY/XXXXY/XXXXXY, and XO/XY/XX/XXY, and 3) mosaicisms or aneuploidies with structural anomalies such as XXX_y, $XXXX_{DL}Y$, $XY/XX_{DL}Y$, $XY/XX_{DL}/XX_{DL}Y$, $XXY/XXX_{DL}Y$, $XO/XX_{IL}/XX_{IL}Y$, and XX plus a fragment of the Y translocated onto one of the 21–22 autosomes. There is a general trend in chromatin-positive Klinefelter patients that certain physical and mental disorders increase with the increase of the number of the X chromosomes. For example, a certain degree of mental retardation, as revealed by the I. Q. test, is present in about 50 per cent of the XXY patients, while the incidence is almost 100 per cent in the XXXY and XXXXY cases. Probably, the genetic inactivation for the second, third and fourth X chromosomes is incomplete. It is also interesting to note that men of disordered personality tend to occur rather frequently in association with extra X and Y chromosomes.

It has been estimated by sex-chromatin surveys that the incidence of chromatin-positive Klinefelter's syndrome is about 0.2 per cent of all liveborn males, while the incidence is 0.85 per cent for mentally defective males and 3.3 per cent for subfertile patients. The incidence of Down's syndrome with an autosomal trisomy, is known to increase with maternal age. A similar situation has been noted in chromatin positive Klinefelter's syndrome. A more obvious maternal age effect was noted in patients who had both the Klinefelter's and Down's syndromes.

Of 16 patients with *hypospadias* studied, 13 cases were chromosomally normal having a 46,XY complement. The remaining 3 cases were noted to have an abnormally long Y chromosome. All nine cases of *hypogonadism* concerned here showed also a normal male karyotype (46,XY).

The chromosomes of 35 cases with *cryptorchism* characterized by bilateral or unilateral undescended testes were studied. With two exceptions, all the patients were found to possess a normal male karyotype (46,XY). One of the exceptional cases was remarkable by showing an unusually elongated short arm in one of the D group chromosomes (probably no. 15), other elements being normal. Since the same abnormality was found in his father, paternal grandfather, a female cousin and two paternal aunts, all being phenotypically normal, this abnormality is apparently an inheritable character and is not essentially associated with a specific phenotypic irregularity.

The chromosomes were investigated in 5 patients with *gynecomastia.* Four of these cases showed a normal male karyotype of 46, XY, leaving one interesting case characterized by a mosaicism with a 45,XO/46,XY complex. It has been reported that an XO/XY mosaic sex-complex exerts variable effects on the sexual manifestation from subject to subject, depending on the difference in relative proportion of the two cell lines, so that the patients do not always exhibit a definite phenotypic similarity. Among 17 cases of *azoospermia* and 1 case of *oligozoospermia* who complained of infertility, a normal male karyotype (46, XY) was established in 16 cases, leaving one patient who had a slightly long Y chromosome. Three cases of *monorchism* showed a normal male karyotype. Out of 3 patients with *small penis,* 2 had a normal male complement, while one case was outstanding in showing a mosaic complex of 46,XY/47,XXY in a proportion of 48 : 13. Reported instances indicate that, in XY/XXY mosaic patients, the XY cell line has a beneficial effect on the phenotype in many cases, so that a wide range of phenotypic expression occurs from a normal male pattern to Klinefelter's syndrome. Our study revealed one suspected Klinefelter patient having rather normal external genitalia and one with small penis, both of whom possessed an XY/XXY mosaicism. Five cases of *eunuchoidism,* 1 case each with *ectopic testis* and *atrophic testis* possessed a normal male chromosome pattern, except for the fact that a long Y chromosome was detected in one of the eunuchoid cases.

Phenotypic females: Patients generally designated by the term of *Turner's syndrome* are phenotypic females characterized by ovarian dysgenesis, small stature and multiple congenital malformations, together with amenorrhoea, infantile or absent ovaries, and infantile external genitalia. Mental retardation is not so common nor so severe as in Klinefelter patients. A large number of the cases with this syndrome was shown to be chromatin negative. Three of these chromatin negative cases were chromosomally examined in our study and showed invariably consistent counts of 45 chromosomes which were associated with an XO sex-complex, a standard chromosome abnormality for this syndrome.

In the literature there are reports of patients with clinical features very similar to those of XO individuals who had mosaicism or structural abnormalities of the X chromosome. The known abnormalities of the X chromosome are isochromosome for the long arm, deletion of either the short arm or the long arm, and ring chromosomes. Further, many mosaic conditions have been recorded in Turner's syndrome and related disorders: they are XO/XX XO/XY, XO/XXX, XO/XYY, XO/XX$_{DL}$, XO/XX$_{DS}$, XO/XX$_{IL}$, XO/XX$_R$, XO/Xy, XO/XY/XX, XO/XX/XXX, XO/XX/XX$_R$, XO/XX$_R$/XX$_R$X$_R$, XO/XX$_{IL}$/XX$_{IL}$X$_{IL}$, and XO/Xy/XXXy. In every case an XO line is present. The phenotypes of the mosaic cases are more variable than those of the standard XO cases. For example, the phenotypic expression of the XO/XY mosaics varies from the standard XO pattern to males with testes. The XO/XX mosaics had phenotypes ranging from

Turner's pattern to women with normal stature.

Sex-chromatin surveys in a total of more than 25,000 liveborn babies report that the incidence of chromatin-negative XO individuals is about 0.4 per 1,000 liveborn females, the value being about one fifth that of chromatin-positive XXY males. Recent information has made it clear that the XO condition is observed in about 4 per cent of spontaneously aborted conceptuses. It is therefore evident that the rarity of the XO individuals at birth is due to the high prenatal death rate of XO zygotes.

Twelve patients with an *enlarged clitoris* were found to have a normal female complement (46, XX). In 12 pateints with *atresia vaginae,* 11 cases were chromosomally normal as 46,XX, while one patient had a G group chromosome with an enlarged short arm, other elements being normal. Ten cases of *adreno-genital syndrome* showed a normal female complement (46, XX). This syndrome is said to be a condition of pseudohermaphroditism or virilism induced endogenously by increased secretion of androgens from the adrenal gland. Seven patients with *testicular feminization* characterized by completely female external genitalia, well-developed breasts but without a uterus and with underdeveloped or maldeveloped testes, were found to possess an apparently normal male karyotype (46, XY). Testicular feminization is therefore a type of clearly marked intersex, being usually sex-chromatin negative.

Of 3 cases with *sexual hypoplasia* studied, remarkable chromosomal abnormalities occurred in 2 cases, and one had a normal female complement. One of the abnormal cases had a 47,XXX complement, and the other was mosaic of a 45,XO/46,XX complex. Generally, females with the XXX constitution are phenotypically normal and fertile, but some of them are known to show underdeveloped sexual characters associated with secondary amenorrhoea. The most common feature of the XXX females is mental retardation, its degree being usually mild. On the basis of sex-chromatin surveys, it is estimated that the incidence of the XXX women is 1.2 per 1,000 liveborn females. A few cases of the XXXX female and one case of the XXXXX female have hitherto been recorded. Generally, the clinical picture of the XO/XY mosaic patients is described to be variable showing intersexual tendency in general, because of different effects of cell lines on the phenotype manifestation.

Among 17 cases diagnosed as *primary amenorrhea*, seven were chromosomally abnormal, leaving nine cases with a normal female karyotype and one showing a normal male complement. The seven abnormal cases were: one case with a 45, XO complex, a pattern common to Turner's syndrome, one characterized by a 45,XO/46,XX mosaicism, one showing a long arm deletion of the X chromosome with a minute fragment, one associated with an isochromosome for the long arm of the X, one having an additional minute fragment, one showing a well-defined secondary constriction in an A-chromosome, and one showing an enlarged short arm of a G-chromosome. Of 2 cases with *hypoplasia uteri*, one showed a normal female karyotype of 46,XX, while the other was exceptional by having a normal male chromosome pattern of 46,XY. One case each with *oligomenorrhoea, epispadia* and *sterility* showed a normal female chromosome complement (46, XX).

Hermaphroditism: On the basis of clinical conditions and phenotypic manifestations, chromosomal descriptions are given separately for true hermaphroditism and pseudohermaphroditism.

True hermaphroditism is a condition in which both ovarian and testicular tissues are present, together with equivocal external genitalia. These individuals are sterile, and in Goldschmidt's terminology, intersexes. Two true hermaphrodites were investigated for chromosome abnormality, and both showed the chromosomes of a normal female pattern as 46, XX. On the basis of chromosomal diagnosis, the genetic sex of these two hermaphrodite individuals is evidently female.

Pseudohermaphroditism is generally categorized into male and female pseudohermaphroditism. Generally, male pseudohermaphrodites possess equivocal genitalia showing varying degrees of feminization, most being chromatin negative, while female pseudohermaphrodites are females in general appearance with atrophic ovaries and masculinized external genitalia in varying degrees. Among 10 cases of *male pseudohermaphroditism* studied by us, 8 were chromosomally males having a 46,XY constitution: one was characterized by a 45,XO/46,XY mosaicism, and the remaining one showed a 46,XY complement with an extraordinary long Y chromosome. All of 3 *female hermaphrodites* studied had a female pattern of the chromosomes as 46, XX.

To date. several cases of true hermaphrodites having a normal female chromosome constitution have been reported. Further, several mosaic cases, such as those of XO/XY, XX/XXX (or XO/XX/XXX), XX/XY (or XX/Xx) and XX/XXY/XXYYY, were recorded in patients diagnosed as true hermaphrodites. Generally, the clinical manifestation in a series of mosaics is variable, due probably to different effects of each cell line on the phenotypic expression. FRACCARO et al.[2] stated that at the origin of human hermaphrodites there is consistently a sex-chromosome mosaicism, and that most authors who reported an XX constitution in human hermaphrodites have based their conclusion on limited tissue samples. The other plausible interpretation for the establishment of true hermaphroditism is a hormonal influence probably exerted during the fetal stage. Though many types of sexual abnormalities or defects of sexual development in man have been reported to be associated with the sex-chromosome abnormalities, it is likely that abnormalities of sexual development such as hermaphroditism are not necessarily correlated with chromosomal disturbances, and that there are cases that may occur in association with hormonal imbalance or allied environmental factors.

Agonadism. A 3–year-old patient who had no internal sexual organs was screened for chromosome abnormality, and was found to have a normal male karyotype (46, XY).

Abnormalities of the Y chromosome: There are reports of a variety of cases with abnormality of the Y chromosome in man. General conclusion reached by recent authors is that: 1) a considerable variability occurs in the size of the Y chromosome, 2) the abnormality in size of the Y is not essentially correlated with an abnormal phenotype, 3) the unusual length of the Y is an inheritable character, and 4) the Y chromosome carries an effective masculinizing factor or factors. Morphological or numerical abnormalities of the Y chromosome have been studied less extensively than those of the X, probably because of the fact that no apparent phenotypic abnormalities occur in association with morphological abnormality of the Y, and the sex-chromatin test contributes no ancillary evidence with respect to the Y.

We know that current human cytogenetics has demonstrated a variety of diseases associated with abnormality of the Y chromosome. Further, evidence has been provided on the genetic implication of the Y, the localization of a masculinizing factor, the role of the Y in human sexual development, and behavior disorders of patients with an abnormal Y chromosome. It has been shown that the length of the human Y chromosome varies considerably from case to case. An unusually long Y chromosome has been reported to occur in both phenotypically normal males as well as in male patients with a variety of congenital and sexual disorders. We found some 30 long Y cases associated with varying disorders, such as Marfan's syndrome, Down's syndrome, azoospermia, multiple malformations, various types of hypogonadism, hypospadia penis, male pseudohermaphroditism, hyperammonemia, mental retardation, heart defects, Klinefelter's syndrome, cryptorchism, eunuchoidism, incomplete Laurence-Moon-Biedl syndrome, choreoathetosis, brain arterio-venous malformation, schizophrenia, and so on. It is then generally agreed that the long Y is not necessarily associated with definite phenotypic anomalies. This fact suggests that the Y chromosome exerts no effective or direct influence in the cause of congenital disorders. It seems, however, of some interest to note that, among 17 patients with neuropsychiatric diseases examined in our study, 8 cases showed an abnormality in length of the Y. The length of the long Y chromosome usually exceeds the average length of the 19–20 autosomes, and in some cases it is almost the same in size as the 13–15 autosomes. Evidence has been presented by our studies and some others that the increased length of the Y is a heritable character. Also it has been reported that racial differences in mean length of the Y seem to exist. The extra length of the Y chromosome may be ascribed either to an actual increase of chromatin content resulting from duplication or translocation, or to reduced contraction of the normal length of chromatin because of its heteropycnotic nature. Usually, the long Y is marked by the same morphological characteristics as those of the normal Y, except for the unusual length. On the other hand, evidence has been presented that the silver-grain content in the long Y as revealed by autoradiographic techniques is almost the same as that in the normal Y. Even if the long Y reflects an increase of the Y chromosome material, this may not always exert a direct influence upon phenotype, because there is evidence that a double dose of normal Y chromosome material does not essentially affect the phenotype in man. XYY males, for instance, are mostly fertile men, and the XXY, XXXY and XXYY Klinefelter patients are clinically indistinguishable.

In contrast to the elongated Y chromosome, an extraordinarily short, or partially deleted Y chromosome has also been reported in both phenotypically normal and abnormal males. Likewise, the short Y does not seem to be associated with specific phenotypic anomalies. An extremely small Y, that is regarded as a minute centric fragment of the Y, also results in an apparently male phenotype. Evidently the minute Y is functional for the differentiation of male sex. No positive evidence has been presented for the belief that the small Y is responsible for infertility, though a case with oligospermia has been reported.

Recent evidence point to the relative inertness of the Y chromosome: the unusually long Y as well as the deleted Y, or Y chromosome excess in number, does not usually affect the phenotype in man. The human Y chromosome is mostly heteropycnotic and carries in its long arm a large achromatic structure. Autoradiographically, the Y shows a late DNA replication. The heteropycnosis and late DNA replication of the Y may be an indication of its genetic inertness.

Worthmentioning is the behaviour disorder of patients associated with the extra Y chromosomes. Fifteen XYY males have been reported in the literature. Hypogonadism and mental retardation with occasional schizophrenia were noted in some cases, but others were seemingly normal and fertile. Although certain physical and mental disabilities of Klinefelter patients tend to increase with the increase in the number of the X chromosome, our interest is called to the recent observation that disordered personality has occurred in association with patients bearing an XYY sex-constitution. PRICE and WHATMORE[11] analysed the behaviour of nine criminals with an XYY complex and found that they suffered from a severe disorder of personality in most cases associated with intellectual impairment, due probably to the extra Y chromosome. The findings that the XYY males tend to have criminal records, on account of their disordered personalities and an unusually high stature over six feet tall are a subject of utmost importance in connection with social problems. A similar trend of disordered behaviour has been noted also in XXYY males. Autoradiographically, one of the two Y chromosomes was found to replicate its DNA early.

Sex-determination: One of the striking contributions of human cytogenetics to biology is the finding of the Y chromosome as a carrier of effective masculinizing factor or factors in man. The existence of a Y chromosome is always associated with male differentiation irrespective of the number of X chromosomes. Thus the masculinizing effect of the Y is very striking: a single Y sufficiently overrules the presence of two or more extra X chromosomes. For instance, XXY, XXXY, XXXXY, XO/XY, XO/XXY, XXXX/XXXXY and XO/XY/XX individuals are all phenotypically males, in striking contrast to the fact that female sex-differentiation always occurs in association with the absence of the Y chromosome, since individuals with XO, XX, XXX and XXXX are phenotypically females. The existence of two or more X chromosomes in males affects their sexual phenotypes to a certain extent, leading to Klinefelter's syndrome In contrast, two Y chromosomes do not seem to enhance the male characters: the XYY, XXYY and XXXYY individuals show a similar degree of masculinity to the XY, XXY and XXXY males, respectively. Recent information indicates that at least one normal X chromosome may be important for survival. The nullo-X individuals such as those with OO, OY and YY sex-chromosome constitutions are almost certainly nonviable. The structurally abnormal X chromosomes usually occur only in one member of the two X's in the female complement, the other member being normal morphologically and functionally.

In this connection, mention should be made of some structural abnormalities of the human Y chromosome which are characterized by pericentric inversion and isochromosome for the long arm (Y_{IL}). Of special interest is the Y_{IL} in relation to genetic basis of sex determination. Individuals with an XY_{IL} constitution so far recorded are phenotypically females in spite of the presence of the

Y. They were found to carry some anomalous sexual characters, and consequently they are infertile. It has been speculated that the male determining factor in men may be located on the short arm of the Y, and that the genes on the long arm are not primarily involved with the determination of male sexual characters.

Clinical cytogenetics is as yet at a young stage of development. Reliable data derived through survey work on a large scale are required in order to provide information on the significance of chromosome aberrations in the etiology of congenital syndromes and developmental anomalies. Rapidly expanding knowledge in this field has rendered it difficult to make any generalization regarding etiological problems in relation to congenital anomalies.

REFERENCES

1. FORD, C.E., POLANI, P.E., DEALMEIDA, J.C., and BRIGGES, J.H.: A sex-chromosome anomaly in a case of gonadal dysgenesis (Turner's syndrome). Lancet 1: 711-713, 1959.

2. FRACCARO, M., TAYLOR, A.I., BODIAN, M., and NEWNS, G.H.: A human intersex ("true hermaphrodite") with XX/XXY/XXYYY sex-chromosomes. Cytogenetics 1: 104-112, 1962.

3. JACOBS, P.A. and STRONG, J.A.: A case of human intersexuality having a possible XXY sex-determining mechanism. Nature 183: 302-303, 1959.

4. LEJEUNE, J., GAUTIER, M., and TURPIN, R.: Étude des chromosomes somatiques de neuf enfants mongoliens. C.R. Acad. Sci. 248: 1721-1722, 1959.

5. LELE, K.P., DENT T., and DELHANTY, J.D.: Chromosome studies in five cases of coloboma of the iris. Lancet 1: 576-578, 1965.

6. MAKINO, S.: Chromosomal studies in normal human subjects and in 300 cases of congenital disorders. Pt. I-III. Cytologia (Tokyo) 29: 13-31, 125-150, 233-262, 1964.

7. MAKINO, S.: Chromosomal studies in 150 sexually abnormal patients. A summarized report. Pt. I-II. Cytologia (Tokyo) 31: 309-323, 349-374, 1966.

8. MAKINO, S.: Screening data of the chromosomes in congenital disorders and maldevelopment, from a survey in a Japanese population (1964-1967). Jour. Fac. Sci. Hokkaido Univ. Ser. VI, Zool. 16: 315-323, 1968.

9. MAKINO, S.: Chromosomal screening data in congenital disorders and sexual defects. From a survey work in Makino Laboratory, 1964 to 1967. Mammalian Chromosome Newsletter Vol. 9, No. 4: 217-230. 1968.

10. MAKINO, S., AWA, A. and SASAKI, M.: Chromosomal studies in normal subjects. New York Acad. Sci. (in press), 1968.

11. PRICE, W.H. and WHATMORE, P.B.: Behaviour disorders and pattern of crime among XYY males identified at a maximum security hospital. Brit. Med. J. 1: 533-536, 1967.

12. SASAKI, M. and MAKINO, S.: Sex-chromosome abnormalities in man. A review. Gunma symposia on endocrinology 4: 3-22, 1967.

13. TJIO, J.H. and LEVAN, A.: The chromosome number of man. Hereditas 42: 1-6, 1965.

THE DIRECT AND INDIRECT EFFECTS OF IRRADIATION UPON THE MAMMALIAN ZYGOTE, EMBRYO AND FETUS

Robert L. Brent

*Professor, Department of Pediatrics and Radiology,
Jefferson Medical College, Philadelphia, U.S.A.*

INTRODUCTION

Although there has been an increase in our understanding of the qualitative and quantitative aspects of radiation embryology, we are still not in a position to identify clearly the mechanism of the multiple effects of irradiation upon the developing mammalian embryo. In spite of this void in our knowledge, some important information has become available over the past 15 years that is important to the embryologist, health physicist and radiologist.

ACUTE EFFECTS OF X–IRRADIATION AT VARIOUS GESTATION STAGES

In the late 1940's and early 1950's, a great deal of information was published dealing with the effects of X-irradiation on embryonic development[4,13,15,18,19,20]. Because of the wealth of data available, a number of generalizations were made. Some of these generalizations have proven to be correct, others have proven to

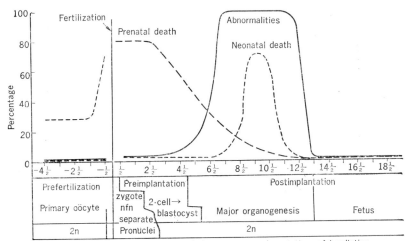

Day, stage, and chromosome number at time of irradiation
(Doses used were 400r for prefertilization, 200r for postfertilization irradiation)

Fig. 1 Radiation and CNS disturbances (Russell, 1954)

be wrong and some generalizations are still in doubt.

Figure 1 is a graph summarizing RUSSELL's work published in 1954. The generalizations that are obtained from this graph are that 200 R of acute radiation administered to the pregnant mouse on various days of gestation will have the following effects.

1. Very few or no congenital malformations are produced in the preimplantation period.
2. The peak incidence of malformations occurs during the organogenetic period.
3. The prenatal death rate (resorptions) is highest in the preimplantation period and gradually approaches control levels in the early fetal stages.
4. The neonatal death rate seemed to be highest in the surviving embryos irradiated during the organogenetic period.
5. Few, if any, malformations were observed in embryos irradiated during the fetal stages.

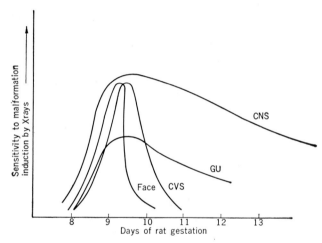

Fig. 2 Relative sensitivity of various organ systems of the rat embryo to X-irradiation on different gestational days. The four curves depict the relative overall sensitivity of the central nervous system (CNS), the cardiovascular system (CVS), the genitourinary system (GU) and the face. The central nervous system has broadest period of overall sensitivity. This graph was prepared in 1952 in our laboratory and is presented only to indicate the prolonged sensitivity of the central nervous system and the insensitivity of the rat embryo to teratogenesis before the 8 th day of rat gestation.

About the same time as RUSSELL published her summary, we prepared a similar graph in our laboratory which also indicated that malformations were more likely to occur in the organogenetic period and that malformations were difficult to produce prior to the inner cell mass stage (Fig. 2). This graph differs in one respect from RUSSELL's early data in that it indicates that malformations of the central nervous system can be produced throughout the entire period of rat gestation.

Over the past 15 years a number of important changes have occurred in the generalizations published in the early 1950's and some important new information has become available.

A. Preimplantation Period

Although the earlier observations were correct in that it is difficult to malform embryos with irradiation at this stage of gestation, they are not absolutely correct in that in some species malformations have been reported but in low incidence. RUSSELL, herself, reported that the sensitivity of the fertilized ovum to irradiation varies during the first few days of gestation (Table 1)[16]. This variability in zygote susceptibility is believed to be due to the fact that the synchronized stages of cell division during the very early stages of development result in marked changes in radiosensitivity of the entire zygote. This is true for the lethal effects of X-ray and for the induction of non-disjunction of chromatin material (Table 1).

Table 1 Summary of the work of L.B. RUSSELL

Effect of time of day on the stage of zygote development and sensitivity to irradiation on the first day of mouse gestation (Percent).

	No pronuclei	One pronucleus	Two pronuclei	Frequency of loss of sex chromatin following 100 R and 200 R	Fraction of control offspring per vaginal plug following 200 R
8:45AM	86	3	11	—	—
11:00AM	26	4	70	5.2	0
2:00PM	0	7	93	4.5	—
3:30PM	5	5	90	1.4	80.6
				No irradiation control 1.0%	

RUSSELL demonstrated that 200 R can produce an increase in the incidence of chromosome aberrations in the irradiated offspring. Just as lethality was dependent on the time of day that the embryos were irradiated, so too was the frequency of induction of non-disjunction related to the time of irradiation.

The induction of mosaicism and mutations during the first four days of development are of interest because of the fact that a large percentage of the adult organism's cells will contain these defects. There is little quantitative data available in the human to evaluate the importance of these effects during this stage of development.

B. Postimplantation—Preorganogenetic Period

Following implantation but before organogenesis begins, the embryo is less sensitive to the lethal effects of irradiation and still has a low incidence of malformations following irradiation. On the other hand, growth retardation does not result from preimplantation irradiation but can be produced in the implanted embryo even before organogenesis begins (Table 2). It can be observed in Table 2 that 150 R to the rat embryo results in a reduction in term fetal weight but only produces a 28% mortality. This same dose of irradiation when administered on the first day of rat gestation results in a term mortality of approximately

Table 2   The effect of irradiation on the 6-day-old rat embryo

	0 R	150 R
Zygotes	217	204
Term fetuses	201	159
Mortality	8%	28%
Term weight	4. 87 g	4. 38 g

70% and no growth retardation observed at term.

C.   Organogenetic Period

Most of the studies in this field of radiation embryology have been concerned with teratogenesis.   A high incidence of malformations can be induced with a relatively low dose of irradiation around the period of the formation of the germ layers and the formation of the first somites.   This period of great sensitivity to the teratogenic effects of X-irradiation occurs in the mouse in 7½ and 8½-day-old embryos and in the rat in 8½ and 9½-day-old embryos.   The equivalent stages in human gestation would be approximately 12 to 22 days.

It is important to note that growth retardation can be induced with low dosage irradiation prior to the induction of a high incidence of malformations. This concept is supported by data from our own laboratory which is presented in Table 2.   When 6-day-old rat embryos receive 150 R they exhibit growth retardation and an increase in mortality at term.   Yet, the surviving embryos do not have a marked increase in the incidence of malformations.   SKREB and coworkers[17] have also demonstrated that the rat embryo is susceptible to the growth retarding effects of X-ray several days before the embryo can be malformed by X-irradiation.   Although growth retardation can be produced by X-irradiation before the stages of differentiation, it should be noted that the stage most sensitive to the growth retarding effects of X-ray is during the period of differentiation which is the same as the stage for the maximum production of malformations.

One of the important applications of this information is in the field of clinical medicine.   The controversy at the present time concerns the lowest dose of irradiation which will result in alterations of the embryo which are not recuperable and leave the embryo with a deficit that is deleterious.   At the present time, a number of clinicians and one country advise a therapeutic abortion if a pregnant woman has received greater than 10 R of irradiation and in some circumstances interruption of pregnancy is recommended when less than 10 R has been received.   We have no information about the effect of irradiation on human embryos in this dose range.   Even if we examine the quantitative data from mouse and rat experimentation, the results do not consistently support the concept that 10 R causes significant permanent damage, although this point is controversial.   When the dosage is raised to 25 R, there have been reports of reproducible morphological and histological alterations in the irradiated embryos. RUSSELL reported that 25 R would alter the number of ribs and vertebrae in strains of mice[14].   RUGH reported that the incidence of resorptions increased with as little as 25 R in the mouse, although RUSSELL reported that a much higher dose was necessary to kill the preimplanted embryo. Although 25 R produces some growth retardation in 8- and 9-day-old rat embryos, the embryos that survive the irradiation are not stunted when they reach adulthood.

Rosette formation has been observed in rat embryos irradiated after 9 days of gestation with 25 R, although all the rosettes disappear and are not seen in survivors at term.

In an early publication we reported that 6% of fetuses irradiated after 9 days of gestation with 25 R were microphthalmic at term[1]. Yet, if we examine Table 3, we find that one has to be careful not to equate growth retardation and congenital malformations. The fetuses described in Table 3 received 100 to 300 R on the 12 th day of rat gestation. Although the eyes were observed to be small they were no smaller than other structures in the stunted animals. This Table indicates the importance of analyzing all the growth data before one describes an easily accessible or easily visible organ as preferentially affected. In some instances growth retardation is not recuperable and the organ remains small in the adult. This can be considered a congenital malformation. One must differentiate between a small eye in a proportionately small animal and a small eye in a proportionately larger animal. One should not label an eye microphthalmic unless the growth of the organism as a whole has been evaluated and the eventual size and structure of the eye determined.

Table 3 Percent growth retardation of various organs and structures of term rat fetuses irradiated on the twelfth day of gestation. Linear measurements were cubed in order to compare them with weight measurements. This data indicates that, although the eyes appeared small, they were no more retarded than other organs. Thus, microphthalmia may be a misnomer in this instance.

Dose	Fetal weight reduction	Occipital nasal length	Palate length	Eye diameter	Liver weight
100 R	21. 8	18. 3	18. 7	21	19. 8
200 R	46. 6	43. 8	45. 5	42. 6	48. 0
300 R	50. 7	—	—	44. 6	—

The effect of 50 R irradiation during the period of maximum sensitivity is without question teratogenic. Even though anophthalmia occurred in only 6% of animals irradiated, it is an irreversible effect. Any embryo that has received 50 R during the organogenetic period should be considered to have been affected, although the incidence of effects is low and the amount of growth retardation is relatively small.

Embryos that have been exposed to 100 R during the early organogenetic period will have a high incidence of congenital malformations, increased mortality and permanent growth retardation.

Many malformations involving all organ systems have been observed in embryos irradiated during the period of organogenesis. The central nervous system and eye are the organs most consistently malformed by X-irradiation.

The period of early and late organogenesis is also the stage when overall permanent growth retardation is produced. Dosages which result in growth retardation at term also result in a reduction in the size of adult organisms if they were irradiated in utero. Permanent growth retardation can be produced by administering 100 R during the period of organogenesis and higher doses have resulted in growth retardation even when administered during the late fetal stages in mouse, rat or human. At the present time we do not know the lowest dose that will result in permanent growth retardation at various stages of gestation. Our own work indicates that it is below 100 R. This may be one of the most important effects of embryonic irradiation and one that should most concern the health physicist.

D. Fetal Stages

Over the past 20 years it has become increasingly apparent that the fetus is not insensitive to the effects of X-irradiation and that although grotesque abnormalities of major organ systems do not occur, permanent alterations can be produced in many organs and systems. HICKS[3-7], BRIZZEE[2], RUGH[8-12] and others have been interested in the selective ability of X-irradiation to affect specific parts of the central nervous system. The specificity of the effects are related to the stage of gestation when irradiation is administered and the severity is related to the dose of X-irradiation. HICKS compared the gross size and structure of a normal adult rat brain with three animals that received 200 R on the 13th and 17th day of gestation and then on the 1st day after delivery. It was determined that the degree of cortical atrophy varies with the stage of gestation when X-irradiation was administered. A cross section of the most severely affected animals revealed marked atrophy, but reasonable gross organization. In fact HICKS and coworkers originally reported that many of these adult animals with abnormal brains exhibited normal motor and behavioral activities. Microscopic pictures of the irradiated brains exhibit irregular and bizarre neuron formation.

There is no question that 150 R fetal irradiation can produce atrophy and microscopic changes in the adult cortex. It has been reported that 20 R acute irradiation produces discernible microscopic changes in the cortex, although of a subtle nature. It is interesting that these animals show no neurological dysfunction. It would be important to extend these studies to determine the extent to which some of the histological changes observed in the newborn are partially or wholley repaired by the time the animal reaches a later stage in development.

There have been some quantitative studies performed by BRIZZEE and coworkers[2] demonstrating that the reduction in depth of the cortical plate is related to the dose and method of irradiation. It is interesting that extended fractionation of the dose drastically reduces the effectiveness of the irradiation.

Other organ systems that have been specifically affected during the fetal stages are the thyroid and diaphragm on the 12th and 13th day of gestation in the rat. Another interesting finding has been that testicular atrophy can be produced by late fetal irradiation. This effect of irradiation is manifested at a relatively low dose of irradiation in that as little as 50 R administered to 18-day-old rat embryos resulted in a reduction in the size of the adult testes. Thus, there exist two separate peaks for the induction of testicular atrophy during rat gestation, since 100 R can result in this malformation if administered to 9-day-old or 18-day-old rat embryos. The fact that testicular atrophy can

Fig. 3 Testicular atrophy is presented in an adult rat which received 100 R when it was a 9-day-old embryo. The non-irradiated littermate control is on the right. Testicular atrophy can also be produced late in gestation with 150 R as demonstrated by MURPHREE and coworker. It is very likely that the mechanism of radiation induced testicular atrophy in the 9-day-old and 18-day-old embryo is different.

be induced at two widely separate stages of embryonic and fetal development is an unusual phenomenon (Fig. 3).

It is perfectly obvious that fetal irradiation can change the structure of adult organs and tissues. In many instances it is difficult to evaluate the significance of these alterations, since they consist of cell and tissue depletions and, in some instances, organ hypoplasia.

Before leaving the topic of the effects of acute irradiation upon the mammalian embryo, it might be worthwhile to update Figures 1 and 2 with their many generalizations. The updated figures will include the fact that (1) non-disjunction can be produced by X-irradiation during the first day of development; (2) radiosensitivity of the zygote varies with the stages of cell division and, therefore, the time of day during the first few days of development; (3) the fetus is not resistant to the teratogenic effects of X-ray; (4) low level effects of X-irradiation are manifested at all stages of gestation—death during the preimplantation period, malformations during the organogenetic period and cell deletions (hypoplasia) during the fetal periods (Figs. 4, 5 and 6).

A recent publication[21] listed low level effects reported in the literature. The abnormal findings occurred in embryos receiving between 15 and 40 R. Some of these findings are real and others need corroboration. One has to be careful not to exaggerate the effects of low level embryonic irradiation.

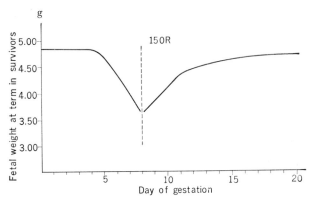

Fig. 4 The effect of 150 R X-irradiation to the rat embryo on the weight of the fetus at term. The rat embryo is very resistant to the growth-retarding effects of X-irradiation before implantation. Growth retardation is produced by X-ray following implantation and before differentiation. Growth retardation is readily produced during differentiation. This effect diminishes as the fetus matures, but never disappears following 150 R. The dotted line refers to the stage after which malformations can be readily induced by irradiation.

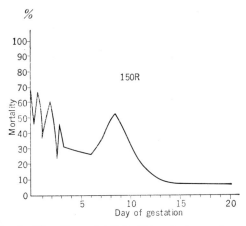

Fig. 5 The effect of 150 R X-irradiation to the rat embryo on the percent mortality observed at term. The graph points out that during the early stages of zygote development, the effect of irradiation may vary at different times of the day because of the synchronism of cell division in the zygote. During the late fetal stages, 150 R does not increase the mortality observed at term.

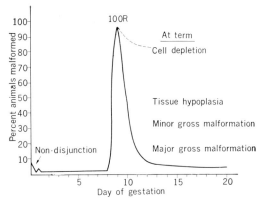

Fig. 6 The effect of 100 R X-irradiation on the percent of animals that are malformed at term. RUSSELL's work indicates that non-disjunction can be induced in a low incidence on the first day of gestation but that it is difficult to induce malformations before the period of active differentiation. It is interesting that at one narrow point during differentiation in the rat, 100 R can induce almost 100 percent malformations. Although major malformations occur in a low incidence during the fetal stages, we realize that cell depletions and tissue hypoplasia do occur. We are just beginning to study the extent and significance of these changes at the tissue and cellular level.

DISCREPANCIES IN THE RESULTS OF X–IRRADIATING THE MOUSE AND RAT EMBRYOS

RUGH has reported on numerous occasions that exencephalia can be induced in the preimplanted embryo with as little as 15 R. The lesion is familiar to all of you and may appear in only one of the members of an irradiated litter or occasionally may affect more than one litter mate. Control litters are reported by RUGH to rarely have animals with exencephlia. We have observed exencephalia in non-irradiated mouse embryos in our own laboratory. Furthermore, RUGH reports the incidence of exencephalia following 50 R and this does not differ greatly from the incidence following 15 R.

We have irradiated several thousand rat embryos during the preimplantation period with doses between 30 R and 150 R. In not one instance have we observed exencephalia, although a significant number of embryos in the higher dose groups resorb after implantation. Thus, there appears to be a marked discrepancy between the response of the preimplanted mouse and rat embryo to irradiation.

Another interesting occurrence that appears to be peculiar to the mouse is the phenomenon of whole-litter resorptions following irradiation. It appears that in certain instances the pregnant mouse responds with an all or none phenomenon following irradiation and an entire litter may be resorbed very early in gestation. The phenomenon is somewhat dose related. RUSSELL postulated that whole-litter resorptions were due to maternal pituitary irradiation, but in our own studies we have always shielded the head and upper chest and still observe whole-litter resorptions.

Irradiation of the pregnant rat during the preimplantation period does not result in whole-litter resorptions. As much as 150 R administered to inseminated females on the first day of pregnancy will result in the same incidence of pregnancy as in the unirradiated inseminated females.

Thus, there appears to be a discrepancy between the response of the (Fig. 1) mouse and rat embryo to X-ray "induced" exencephalia and whole litter resorptions. These findings emphasize the difficulty in applying specific radiation findings from one species to man, since there appears to be unexplained differences even in the rodent category. These variation in species response must be explained before attempting to apply these data to the human.

ACKNOWLEDGEMENT

The original works of the author cited above were made possible by a grant from the Atomic Energy Commission NYO 2071–39.

REFERENCES

1. BRENT, R.L.: The modification of the teratogenic and lethal effects of irradiation to the mammalian fetus. In: Effects of Ionizing Radiation on the Reproductive System, W.D. CARLSON and F.X. GASSNER (editors), Pergamon Press, New York, 451–462, 1964.
2. BRIZZEE, K.R., JACOBS, L.A. and BENCH, C.J.: Histologic effects of total-body X-irradiation in various dose fractionation patterns on fetal cerebral hemisphere. Rad. Res. 31: 415–429, 1967.
3. D'AMATO, C.J. and HICKS, S.P.: Effects of low levels of ionizing radiation on the developing cerebral cortex of the rat. Neurology 15: 1104–1116, 1965.
4. HICKS, S.P.: Effects of Ionizing Radiation on the Adult and Embryonic Nervous System. In: Metabolic and Toxic Diseases of the Nervous System. Proceedings of the Association for Research in Nervous and Mental Disease (Chapt. XXIV, 439–462), Williams and Wilkins, Baltimore, 1953.
5. HICKS, S.P.: Radiation as an experimental tool in mammalian developmental neurology. Physiol. Rev. 38: 337–356, 1958.
6. HICKS, S.P. and D'AMATO, C.J.: Low dose radiation of developing brain. Science 141: 903–905, 1963.
7. HICKS, S.P., D'AMATO, C.J. and LOWE, M.J.: The development of the mammalian nervous system. I. Malformations of the brain, especially the cerebral cortex, induced in rats by radiation. J. Comp. Neur. 113: 435–469, 1959.
8. RUGH, R.: Vertebrate radiobiology: embryology. Ann. Rev. Nuclear Sc. 9: 493–522, 1959.
9. RUGH, R. and GRUPP, E.: Fractionated X-irradiation of the mammalian embryo and congenital anomalies. Amer. J. Roentgenol. 84: 125–144, 1960.
10. RUGH, R., DUHAMEL, L., OSBORNE, A.W. and VARMA, A.: Persistent stunting fol-

lowing X-irradiation of the fetus. Amer. J. Anat. 115: 185–198, 1964.

11. RUGH, R. and WOHLFROMM, M.: Prenatal X-irradiation and postnatal mortality. Rad. Res. 26: 493–506, 1965.

12. RUGH, R. and WOHLFROMM, M.: Resistance of the prenatal female mouse to X-ray sterilization. Fertil. Steril. 17: 396–410, 1966.

13. RUSSELL, L.B.: The Effects of Radiation on Mammalian Prenatal Development. Radiation Biology 1: Part II. A Hollaender (editor), McGraw-Hill, New York, Chapt. 13, 861–918, 1954.

14. RUSSELL, L.B.: Effects of low doses of X-rays on embryonic development in the mouse. Proc. Soc. Exper. Biol. Med. 95: 174–178, 1957.

15. RUSSELL, L.B. and RUSSELL, W.L.: An analysis of the changing radiation response of the developing mouse embryo. J. Cell. Comp. Physiol. 43: 103–149, 1954.

16. RUSSELL, L.B. and MONTGOMERY, C.S.: Radiation-sensitivity differences within cell-division cycles during mouse cleavage. Int. J. Radiat. Biol. 10: 151–164, 1966.

17. SKREB, N., BIJELIC, N. and LUKOVIC, G.: Weight of rat embryos after X-ray irradiation. Experientia 19: 263, 1963.

18. WILSON, J.G.: Differentiation and reaction of rat embryos to radiation. J. Cell. Comp. Physiol. 43: 11–37, 1954.

19. WILSON, J.G. and KARR, J.W.: Effects of irradiation on embryonic development. I. X-rays on the 10 th day of gestation in the rat. Amer. J. Anat. 88: 1–34, 1951.

20. WILSON, J.G., JORDAN, H.C. and BRENT, R.L.: Effects of irradiation on embryonic development. II. X-rays on the ninth day of gestation in the rat. Amer. J. Anat. 92: 153–188, 1953.

21. YAMAZAKI, J.N.: A review of the literature on the radiation dosage required to cause manifest central nervous system disturbances from in utero and postnatal exposure. Pediatrics 37: 877–903, 1966.

DISCUSSION

MILLER, R.W. (U.S.A.)

What is the value of study of radiation teratogenesis as compared with other ways of inducing congenital anomalies?

BRENT

Obvious advantages of X-ray induced teratogenesis are:

1) Ability to confine the offending agent to a specific stage of gestation. The exposure of the embryo to a drug cannot be controlled since the mother also is exposed to the drug and the embryo's exposure is dependent on the excretion and detoxification carried out by the mother.

2) Ability to irradiate parts of the embryo or an embryonic site without irradiating the maternal organism. It is obvious that irradiation is one of the few teratogenic tools that can be utilized in this way.

3) It is important for us to study ra-diation teratogenesis because of the fact that the human embryo has many potential sources of irradiation and maximum permissible levels of irradiation must be determined for the human zygote, embryo and fetus.

SISODIA (India)

Is there any correlationship between the effects of irradiation and mutagenic drugs on the embryo? As both X-ray and drugs, like nitrogen mustard, bring about cell mutation, is it likely that both may be influencing the embryo through a similar mechanism of action?

BRENT

It has been shown that point mutation can be produced at various loci at the rate of 10^{-7} to 10^{-8} per R of irradiation. This low mutation rate could not in itself account for the teratogenic effects of X-ray. On the other hand drugs and irradiation do produce "intergenic" effects (morphological chromosome abnormalities). These intergenic effects may account for a high percentage of cell deaths observed in the growing embryo. Thus it is possible that nitrogen mustard and X-irradiation may have important mechanisms of action in common.

ISHAQ (India)

Adult and even growing rats and mice are known to exhibit diurnal variations in thier mitotic indices, being highest in the early hours of the morning and lowest in the afternoon. Do you think that the variations you have described due to irradiation may be due, possibly, to similar variations in the developing embryos and fetuses?

BRENT

There is no question that the variation in radiation response of the 1, 2 and 4 cell stage zygote varies with the stage of mitosis. This is the "Epitome" of diurnal variation. We have no evidence to indicate that there is a significant diurnal variation in the mitotic index of older embryos. The reason why I believe that diurnal variation is less important in the embryo than in the adult is because the mitotic index is so much higher in the embryo and therefore small fluctuations would be less significant. This is purely conjectural on my part and we would need experimental studies along these lines to accurately answer your question.

MILLER, R.W. (U.S.A.)

Will the response of man to radiation teratogenesis be as diverse as in the experimental animal?

BRENT

There is no reason to believe that the spectrum of malformations induced by X-irradiation in man will be any less diverse than in experimental animals. One reason why central nervous system malformations appear to predominate in the reports of radiation induced human malformations is that the percentage of time devoted to fetal development is 80–90% of the pregnancy while the rat fetal stages makes up only 35% of the pregnancy. Similarly the sensitive organogenetic stages makes up 35% of rat pregnancy and only 10% of human pregnancy. Thus, on a statistical basis, randomly administered irradiation would less likely produce severe generalized malformations in man than in the rat.

MURAKAMI (Japan)

You have shown examples of histological findings in microcephalias, in which the structure of the brain was not altered much. In my experience, however, such microcephalias are always hydromicrocephalias. What is your experience?

BRENT

The "hydromicrocephalics" are more commonly produced by irradiation during the organogenetic period and in this respect my experience is the same as yours. HICKS' experiments, describing primarily hypoplastic brains, is concerned more with the effects of irradiation during the late fetal stages.

WILSON (U.S.A.)

Please summarize the behavioral and psychological effects of low dosage irradiation.

BRENT

There are several investigators who have been interested in this area of research (FURSCHKOFF, WERBOFF, FALK, MEIER and several Russian investigators). HICKS and FALK have been able to demonstrate that rats irradiated during pregnancy with 200 R have severe morphological and histological changes in the brain and minimal behavioral changes. Other investigators have reported that as little as 20 R (1 R per day) administered during rat gestation results in adult rats with behavioral disorders. This field is both important and controversial but until the techniques used to evaluate animal behaviour become more sophisticated it is difficult to evaluate the meaning of these data. Finally the results of many of the behavioral studies do not conform with our knowledge of embryonic development which makes us wonder somewhat about the objectivity of some of these psychological experiments.

MOON (Korea)

Do you have any observed data on leukemic changes in radiated animals especially during the late period?

BRENT

The reports in the human literature are somewhat controversial in that irradiation received by human fetuses during diagnostic roentgenographic procedures has been reported to increase the incidence of leukemia. Animal experiments and the data from the ABCC where higher doses of irradiation were received, do not indicate that irradiation increases the incidence of leukemia. One must be careful not to infer that a statistical relationship between diagnostic irradiation during pregnancy and leukemia in the offspring is interpreted to mean a causal relationship. More investigation must be performed before this question can be finally answered.

NUTRITION AND TERATOGENESIS

C. Willet Asling

Professor, Department of Anatomy, University of California,
San Francisco, U.S.A.

The title of this paper recalls that long ago, before the present century's burst of biomedical research activity, problems of food and problems of reproduction had already been associated. Malthus, 170 years ago, stated two postulates:

1. Food is necessary to man's existence.
2. Human reproductive drive (Malthus: "the passion between the sexes") is a constant.

As you know, Malthus concluded that population pressure can exceed food sources[28]. At this conference Malthus' warnings may not be neglected. The first thought, to present a critical review of animal research with specific dietary deficiencies and their teratologic relationships, might have been acceptable, where the advance of food technology is expected to keep pace with population. But within a decade many members of this conference may see, and possibly have to work with, the consequence of human starvation on a scale never before known. An exclusively laboratory approach therefore is unrealistic and callous. The broader approach should first mention human problems, next, animal experimentation with teratogenic nutritional alterations, and finally, some illustrations of the implications of nutrition for other teratogenic experimentation.

HUMAN PROBLEMS

The human body contains some 8–10,000 different chemical compounds. It manufactures most of these. About 40 are not manufactured, but must be eaten. These include some 14 vitamins, 8–10 amino acids, 1 fatty acid, and 13 inorganic minerals[12a]. Lower life forms (especially plants) can make most of these organic compounds. (It is remarkable to notice, in passing, that for 1 ¢ or less than 4 yen an individual's entire daily need of 27 of these—the vitamins and minerals—could be supplied; for about 9 ¢ or 35 yen the entire needs of all 40 could be provided, although perhaps not in a palatable form.)

One and a half billion people—over half of the world—are undernourished today. In order not to fall farther behind, a 50% increase in total world food supplies will be required by 1975[14]. Lacking this, food deficits in the next two decades will increase 4-fold in slow-growth countries and 10-fold in rapid growth countries[12a]. Although ingenious advances in food technology hold the promise of providing needed nutrients[6], the tonnages necessary are not in sight; barring some unlikely acts of intelligence on the part of the world's nations and peoples, starvation of terrifying magnitude may prevail in a decade. What has this to do with teratology? Is there any likelihood that there lies ahead an epidemic of congenital defects of dimensions to make the thalidomide disaster and the measles problem insignificant by comparison?

If one searches the literature on human nutritional requirements for an association with the etiology of congenital disorders, it is remarkable how incomplete is the scientific documentation for our species in comparison with the thousands of excellent research reports dealing with sub-human forms. It is true that in starvation there is failure of the reproductive functions, to the point where conception fails to occur; this is a cold comfort. What of lesser levels of inanition?

The commonest form of human nutritional deficiency is protein-calorie malnutrition, followed by vitamin A deficiency, and thereafter by deficiencies of the B-vitamin group[12a]. Last year the Panel on World Food Supply reported that in the United States 25 out of 1,000 liveborn infants do not survive one year, principally because of prematurity or congenital defects. In Asia, Africa, and Latin America the figure is 4–8 times as high. This difference is believed to result directly or indirectly from protein-calorie malnutrition[45].

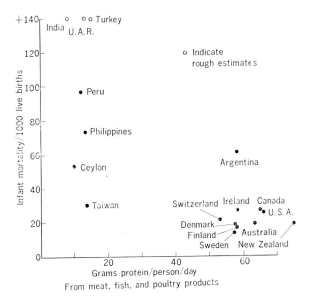

Fig. 1 Infant mortality in relation to animal protein consumption selected countries*
* Data from: REVELLE, 1966 & WILCKE, 1966

More specifically, JACOBSON[25] has combined data from REVELLE[38] and WILCKE[52] into a graph relating infant mortality to animal protein intake in a variety of countries throughout the world. The very strong inverse correlation demands humanitarian concern. But is there not hidden here a matter of added scientific substance? The cluster of countries where protein intake and infant welfare are favorable are also those where many investigators work in problems of teratology. Should not the search be made intensively in the other group of countries instead? This, of course, is one reason why this conference has been convened.

Do epidemiological studies, combined with laboratory and clinical work, give promise of a strong association between human nutrition and teratology? One retrospective and one prospective study are offered in illustration.

In retrospective studies one selects a group which has already experienced the medical problem under study and searches for evidence which significantly implicates the theoretical etiologic factor under study. PITT and SAMSON[36] made critical evaluations of the nutritional habits of 99 mothers who had borne mal-formed children and compared them with 99 mothers who had borne normal babies. The two groups were suitably matched otherwise. The probable food intake of each was broken down into 11 specific criteria and the values were com-pared according to 7 categories of anomalies. Of the 77 statistical correlations thus explored, two showed substantial significance ($p < 0.01$)—low niacin and carbo-hydrate intakes correlated with congenital heart defects—and 10 others were possibly significant ($p < 0.05$). Thus, from a statistical standpoint only 15% of the relationships examined showed a possible association; half of these were in the group associated with congenital heart disorders.

Turning to prospective studies, where one tests the presumed etiologic factor in a chosen group of patients and determines whether some predictable outcome is altered, the study of PEER et al.[34], on vitamin supplementation and cleft palate, may be cited. A group of 594 women, all of whom had previously given birth to babies with palatal or labial defects, were studied. During the first 3 months of a subsequent pregnancy, 176 received a vitamin supplement emphasizing the B-group and ascorbic acid. The remaining 418, also again pregnant, were unsupplemented controls. Whereas almost 5% of the controls again bore babies with labial and/or palatal defects (and the overall incidence of deformities was 8%), the incidence of corresponding defects was halved in the vitamin-supplemented group. The authors expect that with a larger group of vitamin-supplemented patients a statistically significant association will be established.

Thus, it is difficult to locate human studies with proven strong associations between nutritional deficiency and teratology. It is not surprising that BARNES, at a major symposium on congenital defects, could discuss the preventive ap-proach with only passing reference to diet and nutrition[5]. Yet, on the basis of animal experimentation it is likely that important relationships will eventually be shown.

NUTRITIONAL ALTERATIONS AS EXPERIMENTAL TERATOGENS

The basic experiments and methods employed in teratological research, es-pecially on laboratory mammals, using maternal nutritional alteration as an ex-perimental tool, are described in the reviews and summaries of FAVE[11], GIROUD[15,56a], HURLEY[21,56c], KALTER and WARKANY[27], NELSON[30b] and JOHNSON[43b]. In the main, these articles deal with listings of specific nutritional factors and citations of reports on their influence as a teratogen (usually in deficiency states but in some instances, in excess), and sometimes with inquiry into mechanisms involved.

Many hundreds of important investigations have been brought together in these articles. Rather than repeat such summaries, the present paper will describe the kinds of experimental design which have been used and the problems encountered in such investigations. Such an approach will inevitably omit the names of able workers who have made major specific contributions, but they have been clearly identified in the reviews listed above.

The first well-documented reports of a teratogenic nutritional deficiency were those of HALE[19], starting in 1933. With vitamin A deficiency in swine he established the occurrence of a series of anomalies, principally but not exclusively ocular. KALTER and WARKANY[27] have dealt with the significance of this work. Among major contributions HALE established that maternal (and not paternal) nutritional deficiency was the cause, and excluded the possibility that it had operated through genetic alteration.

These studies demonstrate certain problems that recur throughout most nutritional investigations. *First* is the problem that one can rarely work with acute deficiencies—i.e., one can rarely use nutritional deficiency as a short-acting teratogen. HALE placed the pigs on deficient diets early in life (e.g., 4 months of age) and continued this regimen for a prolonged period (e.g., over 5 months) before breeding. Even more stringent maneuvers of this sort may be necessary, as will be described in situations where body stores of a nutrient may be high and requirements of the embryo relatively low. *Second,* if malformed young are to be obtained it is necessary to strike a balance between total parental infertility on the one hand and embryonic death on the other, such that fertilization can occur. HALE'S solution, like that of others since, was to give a small supplement of the nutrient after pregnancy had been well-established (e.g., a month). *Third* is the problem of multiple deficiencies—i.e., of a diet adequate otherwise and hence the study of a specific deficiency. Even nowadays, with far better information on nutritional requirements than in HALE'S time, this factor requires first attention. *Fourth,* as noted by KALTER and WARKANY[27], the technical problem of coprophagia—the consumption of feces—and the possibility of obscuring the nature and level of deficiency; this problem, extended into the laboratory, brings up such technical matters as raising the animals on screens, on using cages which have been scrupulously cleaned from remnants of rations and excreta from previous experiments, and like matters of good nutritional practice[44].

The next great classical series of studies is that of WARKANY and his colleagues; it is a measure of the youth of the field which is being considered that his studies are still continuing and that in great part this work has taken place within the professional lifetime of most workers here. From the first report in 1940[49] to the definitive paper in 1943[50] WARKANY showed by a series of experiments that a broad range of defects, mostly skeletal, developed in rat offspring after maternal dietary riboflavin deficiency. Again, classical experiments can teach some of the problems in such work. *First,* as with HALE'S experiments, the diet originally used did not allow achievement of specific deficiencies. A STEENBOCK and BLACK rachitogenic diet was used, but viosterol supplementation did not avert the deficiencies; furthermore when it was found that the diet was also goitrogenic, iodine supplementation improved maternal but not fetal condition. Finally, with knowledge that crude liver extract was a sufficient supplement, exploration of the B vitamin group became necessary and with various combinations of specific supplements the role of riboflavin was disclosed. *Second,* strain differences may enter; KALTER and WARKANY[27] have discussed the reconciliation of minor differences in experimental results with those of GRAINGER et al.[18] on this basis. *Third,* the level of deficiency attained may vary. As will be seen later when we discuss antimetabolites, the riboflavin deficiency achieved in these experiments resulted in a lower incidence and narrower range of abnormalities than were encountered when it became possible to achieve a more profound deficiency by use of the riboflavin antagonist, galactoflavin[32]. Anomalies of soft tissues became commoner under the latter circumstance.

By the mid-1940's investigators in other laboratories were beginning to contribute to the subject. However, it is not easy to follow a historical sequence in considering their contributions. Having mentioned vitamin A, and having mentioned the colleagues of WARKANY, an association of major importance should be noted. WILSON, also in Cincinnati, was expanding an interest of long-standing in reproductive physiology into the field of "specificity" in teratology—time-specificity and agent-specificity. His views, developed from findings in a broad span of teratogens, have been described elsewhere[43f,53] and will also be described at this conference. At this point one should note his work on maternal vitamin A deficiency, which was already under study by WARKANY and associates. The range of anomalies described by HALE had been markedly extended by studies on rats. In a series of studies culminating in the 1953 report of WILSON, ROTH, and WARKANY[54], the principle of timing nutritional deficiencies was worked out. By giving a vitamin A supplement to rat mothers on a continuous deficiency regimen, and by varying the day on which this supplement was given by 24 hour intervals between the 10th and 15th days of gestation, it was demonstrated that the syndrome of malformations which resulted could be varied accordingly. In addition, seemingly paradoxical increases in incidence of deficiency could be explained on the basis that the additional defective young had been salvaged, by a vitamin supplement, from the embryonic death which would otherwise have occurred. A close association between embryonic death on the one hand and embryonic deformities, on the other hand, could thus be presumed.

At this point one must consider the choice of objectives which must be made in this kind of experiment. There is, as one possibility, the exploration of the extent to which minor or moderate degrees of deficiency will result in deformed offspring, even in low incidence. This approach has been developed strongly by GIROUD, again one of the pioneers in experimental teratology. His viewpoint has been well presented[14,15]. If the findings of experimental teratology are to be useful in disclosing the etiology of human malformations, one must note that it is uncommon for human beings to experience severe degrees of single (specific) nutritional deficiency such as can be established in laboratory animals. It therefore becomes important to know whether milder degrees of specific deficiencies, such as might be encountered clinically, can be held responsible for congenital disorders, in moderate incidences corresponding to those encountered among human beings. With graded deficiencies GIROUD and colleagues have been able to establish this probability. The fact that the mother need not show deficiency manifestations herself, but may still be carrying deformed young, has shown the low level at which fetal requirements may be critical. Finally, GIROUD has contributed substantially to the concept that a nutritional deficiency, itself at a sub-threshold level, may join forces with other teratogenic circumstances to bring about malformations. This idea has been developed in general terms for additive or synergistic effects of separate teratogens, by FRASER[43a]. Some of its applications in nutritional terms will be mentioned later in this lecture.

The other choice—not to work with minimal teratogens and low-level consequences, but rather with high-level teratogenicity and corresponding maximal incidence of deformities—leads to the work of NELSON, another pioneer in the field. If special attention is given to her work here, it is because of a close association with her in the laboratory of Professor HERBERT M. EVANS, from 1945 until her untimely death in 1963. Were she to have survived, the work would be substantially ahead of its present position, and she would have been the person of choice to present this lecture. The techniques and concepts which she refined, and her demonstration of the importance of antimetabolites in teratology research, deserve analysis.

For a number of vitamins there exist chemical analogues, in which the structure of the substance is modified very slightly by the addition of sidechains or prosthetic groups. Administered to animals these substances are handled like the corresponding vitamin, but are inert so far as promoting the metabolic processes which are supported by the true vitamin[30a]. Their presence, especially in a diet deficient in the specific vitamin, will accentuate the deficiency and allow its acute manifestations to develop. One may, in control groups, administer such a vitamin antimetabolite and over-ride its effects by addition of extra amounts of the natural vitamin, thus restoring normal dietary balance.

Among such vitamin analogues are included galactoflavin (for riboflavin), deoxypyridoxine (for pyridoxine), methyl pteroylglutamic acid and aminopterin (for folic acid or PGA), omega-methyl pantothenate and pantoyltaurine (for pantothenic acid), and 6-amino nicotinamide (for niacin)[55].

Doctor NELSON is credited with being the first to employ vitamin antimetabolites as teratogens in mammals. She had been conducting a long-range study on the effects of the various B-vitamins on reproduction and lactation in rats, and when she undertook to study folic (pteroylglutamic) acid (PGA) she had encountered difficulty in achieving deficiency by simple omission of the vitamin from purified diets. Addition of succinylsulfathiazole (to suppress vitamin synthesis by intestinal bacteria) intensified the deficiency slightly. Finally, in 1949, she added the recently developed folic acid antagonist "x-methyl PGA" to the ration. Early that autumn she found some newly-littered rats to be grotesquely swollen so that limbs and head were barely definable. When these translucent young were placed on ground glass with a bright light showing through from beneath, some of their very obvious skeletal defects were visualized crudely. It was at that time the custom in our school to have first-year medical students undertake simple research problems under faculty guidance. Several litters of these interesting creatures were given to two young women students of promise, for preparation for skeletal study by the modified Spalteholz and alizarin technique. These two (now Doctors MARILYN GIST FARQUHAR and SHIRLEY GAEBLER HALL, successful medical scientists) were thus the first to actually examine the deformities. Following repetition of this experiment, the findings were presented at anatomy association meetings in early 1950[3,31]. As others joined in studying such fetuses, either as students and research assistants (BAIRD, JOHNSON, WRIGHT, DOUGHERTY) or staff members (MONIE), exploration of the range of defects encountered was broadened. In virtually every system examined, under some variation of the original experimental regimen, deformities were encountered, and WILSON has called this procedure a "universal teratogen"[53c].

Meanwhile, RICHARDSON and HOGAN[38] were also using this antimetabolite, in what has proved to be a double deficiency of PGA and B-12, and THIERSCH and PHILIPS were at the same time using another very potent PGA-antagonist, aminopterin[47]. Subsequently JOHNSON[26] clarified the relationships between the crude x-methyl and the more potent and refined 9-methyl PGA in teratogenesis. As still another matter of interest is the very recent demonstration by ARMSTRONG[1] that in tissue culture media incorporating 9-methyl PGA one may produce retardation of ocular development comparable to that found *in vivo* in offspring of mothers made nutritionally deficient by the same antimetabolite.

NELSON and her colleagues recognized and clarified some of the special opportunities and limitations of using antimetabolite-induced deficiencies as teratogens[30a]. *First,* the antimetabolite itself is not the teratogen; this was established by control groups in which the substance was present in the diet, but with the addition of substantial amounts of the true vitamin; offspring of such animals were as free from congenital defects as those from mothers fed on a nutritionally adequate stock diet of natural foodstuffs. *Second,* a greater flexibility of time of dietary deficiency was possible. WILSON's device of continuous deficiency with a short-term dietary repletion at different times in pregnancy could be reversed; the acute deficiencies possible with antimetabolites made it possible to carry out studies with short deficiencies induced at specific periods during pregnancy. NELSON worked first with continuing deficiencies started at about mid-pregnancy and subsequently reduced this to 72-hour, than 48-hour, and even 36-hour periods on the deficiency regimen. Adjusting the actual days of pregnancy during which the mothers were exposed to the deficiency resulted in varying the spectrum of defects evoked. There is, however, a limit to the specificity of timing which can thus be procured. Teratogenic levels of deficiency are not achieved until an appropriate amount of diet containing the antimetabolite has been consumed by the mother. It appears that at least one day on the special diet is required, and hence 36-hour deficiencies have seemed the shortest practicable regimens. Because some mothers, transferred from the natural diet to the deficient ration, eat little during the first day of exposure, it is necessary to measure the actual amount of food consumed and reject from further consideration those whose consumption of food (and antimetabolite) is inadequate. (While injection of aminopterin would seem to avoid this ambiguity in timing, the narrow margin between teratogenicity and lethality in rats[47] makes it of questionable usefulness.) *Third,* the possibility of provoking a severe deficiency restricted to only a portion of pregnancy allows one to carry to term considerable numbers of living young, virtually all of whom show malformations. (The significance of minor deficiencies and low incidence of abnormalities has been mentioned above.) In the converse, in the words of WARKANY, ".....development (of malformations)..... could be

followed through various embryonic and fetal stages."[43e]   That is, if the expect-
ancy of a given abnormality is nearly 100% at term, one may recover embryos
and fetuses at earlier times in pregnancy with a high degree of confidence that
such young are on the way to such an abnormality.   Early deviations from
normal morphogenesis may thus be examined.   When this possibility was ap-
proached in the instance of cleft palate, there were only two other reported
experimental circumstances in which such high incidence of that defect had been
achieved—cortisone injections into susceptible strains of mice[13] and hypervitaminosis A[16].   The PGA-deficiency material allowed exploration of some aspects of
the genesis of palatal and facial defects[2,3,4].   By this study, experimental confirmation could be obtained for one of the several mechanisms proposed for
cleft palate genesis—early deficient mandibular development.

Before leaving the topic of folic acid antagonists some of the human implications should be mentioned.   This is perhaps the best-documented instance
of a nutritional deficiency which has teratogenic consequences in animals and in
which similar spectra of defects appear in human beings under related conditions.   The antimetabolite aminopterin (4-amino PGA) was studied by THIERSCH
as a therapeutic abortifacient in early human pregnancy, and some of the older
fetuses obtained in this way showed malformations[46].   Subsequently several cases
have been studied in which patients attempted abortion by this technique.   The
reports of MELTZER[29], WARKANY et al.[48], and most recently, SHAW[41] provide interesting confirmation of the experimental observations in animals.   The last report
is especially interesting, for it reports a case much like that of WARKANY et al.
but in which the child is still surviving, at 5 years of age.

Of other antimetabolites used in teratogenesis, JOHNSON[43b] has reviewed the
information on riboflavin (galactoflavin) and pantothenic acid (pantoyltaurine,
omega-methyl pantothenate).   To these should be added several studies of PINSKY
and FRASER[35] and CHAMBERLAIN[8] on niacin (6-amino nicotinamide).   CHAMBERLAIN's
studies contain a point of special interest.   In the main, experimentally-induced
congenital deformities have resulted following teratogenic procedures early in
pregnancy; in rats, the period between 8 and 13 days conception age has been
that most involved.   With single injections of 6-aminonicotinamide, deformities
were encountered in appreciable incidence in deficiencies instituted even late in
pregnancy; thus, palatal defects were encountered in half of the offspring following treatment as late as 15 days, and ocular defects in corresponding incidence
following treatment at 20 days.

Teratogenicity late in pregnancy was also demonstrated in another type of
nutritional deficiency—that of the trace element manganese.   HURLEY, in a well-
developed series of studies on the congenital ataxia in offspring of manganese-
deficient mothers (rats, guinea-pigs), showed that if dietary repletion was conducted on the 14th day it was adequately preventive, but if delayed until the
18th day, most of the offspring displayed ataxia; manganese supplementation on
the 16th day gave intermediate incidences.   Animals also showed skeletal defects;
those of the cranium were especially noticeable, and the region of the inner ear
was implicated[22,24,56c].

Work with teratogenic trace element deficiencies presents the special problem
of achieving sufficiently severe deficiencies, because of the low requirements and

relatively high body stores. Commonly it becomes necessary to work with mothers on a deficiency regimen from birth, or even the second generation of deficiency. Workers desiring to study such deficiencies may be forced to unusual techniques. NISHIMURA, in his work with zinc deficiency, used an ingenious device to obtain parents depleted of zinc[33]. Knowing that milk is low in trace elements, but that colostrum is reportedly higher in zinc content than the later milk, he avoided this normal supply of extra zinc to the newborn by transferring the young immediately to mothers who had been lactating for several days. These young, continued on zinc-deficient rations, subsequently showed developmental defects.

Zinc-deficiency teratogenesis has also been explored by HURLEY[23]. She took advantage of a fact which had emerged in research on poultry nutrition—that when soy-bean served as a primary dietary source of protein the zinc-deficiency disease "perosis" (lameness and deformity of extremities) developed; the dietary zinc was unavailable unless the soy-bean had been modified by autoclaving or treatment with a chelating agent. By use of this dietary blockage of zinc assimilation (and rigid exclusion of the element from diet and environment) she was able to demonstrate the development of congenital defects in offspring. Such a procedure is not to be regarded as an example of an antimetabolite, for the antagonistic action was against absorption of zinc rather than its utilization in metabolic pathways.

Details of many other teratogenic nutritional alterations have been omitted; they are given in the reviews which have been mentioned (and especially KALTER and WARKANY[27], and GIROUD[56a]. It would be a major omission not to cite the remarkable effects of 24 hours of fasting in mice described by RUNNER[39,40], or to omit mention of hypervitaminosis A, shown to be broadly teratogenic by COHLAN[9] and GIROUD and MARTINET[17].

THE INTERRELATIONSHIP OF NUTRITION WITH OTHER TYPES OF TERATOLOGIC INVESTIGATIONS

There exist several reports in which nutritional alteration, in conjunction with another teratogenic procedure, has affected the incidence of experimentally induced congenital defects. RUNNER[43d] has mentioned some of these, such as the interaction of fasting or food restriction and cortisone administration, of insulin and nicotinamide, and of hypervitaminosis A and cortisone or irradiation. KALTER[43c] has discussed the caution which is necessary in interpreting results of such experiments.

A remarkably interesting study displaying the relationship of genetics and nutritional requirement was described by ENWAY et al.[10] The studies of HURLEY[21] on congenital ataxia following manganese deficiency in rats were extended into mice. Furthermore, a mouse strain was identified which showed hereditary ataxia. In both circumstances there was defective development of otoliths in the inner ear. The hereditary ataxia was averted by dietary manganese supplementation in the susceptible strain during pregnancy, and otolithic development was brought to normal.

An experiment recently conducted here in Kyoto demonstrates well the advantage of being alert to nutritional problems during experiments with other teratogens. TANIMURA et al.[42] were investigating fetotoxicity and teratogenicity of methyl parathion, an organic insecticide. They detected congenital abnormalities in mice, although not in rats under their experimental conditions. During their experiments they had measured food intake, and found that during parathion administration food consumption dropped very sharply, to below 25% of the former amount, and remained below normal for 3 days. Recalling other demonstrations of teratogenic effect of food restriction on mice, they direct attention to the need for evaluating this effect in relation to a direct methyl parathion influence on embryos.

In view of impressions that severe metabolic stress may have an effect on fetal development, it should be noticed that stress symptoms may be produced in some nutritional experimental procedures. CANNON et al.[7] were studying requirements for essential amino acids in rats. When nutritionally-depleted rats were given a dietary repletion adequate in all respects save for one essential amino acid, the animals reacted very strongly within a few hours. They refused food and fluid, lost weight, went into negative nitrogen and potassium balance, and showed other indications of stress in the course of this massive reaction.

It is thus clear that control of nutritional state becomes important in any animal experimentation, in order to avoid confusing interpretations of results. Nutritional requirements for many laboratory animals have been described. WARNER'S[51] survey for rats may be cited. Several diets which have been in use in the parent colony of the Long-Evans stock for some years are given in the Appendix, and may be of service to those desiring to formulate their own laboratory rations.

SUMMARY

1. There exists a reasonably strong presumption that altered nutrition can have teratogenic consequences in human beings; this possibility deserves further careful study.
2. Maternal nutritional interference itself forms one of the major groups of experimental procedures available for teratological studies.
3. Nutritional control ought to be a primary concern in all experimental design in teratology.

APPENDIX
Diets in Use in Parent Colony of the Long-Evans
Stock of Rats, University of California, San Francisco

1) A diet apparently corresponding to commercial rations consists of

Ground whole wheat	68.5%
Casein, technical	5.0
Alfalfa leaf meal	10.0
Fish meal	10.0
Fish oil (Sardilene)*	5.0
Sodium chloride	0.5

Iodized salt*   1.0

* The fish oil contains approximately 750 U.S.P. units of vitamin A and 300 chick units of vitamin D per gram. Iodized salt at the recommended level yields an iodine content of 0.9 μg/gm of diet. The ration is approximately 19.3% protein, 56.7% carbohydrate, and 6.5% fat.

The foregoing formula is supplemented by feeding of fresh greens (lettuce) twice weekly. It allows satisfactory growth, and will support reproduction and lactation. However, fertility, judged by conceptions, litter size, birth weight, and weaning weight, is not optimal, as would be hoped for in critical experiments in teratology.

2) A preferable formula consists of

Ground whole wheat	67.25%
Casein, technical	15.0
Skim milk powder	7.5
Hydrogenated vegetable fat, melted	6.75
Fish oil (Sardilene)	1.0
Calcium carbonate	1.5
Iodized salt	1.0

This yields approximately 24.5% protein, 54.9% carbohydrate, 8.9% fat, and an iodine content of 0.9 μg/gm of diet. It is supplemented with fresh greens twice weekly. Recently it has been found possible to form this diet into soft pellets, without sacrifice of nutritional value and with substantial reduction in waste.

3) For critical experiments on nutritional factors, including the induction of specific deficiencies, the following basal synthetic diet has been in use. It contains all known essential dietary requirements for rats[51], in purified form.

Casein*	240 gm/kgm
Sucrose	640
Hydrogenated vegetable fat	80
Salts, No. 4*	40

To the above are added the following crystalline vitamins, in mg/kgm.

d-Biotin	0.3 mg/kgm
2-Methyl 1, 4-naphthoquinone	5.0
Thiamine HCI	5.0
Pyridoxine HCl	5.0
Pteroylglutamic acid	5.5
Riboflavin	10.0
p-Aminobenzoic acid	10.0
Nicotinic acid	20.0
d-Calcium pantothenate	50.0
Inositol	400.0
Choline chloride	1000.0

* Purified casein is required. The salt mixture is that of Hegsted et al.[20]. All rats receive a supplement of fat-soluble vitamin mixture weekly, containing 800 U.S.P. units of vitamin A, 115 chick units of vitamin D, 6 mg of synthetic alpha-tocopherol, and 650 mg corn oil. On this regimen reproductive performance is virtually equivalent to that of the preceding optimal natural foodstuff diet.

REFERENCES

1. ARMSTRONG, R.C. and ELIAS, J.J.: Development of embryonic rat eyes in organ culture. II. An *in vitro* approach to teratogenic mechanisms. J. Embryol. Exp. Morphol. 19: 407–414, 1968.

2. ASLING, C.W.: Congenital Defects of Face and Palate in Rats Following Maternal Deficiency of Pteroylglutamic Acid. In: Congenital Anomalies of the Face and Associated Structures, edited by S. PRUZANSKY. pp. 173–187. C.C. Thomas, Springfield, 1961.

3. ASLING, C.W. and NELSON, M.M.: Skeletal abnormalities in the rat fetus resulting from pteroylglutamic ("folic") acid deficiency during gestation. Anat. Rec. 106: 170–171, 1950. (abst.).

4. ASLING, C.W., NELSON, M.M., DOUGHERTY, H.L., WRIGHT, H.V. and EVANS, H.M.: The development of cleft palate resulting from maternal pteroylglutamic (folic) acid deficiency during the latter half of gestation in rats. Surg. Gynec. & Obst. 111: 19–28, 1960.

5. BARNES, A. C.: The clinical approach to the prevention of congenital anomalies. Am. J. Obst. & Gynecol. 90: 1242–1250, 1964.

6. BERG, A. D.: Malnutrition and national development. Foreign Affairs 46: 126–136, 1967.

7. CANNON, P.R., FRAZIER, L.E. and HUGHES, R.H: Studies in amino acid utilization. Arch. Path. 50: 709–720, 1950.

8. CHAMBERLAIN, J.G. and NELSON, M.M.: Congenital abnormalities in the rat resulting from single injections of 6-aminonicotinamide during pregnancy. J. Exptl. Zool. 153: 285–299, 1963.

9. COHLAN, S.Q.: Congenital anomalies in the rat produced by excessive intake of vitamin A during pregnancy. Pediatrics 13: 556–567, 1954.

10. ENWAY, L., HURLEY, L.S. and FRASER, A.: Neurological defect: manganese in phenocopy and prevention of a genetic abnormality of inner ear. Science 152: 1766–1768, 1966.

11. FAVE, A.: Les embryopathies provoquées chez les mammiferes. Thérapie 19: 43–164, 1964.

12. Food and Civilization-A Symposium. C.C. Thomas, Springfield, 1966. (Consult U.S. Information Service offices for special "Voice of America Forum Lectures" edition.)
    a. BRIGGS, G.M. Panel: The Broader Implications of Research. pp. 250–256.
    b. MEHREN, G.L. Geography, Geopolitics and World Nutrition. pp. 121–131.

13. FRASER, F.C. and FAINSTAT, T.D.: Production of congenital defects in offspring of pregnant mice treated with cortisone. Pediatrics 8: 527–533, 1951.

14. GIROUD, A.: In: Environmental Influences on Prenatal Development, edited by B. MINTZ. pp. 6–10. University of Chicago Press, 1958.

15. GIROUD, A.: The Nutritional Requirements of Embryos and the Repercussions of Deficiencies. In: World Review of Nutrition and Dietetics, edited by G.H. BOURNE, 1: 231–263. Pitman Medical Publishing Company, Ltd., London, 1959.

16. GIROUD, A. and MARTINET, M.: Fentes du palais chez l'embryon de rat par hypervitaminose A. Compt. rend. soc. biol. 148: 1742–1743, 1954.

17. GIROUD, A. and MARTINET, M.: Malformations diverses du foetus de rat suivant les stades d'administration de vitamine A en exces. Compt. rend. soc. biol. 149: 1088–1090, 1955.

18. GRAINGER, R.B., O'DELL, B.L. and HOGAN, A.G.: Congenital malformations as

related to deficiencies of riboflavin and vitamin B_{12}, etc. J. Nutrition 54: 33–48, 1954.

19. a. HALE, F.: Pigs born without eyeballs. J. Hered. 24: 105–106, 1933.
    b. ...... Relation of vitamin A to anophthalmos in pigs. Am. J. Ophth. 18: 1087–1093, 1935.
    c. ...... Relation of maternal vitamin A deficiency to microphthalmia in pigs. Texas M.J. 33: 228–232, 1937.

20. HEGSTED, D.M., MILLS, R.C., ELVEHJEM, C.A. and HART, E.B.: Choline in the nutrition of chicks. J. Biol. Chem. 138: 459–466, 1941.

21. HURLEY, L.S.: Studies on nutritional factors in mammalian development. J. Nutrition 91: 27–38, 1967.

22. HURLEY, L.S. and EVERSON, G.J.: Delayed development of righting reflexes in offspring of manganese-deficient rats. Proc. Soc. Exp. Biol. & Med. 102: 360–362, 1959.

23. HURLEY, L.S. and SWENERTON, H.: Congenital malformations resulting from zinc deficiency in rats. Proc. Soc. Exp. Biol. & Med. 123: 692–696, 1966.

24. HURLEY, L.S., WOOTEN, E., EVERSON, G.J. and ASLING, C.W.: Anomalous development of ossification in the inner ear of offspring of manganese-deficient rats. J. Nutrition 71: 15–19, 1960.

25. JACOBSON, H.N.: Social, economic and nutritional patterns of prematurity. Presented at the First International Conference on Prematurity. (Committee on Maternal and Child Care, American Medical Association), 1968.

26. JOHNSON, E.M., NELSON, M.M. and MONIE, I.W.: Effects of transitory pteroylglutamic acid (PGA) deficiency on embryonic and placental development in the rat. Anat. Rec. 146: 215–224, 1963.

27. KALTER, H. and WARKANY, J.: Experimental production of congenital malformations in mammals by metabolic procedure. Physiol. Rev. 39: 69–115, 1959.

28. MALTHUS, T.R.: Essay on the principle of population, as it affects the future improvement of society. London, 1798.

29. MELTZER, H.J.: Congenital anomalies due to attempted abortion with 4-aminopteroylglutamic acid. JAMA 161: 1253, 1956.

30. a. NELSON, M.M.: Mammalian fetal development and antimetabolites. In: Antimetabolites and Cancer, edited by C.P. RHOADS. pp. 107–128. A.A.A.S. Monograph, Washington, D.C., 1955.
    b. ...... Production of congenital anomalies in mammals by maternal nutritional deficiencies. Pediatrics 19: 764–776, 1957.

31. NELSON, M.M., ASLING, C.W. and EVANS, H.M.: Congenital abnormalities in fetal rats resulting from pteroylglutamic ("folic") acid deficiency during gestation. Anat. Rec. 106: 309, 1950. (demonstr.)

32. NELSON, M.M., BAIRD, C.D.C., WRIGHT, H.V. and EVANS, H.M.: Congenital anomalies in the rat resulting from riboflavin deficiency induced by the antimetabolite galactoflavin. J. Nutrition 58: 125–134, 1956.

33. NISHIMURA, H.: Zinc deficiency in suckling mice deprived of colostrum. J. Nutrition 49: 79–97, 1953.

34. PEER, L.A., GORDON, H.W. and BERNHARD, W.G.: Effect of vitamins on human teratology. Plastic and Reconstructive Surgery 34; 358–362, 1964.

35. PINSKY, L. and FRASER, F.C.: Production of skeletal malformations in the offspring of pregnant mice treated with 6-aminonicotinamide. Biol. Neonat. 1: 106–112, 1959.

36. PITT, D.B. and SAMSON, P.E.: Congenital malformations and maternal diet. Australasian Ann. of Med. 10: 268–274, 1961.

37. REVELLE, R.: Population and food supplies. In: Prospects of the World Food Supply, A symposium. pp. 24–47. National Academy of Sciences, Washington, D. C., 1966.

38. RICHARDSON, L.R. and HOGAN, A.G.: Diet of mother and hydrocephalus in infant rats. J. Nutrition 32: 459–465, 1946.

39. RUNNER, M.: Inheritance of susceptibility to congenital deformity–embryonic instability. J. Nat. Cancer Inst. 15: 637–649, 1954.

40. RUNNER, M. and MILLER, J.R.: Congenital deformity in the mouse as a consequence of fasting. Anat. Rec. 124: 437–438, 1956. (abst.)

41. SHAW, E.B. and STEINBACH, H.L.: Aminopterin-induced fetal malformation. Am. J. Dis. Child. 115: 477–482, 1968.

42. TANIMURA, T., KATSUYA, T. and NISHIMURA, H.: Embryotoxicity of acute exposure to methyl parathion in rats and mice. Arch. Envir. Health 15: 609–613, 1967.

43. Teratology: Principles and Techniques, edited by J.G. WILSON and J. WARKANY, University of Chicago Press, 1965.
    a. FRASER, F.C. Ch. 2: Some genetic aspects of teratology.
    b. JOHNSON, E.M. Ch. 5: Nutritional factors in mammalian teratology.
    c. KALTER, H. Ch. 3: Interplay of intrinsic and extrinsic factors.
    d. RUNNER, M. Ch. 4: General mechanisms of teratogenesis.
    e. WARKANY, H. Ch. 1: Development of experimental mammalian teratology.
    f. WILSON, J.G. Ch. 10: Embryological considerations in teratology.

44. The U.F.A.W. Handbook on the Care and Management of Laboratory Animals, edited by A.N. WARDEN and W. LANE-PETTER. Universities Federation for Animal Welfare, London, 2nd. ed. 1957.

45. The World Food Problem, Vol. 1, Report of the Panel on the World Food Supply. President's Science Advisory Committee. U.S. Government Printing Office: 0–263–531, 1967.

46. THIERSCH, J.B.: Therapeutic abortions with a folic acid antagonist. Am. J. Obst. Gynec. 63: 1298–1304, 1952.

47. THIERSCH, J.B. and PHILIPS, F.S.: Effect of 4-amino-pteroylglutamic acid (aminopterin) on early pregnancy. Proc. Soc. Exp. Biol. & Med. 74: 204–208, 1950.

48. WARKANY, J., BEAUDRY, P.H. and HORNSTEIN, S.: Attempted abortion with 4-aminopteroylglutamic acid (aminopterin); malformations of the child. Am. J. Dis. Child. 97: 274–281, 1959.

49. WARKANY, J. and NELSON, R.C.: Appearance of skeletal abnormalities in the offspring of rats reared on a deficient diet. Science 92: 383–384, 1940.

50. WARKANY, J. and SCHRAFFENBERGER, E.: Congenital malformations induced in rats by maternal nutritional deficiency. V. Effects of a purified diet lacking riboflavin. Proc. Soc. Exp. Biol. & Med. 54: 92–94, 1943.

51. WARNER, R.G.: Nutrient requirements of the laboratory rat. In: Nutrient Requirements of Domestic Animals. No. 10, pp. 51–95. Report of the Committee on Animal Nutrition. Nat. Acad. Sci.—Nat. Res. Council, Pub. 990. Washington, D.C., 1962.

52. WILCKE, H.: General outlook for animal protein in food supplies of developing areas. In: World Food Resources. Adv. in Chem. Series 57, Amer. Chem. Soc., Washington, D.C., 1966.

53. a. WILSON, J. G.: Is there specificity of action in experimental teratogenesis? Pediatrics 19: 755–763, 1956.
    b. ...... Experimental studies on congenital malformations. J. Chron. Dis. 10: 111–130, 1959.

c. ......   Experimental teratology. Am. J. Obst. Gynec. 90: 1181–1192, 1964.

54. WILSON, J.G., ROTH, C.B. and WARKANY, J.: An analysis of the syndrome of malformations induced by maternal vitamin A deficiency. Am. J. Anat. 92: 189–217, 1953.

55. WOOLEY, D.W.: Antimetabolites of the water-soluble vitamins. In: Metabolic Inhibitors. Vol. 1, edited by R.M. HOCHSTER and J.H. QUASTEL. Ch. 12. Academic Press, N.Y., 1963.

56. The following reference arrived too late to be listed in order in the text, but will be of great importance to those who wish to read on this subject.
Symposium on Nutrition and Prenatal Development. Federation Proceedings 27: 163–204 (1968). Papers include:
a. GIROUD, A.: Nutrition of the embryo.
b. GRAU, C.R.: Avian embryo nutrition.
c. HURLEY, L.S.: Approaches to the study of nutrition in mammalian development.
d. O'DELL, B.L.: Trace elements in embryonic development.

DISCUSSION

TAKANO (Japan)

To my knowledge, pregnant mice are more or less susceptible to fasting in regard to maldevelopment of the conceptus. In contrast, it is somewhat difficult to induce malformations in rats by fasting. In fact, Dr. CHAMBERLAIN, one of your colleagues, reported recently that fasting for several days, including susceptible periods for teratogenesis, did not induce any spectacular maldevelopment of the conceptus.

What do you think is the reason for this species difference?

ASLING

This difference between rats and mice seems well-established, but its basis is not yet understood. Perhaps we should explore closely such differences in response to fasting as hypoglycemia: mice have very low glycogen reserves and become hypoglycemic in a few hours, whereas rats withstand this blood-sugar change for over a day. Such a fundamental change has numerous secondary metabolic consequences, some of which might be teratogenic.

GREEN (Australia)

As you may know, it has been found that prophylaxis against malaria is more effective when the anti-malarial drug Chloroquine is combined with the folic acid antagonist Pyrimethamine (Daraprim).

In view of experience with Aminopterin, would you not agree that, especially in countries where both malaria and malnutrition are common, women of reproductive age should *not* be exposed to this folic acid antagonist?

ASLING

Inasmuch as testing of antimalarial agents has been conducted in subhuman primates, and inasmuch as it is known that some folic acid antagonists are teratogenic in human beings, this would seem to be a very important question to test in rhesus monkeys. If I were in medical practice I would be reluctant to use folic acid antagonists in women of child-bearing age even to augment other medications, unless the woman's health was severely threatened by disease.

OSATHANONDH (Thailand)

Have you ever found malformations of the placenta in your experiments with nutritional deficiencies?

ASLING

Placental damage was observed by JOHNSON[27] while testing the newer 9-methyl folic acid in rats, under teratogenic circumstances. One should also remember the very early work of EVANS and BISHOP (1922) on damage to the placenta with vitamin E deficiency; this deficiency has subsequently been shown by CHENG and associates to be broadly teratogenic in rats. (The primary references will be found in GIROUD's 1968 review; see reference 57, above.)

VIRUSES AND EMBRYOS

John L. Sever

*Head, Section on Infectious Diseases, Perinatal Research Branch, National Institute
of Neurological Diseases and Stroke, National Institutes of Health,
Bethesda, U.S.A.*

Both rubella and cytomegalovirus are capable of producing severe damage to the developing human embryo. For rubella the primary defects occur in the heart, eyes, brain, and ears. The frequency and type on defects depend on the time of maternal infection (Fig. 1)[7,23,25,38]. Damage to blood vessels may also result in a variety of effects including cerebral lesions and renal ischemia[34].

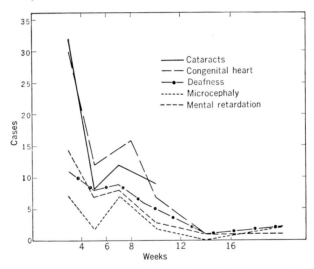

Fig. 1 Frequency of abnormalities in 100 offspring related to time of maternal rubella. (Decaban et al.[7])

There is a generalized infection of the fetus which may persist after birth for a period of months to years[5]. The disseminated involvement results in an actual decrease in the number of cells in the various tissues, and the children are frequently small and microcephalic[14,29]. Cytomegalovirus infections may result in microcephaly, chorioretinitis, mental retardation, and generalized infection which persists after birth[39]. A recent report also suggests an association with inguinal hernias[22]. In the immediate newborn period both types of congenital infections may result in unusual newborn findings including hepatosplenomegaly and thrombocytopenia with bleeding tendencies[35]. For both diseases it appears that infection early in pregnancy results in more severe involvement and permanent damage. However, this is better established for rubella than for cytomegalic inclusion disease.

Data concerning the frequency of rubella and cytomegalovirus infections in pregnant women is becoming available from prospective and specialized studies which are now in progress. One such investigation is the Collaborative Perinatal Research Study. This is a large, prospective study being conducted at ten medical centers throughout the United States. In an analysis of 30,000 pregnancies in the Collaborative Research Study we found that during non-epidemic periods rubella occurred at the rate of 1 to 3 cases per 1,000 while during the 1964 epidemic there were 22 to 30 cases per 1,000[39]. For cytomegalovirus infections in the same population, serologic tests showed that the initial appearance of significant levels of antibody to this virus occurred in $3\frac{1}{2}\%$ of the patients studied[39]. A further investigation of the frequency of cytomegalovirus infections among 200 pregnant women conducted at the National Naval Medical Center showed that seven were excreting virus in the urine at the time of delivery[16]. One of the children of these seven mothers was also excreting virus in the urine and this child had hypospadias. In a recent study, also conducted at the National Naval Medical Center, we investigated the frequency of congenital CMV infection by studing 500 children from whom urine specimens were obtained within the first 24 hours of life[3]. In this group, we found three children excreting virus. These children are now 8 months to $1\frac{1}{2}$ years old and all three have continued to remain infected. While none of the three had the major findings of cytomegalic inclusion disease, in each case there were minimal signs of symptoms in the newborn period which may have been related to the congenital infection. These children and their families are being kept under surveillance for repeated longitudinal study. There is a critical need for additional studies of this type to determine the frequency and spectrum of clinical findings associated with these congenital infections.

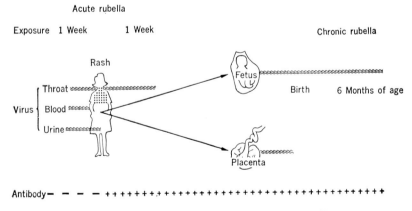

Fig. 2 Acute and chronic rubella (Sever et al.[36])

The mechanism of pathogenesis of rubella has been clarified, to a great extent, by the combined virus isolation, antibody, and histological studies which have been conducted during the last few years. First, the virus is capable of infecting the products of conception and this infection almost always involves the placenta (Fig. 2). In about a third of the cases, the fetus is also infected.

The virus may be disseminated to essentially all organs, or localized in a few sites (Table 1). The disseminated pattern is generally seen more frequently in infections which occur early in the first trimester[1,28]. Other factors must be involved, however, since the disseminated pattern has been found in association with maternal rubella as late as the fourth month of gestation. The possible role of the placenta in restricting the infection and thus protecting the fetus is suggested by the above data and warrants further study. In addition, the

Table 1 Congenital rubella
Recovery of rubella virus from individual organs

Organs	Patients							
	M.E.	M.T.	B.C.	B.K.	E.H.	J.L.	L.K.	O.G.
Brain	+*	−†	−	+	−	−	−	−
Eye	+	−	−	+	−	−	−	−
Inner ear	+	−	−	+	−	−	−	−
Thymus	+	−	−	+	−	−	−	−
Heart	+	−	−	+	−	−	+	−
Lungs	+	−	−	+	−	−	−	−
Liver	−	−	−	−	−	−	−	−
Spleen	+	−	−	+	−	−	−	−
Kidney	+	−	−	+	−	−	−	−
Gastrointestinal tract	+	−	−	+	−	−	−	−
Adrenal gland	+	−	−	N.T.‡	−	−	−	−
Gonads	+	−	−	N.T.	−	−	−	−
Urine	+	U.A.§	U.A.	U.A.	−	U.A.	U.A.	U.A.
Amniotic fluid	+	U.A.	U.A.	U.A.	−	U.A.	U.A.	U.A.
Placenta	+	+	+	+	+	+	+	+
Maternal blood	−	−	−	−	−	−	−	−
Gestational age at the time of rash	15 Days	27 Days	46 Days	55 Days	63 Days	78 Days	92 Days	128 Days
Interval between clinical onset of rubella and therapeutic abortion	77 Days	64 Days	53 Days	48 Days	27 Days	12 Days	38 Days	61 Days

*+, Rubella virus recovered.
†−, Rubella virus not recovered.
‡N.T., not tested.
§U.A., Unavailable.

(MONIF et al.[28])

high frequency of isolation of virus from therapeutic abortions for maternal rubella (approximately 50%) is considerably greater than the known incidence of congenital malformations (approximately 20%).

The mechanism of teratogenesis for rubella appears to be due to a direct virus-cell relationship which persists throughout gestation[1,27,28]. The restriction of damage to certain organs probably reflects, at least in part, the regenerative capacity of a given tissue[36]. Indirect effects, such as those caused by vascular occulusions due to damage of blood vessels, probably account for some of the apparent defects[34]. In addition, it is well established that the virus is capable of interfering with the growth of certain tissues, this in itself provides a direct mechanism for producing abnormalities in the developing fetus[29,32].

Studies with rubella in experimental animals have not been particularly rewarding. Congenital infection can be produced in the monkey, however to date, this appears to be a very transient infection and there is no evidence of persisting infection either in terms of virus isolation from the newborn or active antibody synthesis at the time of birth[31,37]. One recent study using monkeys suggested that lens, optic, cutaneous, chorion, and osseous lesions were produced following inoculation at the 25th day of gestation[8]. Since previous studies had not shown these effects, this work warrants early repetition. Transient congenital infection can also be produced in the ferret. In our studies, however, we have seen no clear virus induced defects[11]. Inoculation of newborn ferrets, however, has resulted in a chronic persisting infection and active antibody production similar to that found in infants with congenital infection, and in approximately 10% of newborn ferrets inoculated intracerebrally, corneal opacities associated with persisting infection in the involved eye have been shown[37]. Runting, scoliosis, visceral, central nervous system, and facial malformations have been observed in some of our studies in ferrets, but we are now inclined to believe that these effects were probably related to indirect factors possibly including deficient diet, seasonal mating patterns, and mixed genetic background of the animals.

One group of investigators, using rats inoculated with rubella recently reported that runting, lense opacities, malformations, and neonatal deaths were produced when the virus was administered on the sixth day of gestation[6]. In view of the ferret studies, these investigations in rats should be repeated with great care and controls.

Cytomegaloviruses tend to be extremely species specific, and while infections can be produced within a given species with its own cytomegalovirus, cross species effects are rarely demonstrable. To date most information is available for cytomegaloviruses by studies in mice with mouse cytomegalovirus[15]. When high titers of animal-passaged virus are used, the mice show a rapidly fatal generalized infection, which has some of the characteristics of the newborn disease in man.

A number of "model systems" are available for the study of the effects of viruses in experimental animals. Many of these are extremely unique and bear little resemblance to diseases known to occur in man. These may represent more curiosities than informative study systems. Some of the systems which may be of value are summarized in Table 2.

Five basic guidelines appear to be useful at the present time in considering experimental viral teratology (Table 3).

1. Infection should be produced in the adult and fetus or newborn.

   Viruses which produce intrauterine or fetal damage are capable of initiating infection in the adult, fetus, or newborn. There is no evidence to date to indicate that damage or teratogenic effects can be produced indirectly without infection. Therefore, in exploring the potential of an

Table 2 Experimental intrauterine and newborn infections

Virus	Animal	Effects	Reference
Rubella	Monkey (*Macaca mulatta*) (*Macaca irus*)	Newborns and adults infected. Limited intrauterine infection. Reported lense, optic, cutaneous, chorion, and osseous lesions.	37, 31 8
	Ferret	Limited intrauterine infection, persistent newborn infection, lense opacity in 10% of newborns following IC infection.	11
	Rat	Reported chronic intrauterine infection, purpura, lense opacities, malformations (rare), frequent neonatal deaths.	6
	Hamster	No transplacental infection.	30
Cytomegalovirus	Mouse	Rapidly fetal, generalized infection in newborns. No congenital infection but increased intrauterine deaths.	15, 24
Herpes simplex	Rabbit	Intrauterine death and readsorption.	26, 2
	Hamster	Direct inoculation in utero gives generalized fetal infection with rapid death.	12
Attenuated blue tongue virus	Sheep	Congenital anomalies of central nervous system (hydroanencephaly, subcortical cysts).	40, 33
Attenuated hog cholera (Myxo virus like)	Swine	Congenital deformed noses, kidneys, edema, ascities. Intrauterine infection. Cerebral hypoplasia and poor myelination (tremor, ataxia).	42, 10
Infectious bovine rhinotracheitis (Herpes like)	Cows	Congenital infection and fetal death.	4
Equine abortion virus (Herpes like)	Horses	Congenital infection and abortion.	9
H-1, RV viruses (DNA, heat and ether resistent. Intra nuclear inclution)	Hamster (Mouse, cat, rat)	Intrauterine and newborn infection and effects exencephalus, microcephalus, facial clefts, abdominal herniation, "Mongoloid faces", hepatitis and cerebellar hypoplasia, virus destroys mitotic cells. Not found in association with similar human malformations.	41, 13, 20, 19
Feline ataxia virus (similar to H-1, RV viruses)	Cats	Congenital infection and cerebellar hypoplasia, ataxia.	21
Mumps	Hamster	Newborn infection produces hydrocephalus due to aqueductal stenosis.	17, 18

Table 3 Guidelines for experimental viral teratology

1. Infection should be produced in the adult and fetus or newborn.
2. The virus used should be well adapted to the animal and passaged in the living animal.
3. Several different intervals during gestation should be studied including inoculation of newborns.
4. Indirect effects on the mother or infant should be considered.
5. The effect should be prevented by specific neutralization of the virus.

agent to produce teratogenic or other effects in an animal species, the first studies should be directed at establishing that infection can be produced in the experimental animal model.

2. In most cases the virus used should be well adapted to the animal and preferably passaged in the living animal.

    Several studies have demonstrated the importance of maintaining the virus in either a very low tissue culture passage or preferably in passages in the animal species itself. With mouse cytomegalovirus, for example, the effect on the experimental animal is lost completely with just one passage of the virus in tissue culture[30]. Furthermore, laboratory adapted strains of the rat virus fail to show transplacental passage of this virus, whereas, fresh field, strains readily produce the infection and disease[9,20]. While in some cases attenuation by tissue culture passage may result in less severe disease and thereby less fetal deaths, in general, attenuation appears to decrease the likelihood of transplacental infection and teratogenic effcects.

3. Several different intervals during gestation should be studied, including the inoculation of newborns. Several dosages and routes should be tried.

    The possible effects of the agent must be considered in relation to various phases of the developement of the embryo and the newborn. The data for rubella in man demonstrates the importance of including infections initiated early in gestation. For herpes viruses, on the other hand, the information for man and horses suggests that inoculation later in pregnancy or near term results in congenital infection and disease, whereas, early infection has not shown significant effects. In the experimental system, RV virus inoculated late in gestation results in cerebellar destruction, severe neonatal hepatitis, while earlier inoculation may produce fetal death or teratogenic effects. Inoculation of newborns and suckling animals with this virus may lead to fatal disease, "funny faces," or cerebellar hypoplasia and hepatic involvement. Some variation may also be caused by the dosages of virus used and route of inoculation.

4. Indirect effects on the mother or infant, environmental factors, mating patterns, and genetic background variables should be considered.

    Since infectious agents frequently produce illness in the mother, the occurrence of generalized effects such as fever, nausea, diarrhea, anorexia, or rejection of the newborn infant must be taken into consideration. Environmental factors including temperature, availability of water, adequacy of bedding should be examined. Nutritional deficiencies, variations in frequencies of naturally occurring defects at various seasons of the year, and genetic background of the animals should be determined whenever possible.

5. The effects should be prevented by specific neutralization of the virus.

    If effects are produced in experimental animal systems, it is the responsibility of investigator to establish that this is the result of the virus infection under study and not due to contaminating infectious agents or to materials in the inoculum. This is best confirmed by neutralization of the virus with specific antibody prepared using a different seed virus in another host.

SUMMARY

A number of viruses are capable of producing intrauterine infection and damage. Both rubella and cytomegalovirus may cause malformations. For rubella the most frequent defects are those involving the heart, eyes, brain, and ears. With cytomegalovirus, children may be microcephalic, small, and mentally retarded.

The mechanism of teratogenesis of rubella apparently relates to the direct infection of the virus in certain tissues of the developing fetus. Indirect effects may also be caused by vascular occulusion due to damage of blood vessels.

Studies of rubella in experimental animals have not been particularly successful. Isolated reports have suggested that congenital damage can be produced in monkeys and rats. Further studies, however, are necessary.

A number of "model systems" are available for the study of viruses in experimental animals. It is now possible to utilize basic guidelines in considerations of experimental teratogenesis in these systems. These guidelines include:

1. Infection should be produced in the adult and fetus or newborn.
2. In most cases the virus used should be well adapted to the animal and preferably passaged in the living animal.
3. Several different intervals during gestation should be studied, including the inoculation of newborns. Several dosages and routes should be tried.
4. Indirect effects on the mother or infant, environmental factors, mating patterns, and genetic background variables should be considered.
5. The effects should be prevented by specific neutralization of the virus.

REFERENCES

1. ALFORD, C.A., NEVA, F.A. and WELLER, T.H.: Virologic and serologic studies on human products of conception after maternal rubella. New. Eng. J. Med. 271: 275–281, 1964.
2. BIEGELEISON, J.Z., SCOTT, L.V. and JOEL, W.: Further evidence of fetal infection with herpes simplex virus. Amer. J. Clin. Path. 37: 289–293, 1962.
3. BIRNBAUM, G., LYNCH, J., LONGERAN, W.M., MARGILETH, A.M. and SEVER, J.L.: Prospective study of congenital cytomegalovirus infection. To be presented at Epidemiology Meeting of Am. P.H. Ass., November, 1968.
4. CHOW, T.L., MELELLO, J.A. and OWEN, N.V.: Abortion experimentally induced in cattle by infectious bovine rhinotracheitis virus. J. Amer. Vet. Med. Ass. 144: 1005–1007, 1964.
5. COOPER, L.Z. and KRUGMAN, S.: Diagnosis and management: Congenital rubella. Pediatrics 37: 335–338, 1966.
6. COTLIER, E., FOX, J., BOHIGIAN, G., BEATY, C. and DU PREE, A.: Pathogenic effects of rubella virus on embryos and newborn rats. Nature 217: 38–40, 1968.
7. DEKABAN, A., O'ROURKE, J. and CORMAN, T.: Abnormalities of offspring related to maternal rubella during pregnancy. Neurology 8: 387–392, 1958.

8. DELAHUNT, C. S. and RIESER, N.: Rubella-induced embryopathies in monkeys. Amer. J. Obstet Gynec. 99: 580–588, 1967.

9. DOMOCK, W.W.: The diagnosis of virus abortion in mares. J. Amer. Vet. Med. Ass. 96: 665, 1940.

10. EMERSON, J.L. and DELEZ, A.L.: Cerebellar hypoplasia, hypomyelinogenesis and congenital tremors of pigs associated with prenatal hog cholera vaccination of sows. J. Amer. Vet. Med. Ass. 147: 47–54. 1965.

11. FABIYI, A., GITHICK, G.L. and SEVER, J.L.: Chronic rubella virus infection in the ferret (Mustela putorius furo) puppy. Proc. Soc. Exp. Biol. Med. 125: 766–771, 1967.

12. FERM, V.H. and LAW, R.J.: Herpes simplex infection in the pregnant hamster. J. Path. Bact. 89: 295–300, 1965.

13. FERM, V.H. and KILHAM, L.: Rat virus (RV) infection in fetal and pregnant hamsters. Proc. Soc. Exp. Biol. Med. 112: 623–626, 1963.

14. HARDY, J.B., MONIF, G.R.G. and SEVER, J.L.: Studies in congenital rubella, Baltimore, 1964–1965, II. Clinical and virologic. Bull. Johns Hopkins Hosp. 118: 97–108, 1966.

15. HENSON, D., SMITH, R.D. and GEHRKE, J.: Non-fatal mouse cyto-megalovirus hepatitis. Amer. J. Path. 40: 871–888, 1966.

16. HILDEBRANDT, R.J., SEVER, J.L., MARGILETH, A.M. and CALLAGAN, D.A.: Cyto-megalovirus in the normal pregnant woman. Amer. J. Obstet. Gynec. 98: 1125–1128, 1967.

17. JOHNSON, R.T.: Mumps virus encephalitis in the hamster. Studies of the inflammatory response and noncytopathic infection of neurons. J. Neuropath. Exp. Neurol. 27: 80–95, 1968.

18. JOHNSON, R.T., JOHNSON, K.P. and Edmonds, C.J.: Virus-induced hydrocephalus: Development of aqueductal stenosis in hamsters after mumps infection. Science 157: 1066–1067, 1967.

19. KILHAM, L. and FERM, V.H.: Rat virus (RV) infections of pregnant, fetal, and newborn rats. Proc. Soc. Exp. Biol. Med. 117: 874–879, 1964.

20. KILHAM, L. and MARGOLIS, G.: Spontaneous hepatitis and cerebellar "hypoplasia" in suckling rats due to congenital infections with rat virus. Amer. J. Path. 49: 457–475, 1966.

21. KILHAM, L. and MARGOLIS, G.: Viral etiology of spontaneous ataxia of cats. Amer. J. Path. 48: 991–1011, 1966.

22. LANG, D.J.: The association of indirect inguinal hernia for the congenital cytomegalovirus inclusion disease. Pediatrics 38: 913–916, 1966.

23. LUNDSTROM, R.: Rubella during pregnancy. Acta. Paediat. Scand. (Stockholm) 51 (Suppl. 133): 1–110, 1962.

24. MEDEARIS, D.N.: Mouse cytomegalovirus. III. Attempts to produce intrauterine infections. Amer. J. Hyg. 80: 113–120, 1964.

25. MICHAELS, R.H. and MELLIN, G.W.: Prospective experience with maternal rubella and the associated congenital malformations. Pediatrics 26: 200–209, 1960.

26. MIDDLEKAMP, J., REED, C. and PATRIZI, G.: Placental transfer of herpes simplex in pregnant rabbits. Proc. Soc. Exp. Biol. Med. 125: 757–760, 1967.

27. MONIF, G., AVERY, G.B., KORONES, S.B. and SEVER, J.L.: Isolation of rubella virus from the organs of three children with rubella syndrome defects. Lancet 1: 723, 1965.

28. MONIF, G., SEVER, J.L., SCHIFF, G.M. and TRAUB, R.G.: Isolation of rubella virus from products of conception. Amer. J. Obstet. Gynec. 91: 143–146, 1965.

29. NAEYE, R.L. and BLANC, W.: Pathogenesis of congenital rubella. J.A.M.A. 194: 1277–1283, 1965.

30. OXFORD, J.S. and SCHIELD, G.C.: Growth of rubella virus in the hamster. Virology 28: 780–782, 1966.

31. PARKMAN, P.D., PHILLIPS, P.E. and MEYER, H.M.: Experimental rubella virus infection in pregnant monkeys. Amer. J. Dis. Child. 110: 390–394, 1965.

32. RAWLES, W.E., MELNICK, J.L., ROSENBERG, H.S. and BAYATPOUR, M.: Spontaneous virus carrier cultures and post-mortem isolation of virus from infants with congenital rubella. Proc. Soc. Exp. Biol. Med. 120: 623–626, 1965.

33. RICHARDS, W.P.C. and CORDY, D.R.: Blue tongue virus infection: Pathologic responses of nervous systems in sheep and mice. Science 156: 530–531, 1967.

34. RORKE, L.B. and SPIRO, A.J.: Cerebral lesions in congenital rubella syndrome. J. Pediat. 70: 243–255, 1967.

35. SEVER, J.L.: Perinatal infections affecting the developing fetus and newborn. Proc. Conference on Prevention of Mental Retardation Thorugh Control of Infectious Diseases. NICHD/NIH Monograph, 1966.

36. SEVER, J.L.: Rubella as a teratogen. In: Advances in Teratology, Vol. 2, edited by D.H.M. WOOLLAM. Logos Press, London, 1967.

37. SEVER, J.L., MEIER, G.W., WINDLE, W. F., SCHIFF, G. M., MONIF, G. R. G. and FABIYI, A.: Experimental rubella in pregnant rhesus monkeys. J. Infect. Dis. 116: 21–26, 1966.

38. SEVER, J.L., NELSON, K.B. and GILKESON, M.R.: Rubella epidemic, 1964: Effect on 6,000 pregnancies. Amer. J. Dis. Child. 110: 395–407, 1965.

39. SEVER, J.L. and WHITE, L.R.: Intrauterine Viral Infection. Annual Review of Medicine, Vol. 19, 1968.

40. SCHULTZ, G. and DELAY, P.D.: Losses in newborn lambs associated with blue tongue vaccination of pregnant ewes. J. Amer. Vet. Med. Ass. 127: 224–226, 1955.

41. TOOLAN, H.W.: Experimental production of mongoloid hamsters. Science 131: 1446–1448, 1960.

42. YOUNG, G.A., KITCHELL, R.L., LUEDKE, A.J. and SAUTTER, J.H.: The effect of viral and other infections of the dam on fetal development in swine. Modified hog cholera viruses. J. Amer. Vet. Med. Ass. 126: 165–171, 1955.

DISCUSSION

MISHALANY (Lebanon)

1. Where was the work associating indirect inguinal hernias with cytomegalovirus published? What is the evidence for the association?

2. At what time during pregnancy did you study the shedding of cytomegalovirus by the mother in the urine?

3. Did the 3 children who were shedding cytomegalovirus in their urine, have any congenital anomalies? Did the 500 children studied have any malformation?

SEVER

The analysis by Dr. DAVID LANG of the high frequency of inguinal hernias in males with cytomegalic inclusion disease was published recently in the New England Journal of Medicine. In our studies, maternal excretion of cytomegalovirus was tested at delivery. Seven of 200 women tested had viuria. The 3 children with congenital infection with cytomegalovirus, as evidenced by viuria in the first 24 hours of life did not have any malformations or other major findings normally associated with cytomegalic inclusion disease. All 3 did have minimal findings which might have been related to the infection. These

included petechia, slight hepatomegaly and "floppiness" in the first 8 months of life.

OSATHANONDH (Thailand)

I would like to ask your opinion about preventive measures for pregnant woman during an epidemic of rubella?

SEVER

The value of gammaglobulin for the prevention of congenital rubella remains controversial. Vaccine studies are in progress but a vaccine will not be available for at least 1 year and its value during pregnancy has not been studied to date.

At present we and most of our associates recommend avoidance of exposure during an epidemic, if possible. If exposure to rubella occurs in the first months of pregnancy, paired serum specimens are obtained and tested for antibody. In this way the susceptibility of the patient can be determined and seroconversion identifies or confirms the occurrence of rubella. In some cases we use virus isolation to establish the diagnosis.

SINGH (India)

You have shown that in rubella infection the fetus is affected in 30% of cases while the placenta shows evidence of the virus in almost 100% of cases. Do you see any abnormality or histopathological change of the placenta?

SEVER

Several studies in our laboratories and elsewhere have shown minor inflammatory changes in infected placentas. In addition vascular damage has been reported.

KLINGBERG (Israel)

1) What experimental animals were used for producing hydrocephalus by mumps virus? 2) Have you information concerning mumps infection during pregnancy and congenital malformations in humans? 3) Have you information about spontaneous abortions caused by mumps infection during pregnancy?

SEVER

The hamster has been used in the studies of mumps (JOHNSON, R.T. Science 157: 1066–1067, Sept. 1, 1967). In our studies of mumps we have found neither congenital malformations nor abortions. A number of reports have suggested that mumps may produce malformations, abortions or possibly endocardial fibroelastosis, however we have found only a slight suggestion of smaller babies in our studies.

MILLER, R.W. (U.S.A.)

In addition to smallpox, what other infections during pregnancy can be studied in particular in the Far East?

SEVER

There are several excellent opportunities for studying infection and congenital anomalies in the Far East:

1. Rubella: Current epidemics in Taiwan and elswhere could be studied for acute and chronic rubella as well as vaccine and gammaglobulin effects.

2. Japanese B encephalitis virus: This virus causes abortions in swine and could be investigated in Japan and elsewhere, particularly when epidemics occur.

3. Malaria: This protozoan produces fetal damage and could be studied in many areas of the Far East.

Other infections of interest might include cholera, various arbor viruses, several of which are quite common here, parasites of various types, plague, and protozool infections.

NISHIMURA (Japan)

Once, doctor friend of mine raised the following question: how long before conception will maternal rubella infection be dangerous to human embryos? I would like to pass this question onto you.

SEVER

We have reported several cases of congenital rubella where the maternal infection appears to have been 2 to 3 weeks before conception. These were pregnancies for which quite accurate information was availabe for both the time of the infection and the date of conception.

MURAKAMI (Japan)

It has been believed by gynecologists that virus infections such as mumps, polyomyelitis and influenza cause malformations. However, Dr. TÖNDURY of Zürich said that these virus infections only cause fetal deaths and malformations were never resulted. What is your opinion?

SEVER

Our data do not show any relation

between mumps or polyomyelitis and malformation. The imformation for influenza is conflicting. In our studies we did not find an association between influenza and malformations or respiratory disease in the newborn; however our data did not include the severe epidemic of influenza A_2 in the late 1950's.

SISODIA (India)

1. Have you any information on malformations in human babies born to smallpox infected mothers?

2. We in Hyderabad, India are using Azaserine as a chemotherapeutic agent for the treatment of smallpox infection. I wonder what would be the effect of Azaserine, which is an antimetabolite, on babies born to human mothers being treated for smallpox.

SEVER

Smallpox causes increased rates of abortion and stillbirth. Children may also be born with smallpox. There are no data indicating that samllpox causes malformations. Azaserine, as an antimetabolite would be a likely candidate to produce malformations.

COMPARATIVE TERATOLOGICAL EFFECTS OF
METABOLIC DISEASES OF THE MOTHER

KIICHI TAKANO

*Associate Professor, Department of Anatomy, Faculty of Medicine,
Kyoto University, Kyoto, Japan.*

Among human metabolic diseases, diabetes mellitus and thyroid dysfunction in the mother have been suspected as a cause of fetal malformations and many investigations using experimental animals have been carried out employing these metabolic errors. There are several other metabolic disturbances which have been induced in pregnant animals in order to determine their effect upon the conceptus: disease state induced by sympatholytic agents[9], anorexia by amphetamine[69] and obesity by goldthioglucose[41]. There are, however, scarcely any clinical reports comparable to the latter three experiments, and I will confine my discussion to the thyroid diseases and diabetes mellitus. At the same time, the effect on the conceptus of agents used in the treatment of these diseases will be discussed, even though it is often difficult to separate the effect of the disease itself from that of medications.

HYPO- OR HYPERTHYROIDISM

HOET et al.[24] emphasized the role of maternal hypothyroidism as well as prediabetes as a cause of congenital malformations but the significance of this study was questioned because of an inadequate statistical treatment of the data.

There is some evidence that antithyroid agents may cause goitrous or non-goitrous hypothyroidism in fetuses when administered to the mother after a certain period of gestation in human, as well as in experimental animals (Tables 1, 2). BARGMAN and GARDNER[5] estimated that the critical period may begin at the 10th to 12th week of pregnancy in man. It is of interest that non-radioactive iodine powder as a medicament for bronchitis of the mother also seems to cause goiter in the offspring[3]. The authors suggested that a high level of plasma-iodines might prevent the organic binding of iodine in the thyroid gland. The ultimate effect was lack of thyroxin and clinical hypothyroidism, and the goiter was thought to be caused by excessive thyroid stimulating hormone released by the pituitary.

Nevertheless on the basis of the report of HOET et al.[24], it is doubtful that fetal abnormalities other than the thyroid dysfunction are induced by maternal hypothyroidism or ingestion of antithyroid drugs. HODGES et al.[23] reported three abnormal, mentally deficient children born to a mother with myxedema. However, they attributed to the maternal hypothyroidism, DOWN's syndrome, which was recognized in one of the children and it is now clear that this condition

Table 1 Reports of abnormal newborns possibly related to maternal hypo-
or hyperthyroidism

Maternal state	Outcome	Reference
Propylthiouracil for hyperthyroidism	Goiter	1
[131]I for hyperthyroidism	Hypothyroidism	5, 18
Non-radioactive iodine for bronchitis	Goiter	3
Antithyroid antibodies by autoimmunization	Athyrotic cretinism	8, 37
Thyroid stimulator	Neonatal exophthalmos	38
Thyrotoxicosis	*ibid.*	37
Thyrotoxicosis	Microcephaly, hydrocephaly, heart disease, etc.	43

Table 2 Effect upon the offspring of hypo- or hyperthyroid agent administered
to pregnant animals

Agent (animal)	Treatment*	Outcome**	Reference
Propylthiouracil (rabbit)	22 mg/kg/d, p.o., day 11–25	Athyrotic cretinism	29
(guinea pig)	25 mg/d, p.o., day 38–term	Goiter	46
Methylthiouracil (mouse)	8–20 mg/d, i.p., day 7–10	No effect	60
(mouse)	400 mg/kg/d, p.o., day 0–17	Death (+)	70
(mouse)	10 mg/kg, s.c., day 9	Death ($\#\#\#$); Clubfoot (5.5 %)	39
Thyrotropin (rat)	20 u/total, i.p., day 7–10	Death($\#\#\#$); Anophthalmia, hydrocephaly, etc. (24.6 %)	7
Thyroxin (mouse)	0.1 mg/d, s.c., day 9–11	Death ($\#\#$); Clubfoot, etc. (11.5%)	39
(mouse)	0.1 mg/d, day 11–12 (route ?)	Incidence of cleft lip decreased	68

* Explanation of abbreviations: p.o., oral administration, either by gastric intubation
or by mixture into food; i.p., intraperitoneal injection; s.c., subcutaneous injection.
** Incidence of fetal death is shown as follows: +, less than 10%; $\#\#$, 10–30%; $\#\#\#$,
more than 30%.

results from a chromosomal aberration.

In experimental animals, fetal mortality may increase after the administration of antithyroid agents but only a small number of minor deformities were produced by one of the investigators[39].

Hyperthyroidism of the mother quite probably causes neonatal exophthalmos of the baby[37,38]. Recently, ORLOVA[43], a Russian obstetrician, reported a very high incidence of microcephaly, heart diseases and other congenital malformations among 50 infants born to mothers with hyperthyroidism. Regrettably, I could not read the original report, but to my knowledge this is the first one which suggests a relationship between major malformations and maternal hyperthyroidism in human beings.

In animal experiments there is a slight controversy about the effect of maternal hyperthyroidism upon the conceptus. BEAUDOIN and ROBERTS[7] reported a teratogenic effect of thyroid stimulating hormone (TSH) upon rat embryos. If a sub-teratogenic dose of trypan blue was injected in conjunction with TSH the incidence of malformations was more than doubled (from 24.6% to 59.7%). On the contrary, thyroxin administered to pregnant animals was reported to decrease the teratogenic effect of vitamin A as well as to suppress the occurrence of a spontaneous malformation in Strong A mice[68]. MIYAMOTO[39] reported that thyroxin decreased the teratogenic effect of ethylurethan, although the agent itself at the same dosage showed a teratogenic effect in a colony-bred stock mouse (Table 2).

DIABETES MELLITUS

Despite great progress in the treatment of this disease, fetal mortality including perinatal death is still very high in the diabetic mother[20,21,40,47]. There have also been many investigations in relation to the disease as a possible cause of human congenital malformations. In Table 3, relatively recent reports of malformed babies born to diabetic mothers are listed. Regarding the type of

Table 3 Reports of malformed babies born to diabetic mothers

Type of malformations*	Reference
Cataract, cleft palate, heart disease, etc. (4.9%)	22
Anencephaly, polydactyly, cleft palate, etc. (18%, including autopsy)	40
Caudal regressions, including vertebra and lower limb deformities	30, 32
Heart disease, limb deformity (6.4% by external examination and 19.5% by autopsy)	45
Hydrocephaly, heart disease, kidney defect (4.7%)	21
Thrombosis, esp. at renal and suprarenal veins (15.8% by autopsy)	42
Heart disease, talipes, etc. (5.3%)	16
Spinal deformities, cleft lip and palate (in relation to insulin antagonism of the mother)	61, 64

* Include only those found by external examinations, unless otherwise stated.

abnormalities, we can recognize several groups: anomalies of the nervous system, heart diseases and skeletal malformations. "Caudal regressions" were first reported by LENZ and MAIER[32] and several similar cases have been noted other than those listed in the table[44,55].

On the other hand, a few authors have reported no relationship between congenital malformations and maternal diabetes[14,49]. An especially severe opinion was presented by RUBIN and MURPHY[49], who criticized some of the early reports on the basis that the infants of diabetic women had been examined much more closely than those of the control. In this regard, the statistical investigations of PEDERSEN et al.[45] on 853 newborn infants of diabetic mother and 1212 controls

are noteworthy. These authors reported that the frequency of major malformations were significantly higher in the infants of women with late diabetic vascular
complications (WHITE's groups D and F) than in those born to women in the
control group. One could argue, however, that it would be impossible to
determine an exact influence of maternal diabetes itself in humans because of
various treatments given to the patients, which alone could be teratogenic. The
effect of antidiabetic agents upon the development of the conceptus will be discussed separately in a later section.

Fortunately, disease states resembling diabetes can be produced in experimental animals through the administration of alloxan. Ross and SPECTOR[48] are
probably the first ones to have observed the teratogenic effect of alloxan treatment. However, it was not clear in their report whether or not a diabetic state
was really induced in the treated animals. Since then, a large number of experiments have been carried out using mice, rats or rabbits to examine the effect
of maternal alloxan diabetes upon the conceptus[10,59]. A high rate of fetal or
perinatal death is generally reported. In Table 4, only those reports in which a

Table 4 Reports of congenital malformations induced by maternal alloxan
diabetes in experimental animals

Animal	Treatment by alloxan*	Outcome	Reference
Mouse	200 mg/kg, s.c. (before mating-day 15)	Cataract and iris anomalies	28
Mouse	100 mg/kg, i.v. (day 8.5-13.5)	Cleft palate (up to 17%) etc. (up to 21% in total)	65
Mouse	200 mg/kg, i.p. (day 8-9)	Cleft palate, polydactyly, etc. (7-12%)	58
Mouse	50 mg/kg, i.v. (before mating)	Agnathus, CNS defects, etc. (7.8%)	17
Mouse	80 mg/kg, i.v. (4th day)	CNS defects, cleft palate, etc. (5.0%)	25
Mouse	200 mg/kg, s.c. (day 0)	CNS defects, cleft palate, etc. (7.2%)	59
Rat	160 mg/kg, i.p. (day 7)	Cataract, hydronephrosis, CNS defects, etc. (50%)	59
Rabbit	200 mg/kg, i.v. (before mating)	CNS defects, etc. (about 9%)	19
Rabbit	100-180 mg/kg, i.v. (2nd or 9th day)	CNS defects (0.9-2.8%)	4

* See the footnote in Table 2 for the explanation of abbreviations.

significant frequency of malformations in fetuses or newborns were described are
listed. There are many reports in which few, if any, malformations were recognized as the outcome of maternal alloxan diabetes. In these negative reports,
however, observation of the offspring was done only after delivery and it is
probable that some destruction of defective young by the mother occurred prior
to this time.

Types of malformation produced include defects of the central nervous system, such as exencephaly and spina bifida, cleft palate and other skeletal abnor-

malities. The incidence of these malformations is usually 10% or less and is quite comparable among different investigators except the following two reports. The first is that of WATANABE and INGALLS[45], who found an extraordinarily high incidence of cleft palate (17%) as compared with the other five experiments in mice shown in Table 4. It might be that the Phipps mice used in their experiment is a peculiar stock, in which cleft palate is easily produced. The second is that of TAKANO and NISHIMURA[59], who reported a very high incidence of fetal abnormalities in Wistar rats. This experiment was done at Dr. JAMES G. WILSON's laboratory in University of Florida by one of the authors (K.T.) and fetuses were examined not only externally, as they were in the other studies reported in Table 4 but also internally by the razor blade sectioning method described by WILSON[66]. The type and incidence of external malformations (exencephaly, microphthalmia and cleft palate) were comparable to those in other experiments in mice and rabbits. However, a high frequency of cataract and hydronephrosis was observed by internal observations. The observation on the hydronephrosis is of interest, because it might explain the frequent neonatal death of the offspring born to diabetic rats in earlier reports. In addition, thrombosis of the renal and suprarenal veins could be a cause of the high perinatal mortality in human diabetes[42].

In conclusion, it seems quite probable that maternal diabetes induced by alloxan and not the direct action of the agent itself was the cause of congenital malformations shown in Table 4. The results following treatment of dams during early stage of pregnancy are comparable to those after the treatment before conception and, though not shown in the table, if the treated animals did not become or became only transiently diabetic, the outcome was just the same as that of the control[59].

HYPOGLYCEMIA

There has been a lot of discussion about the influence of maternal hypoglycemia or of hypoglycemic agents upon the offspring. Although hypoglycemia alone may not be a metabolic disease, I will discuss briefly this problem in relation to diabetes mellitus, becase *hyper*glycemia is a major, if not the only, symptom of the disease.

LUTWAK-MANN[35] reported that maternal hyperglycemia caused only a very slight rise of the glucose level in the blastocyst fluid in rabbits and that insulin-provoked hypoglycemia, on the other hand, is not accompanied by any spectacular decrease in glucose content of the early embryonic fluids, suggesting a mechanism which strictly regulates the supply of carbohydrate to the embryonic cells. If this mechanism exists in man it would be a quite reasonable one, as the supply of carbohydrate to the conceptus is important to its development but maternal blood glucose level may change day-to-day or meal-to-meal even in a normal pregnant woman. However, the existence of such a mechanism in the rat embryo during organogenesis as well as in near-term fetuses was questioned by TAKANO and NISHIMURA[59] (Fig. 1) and KIM[27] respectively. Though data are available for only the last trimester of pregnancy, blood glucose level in the human fetus is considered to change according to that of the mother[54], and the

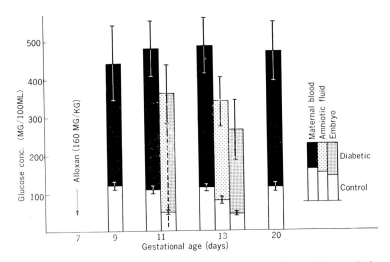

Fig. 1 Comparison of glucose concentration in the embryo, the amniotic fluid and the maternal blood of rats between diabetic group and the control. On the 11th day, the embryo and the amniotic fluid were assayed altogether in each litter. Vertical solid lines indicate 95% confidence limit for the mean[59].

Table 5 Effect upon the conceptus of hypoglycemic agents administered to mothers with or without diabetes mellitus

Agent (treatment)	No. of cases	Outcome	Reference
for psychiatric disease			
Insulin (coma therapy)	17	4 fetal death 2 live malformed	53
for diabetes mellitus			
Insulin and/or diet	50	20% perinat. death	
Tolbutamide	20	23% // //	12
Chlorpropamide	21	65% // //	
Insulin	70	17 perinat. death 1 heart disease 2 minor defect	56
Sulphonylurea or biguanide	34	6 perinat. death (no malfs.)	
Chlorpropamide and/or tolbutamide			
(during 1st–2nd trimesters)	23	1 stillbirth 1 acces. auricle	36
(during only last trimester)	18	5 stillbirth 1 neonat. death	
Carbutamide or tolbutamide	10	1 stillbirth 2 heart disease	26

importance for the health of the fetus of keeping maternal blood sugar levels within certain ranges has been stressed[50].

In the treatment of psychiatric diseases, insulin shock therapy which severely decreases the blood glucose level for a while, may be lethal or teratogenic to the conceptus when it is administered within the first 14 weeks of gestation[53] (Table 5). In various experimental animals, insulin is known to have deleterious effects upon the offspring when large amounts are injected into pregnant females (Table 6).

Table 6 Effect upon the offspring of insulin administered to pregnant animals

Animal (strain)	Treatment*	Outcome**	Reference
Rabbit	20–22 u/d, 2 times on day 6–11	Death (++–+++); CNS defects, heart disease and cataract (++–+++)	11, 13
Rat	7–8 u/d, s.c., day 2–term	Death (++); Rib and sternebrae malfs. (+++)	33
Rat	0.5×2 u/d, s.c., day 15–21 or 8–21	Death (+++)	34
Mouse (BALB/c) (129)	4–5 u/kg, i.p., day 9	Exencephaly and rib-vert. malfs. (3%) *ibid.* (62%)	52

* See the footnote in Table 2 for explanation of abbreviations.

** Incidence of fetal death or of malformation is approximately shown as follows, unless otherwise described: +, less than 10%; ++, 10–30%; +++, more than 30%.

TUCHMANN-DUPLESSIS and MERCIER-PAROT[62,63] first reported teratogenic and lethal effects of oral hypoglycemics in experimental animals. Among several agents tested by them, carbutamide was most teratogenic. Since then, a great number of conflicting reports have been published concerning the teratogenic effect of oral antidiabetics in animals as well as in human pregnancy (Tables 5, 7).

TANIMURA et al.[61] reported that the oral administration of 100mg/kg tolbutamide decreased the blood sugar level from 123mg% in the control to 96mg% at two hours after the treatment in mice but that the treatment showed no significant effects upon conceptuses when given to the pregnant dam once a day throughout the gestation. On the other hand, the dosage which showed significantly lethal and/or teratogenic effect in other experiments is generally very high. As a matter of fact, according to BARILYAK[6], the minimum teratogenic dose of carbutamide by oral administration in rats is 800mg/kg/day. In other words, treatment with less than this dosage may produce a *pharmacological* effect upon the dam but it is not teratogenic. A direct, teratogenic effect of tolbutamide was demonstrated in fish embryo[51]. Available information suggests that the morphogenetic accidents listed in Table 7 are due to an extraordinary hypoglycemia induced by the agents or to other specific or non-specific factors involved in the treatment, which are not directly connected with carbohydrate metabolism. To date, there is no definite evidence that a pharmacological dose of these agents may produce deleterious effects upon the conceptus.

Table 7 Effect upon the offspring of oral hypoglycemics administered to pregnant animals

Agent (animal)	Treatment*	Outcome	Reference
Carbutamide (rabbit)	100 mg/kg/d (parenteral) day 4–6	No effect	2
Tolbutamide (rabbit)	125 × 2 mg/kg/d, i.v., day 7–14	Death (+)**	31
Carbutamide (rabbit) (mouse)	800 mg/kg, p.o., day 6–12	Cleft palate, coelosomia, etc. (13%) Eye malfs. (6%)	63
Carbutamide (rat) Tolbutamide (rat) Chlorpropamide (rat)	about 1,000mg/kg, p.o., day 1–12	Eye malfs. (25–40%) Exencephaly, etc. (2–4%) No effect	62
Tolbutamide (rat)	50–125 mg/kg/d, i.p.. day 1–term	Death (+)**; Reduction in no. of sternebrae	15
Tolbutamide (C57BL mouse) (Strain 129 mouse)	1,000 mg/kg, i.p., day 9	Exencephaly and rib-vert. malfs. (13%) *ibid.* (56%)	52
Tolbutamide (mouse)	100 mg/kg, p.o., day 0–term	No effect	61

* See the footnote in Table 2 for the explanation of abbreviations.
** High incidence of fetal death or resorption was suggested from a decrease in litter size.

SUMMARY

Effects of hypo- or hyperthyroidism and hypo- or hyperglycemia (diabetes) as maternal metabolic diseases, either spontaneous or iatrogenic, upon the development of the conceptus in man and in experimental animals were discussed.

Antithyroid medications to the mother may cause goitrous or non-goitrous hypothyroidism in the newborn in man and other animals. It is questioned, however, whether other fetal abnormalities can be induced by maternal hypothyroidism. Hyperthyroidism of pregnant women may sometimes cause neonatal exophthalmos in the baby, and recently it has been suspected as a possible teratogen in man and experimental animals.

Maternal diabetes in man, as well as alloxan-induced diabetes in animals, may often cause external and/or internal maldevelopment of the offspring and, as a result, a high fetal or perinatal mortality. Severe hypoglycemia of the mother, such as that produced by insulin shock, can be lethal or teratogenic to the conceptus. There is, however, no definite evidence that pharmacological doses of oral hypoglycemics employed as antidiabetic medicament in pregnant women have a harmful effect upon the offspring.

ACKNOWLEDGEMENT

The original investigations reported here were supported in part by grant HD 00074 from National Institutes of Health, Public Health Service, U.S.A.

REFERENCE

1. AARON, H.D., SCHNEIERSON, S.J. and SIEGEL, E.: Goiter in newborn infant due to mother's ingestion of propylthiouracil. J.A.M.A. 159: 848–850, 1955.
2. ADAMS, C.E., HAY, M.F. and LUTWAK-MANN, C.: The action of various agents upon the rabbit embryo. J. Embryol. Exp. Morph. 9: 468–491, 1961.
3. ANDERSON, G.S. and BIRD, T.: Congenital iodine goitre in twins. Lancet 2: 742–743, 1961.
4. BARASHNEV, YU. I.: Malformation of fetal brain resulting from alloxan diabetes in mother. Fed. Proc. (Transl. Suppl.) 24: 382–386, 1965.
5. BARGMAN, G.J. and GARDNER, L.I.: The cloistered thyroidologist. Lancet 2: 562, 1967.
6. BARILYAK, I.R.: The pathologic effect of the antidiabetic sulfonamide Oranil (carbutamide) in the various stages of embryogenesis. Akush. Gynek. (Moskow) 12: 35–40, 1966. (Cited form Excerpta Medica, Section 21, 7: 488–489, No. 3332, 1967)
7. BEAUDOIN, A.R. and ROBERTS, J.M.: Teratogenic action of the thyroid stimulating hormone and its interaction with trypan blue. J. Embryol. Exp. Morph. 15: 281–289, 1966.
8. BLIZZARD, R.M., CHANDLER, R.W., LANDING, B.H., PETTIT, M.D. and WEST, C.D.: Maternal autoimmunization to thyroid as a probable cause of athyrotic cretinism. New Eng. J. Med. 263: 327–336, 1960.
9. BOVET-NITTI, F. and BOVET, D.: Action of some sympatholytic agents on pregnancy. Proc. Soc. Exp. Biol. Med. 100: 555–557, 1959.
10. BRENT, R.L. and JENSH, R.P.: Intra-uterine Growth Retardation. In: Advances in Teratology, Vol. 2, edited by D.H.M. WOOLLAM. pp. 166–170. Academic Press Inc., London, 1967.
11. BRINSMADE, A., BUCHNER, F. and RUBSAAMEN, H.: Missbildungen am Kaninchenembryo durch Insulininjektion beim Muttertier. Naturwissenschaften 43: 259, 1956.
12. CAMPBELL, G.D.: Chlorpropamide and foetal damage. Brit. Med. J. 1: 59–60, 1963.
13. CHOMETTE, G.: Entwicklungsstörungen nach Insulinschock beim trächtigen Kaninchen. Beitr. Path. Anat. 115: 439–451, 1955.
14. DANDROW, R.V. and O'SULLIVAN, J.B.: Obstetric hazards of gestational diabetes. Am. J. Obst. Gynec. 96: 1144–1147, 1966.
15. DAWSON, J.E.: Effect of sodium tolbutamide on pregnant albino rats and their young. Diabetes 13: 527–531, 1964.
16. DRURY, M.I.: Pregnancy in the diabetic. Diabetes 15: 830–835, 1966.
17. ENDO, A.: Teratogenesis in diabetic mice treated with alloxan prior to conception. Arch. Environ. Health (Chicago) 12: 492–500, 1966.
18. FISHER, W.D. and VOORHESS, M.L.: Congenital hypothyroidism in infant following maternal I[131] therapy with a review of environmental radio-isotope contamination. J. Pediat. 62: 132–146, 1963.
19. FUJIMOTO, S., SUMI, T., KUZUKAWA, S., TONOIKE, H., MIYOSHI, T. and NAKAMURA, S.: The genesis of experimental anomalies—fetal anomalies in reference to experimental diabetes in rabbits. J. Osaka City Med. Cent. 7: 62–66, 1958. (Japanese)
20. HADDEN, D.R. and HARLEY, J.M.G.: Potential diabetes and the foetus. J. Obst. Gynacc. Brit. Cwlth. 74: 669–674, 1967.
21, HARLEY, J.M.G. and MONTGOMERY, D.A.D.: Management of pregnancy complicated by diabetes. Brit. Med. J. 1: 14–18, 1965.
22. HIEKKALA, H. and KOSKENOJA, M.: A follow-up study of children of diabetic

mothers. Ann. Paediat. Fenn. 7: 17–31, 1961.

23. HODGES, R.E., HAMILTON, H.E. and KEETTEL, W.C.: Pergnancy in myxedema. A. M. A. Arch. Intern. Med. 90: 863–868, 1952.

24. HOET, J.P., GOMMERS, A. and HOET, J.J.: Causes of Congenital Malformations: Role of Prediabetes and Hypothyroidism. In: Ciba Foundation Symposium on Congenital Malformations, edited by G.E.W. WOLSTENHOLME and C.M. O'CONNOR. pp. 219–240. J. & A. Churchill Ltd., London, 1960.

25. HORII, K., WATANABE, G. and INGALLS, T.H.: Experimental diabetes in pregnant mice. Diabetes 15: 194–204, 1966.

26. HORKÝ, Z.: Perorale Antidiabetika in der Schwangerschaft. Zbl. Gynaek. 87: 972–975, 1965.

27. KIM, J.N.: Prevention of reversal of glycogen infiltration in the pancreatic islets of fetuses from diabetic rats. Anat. Rec. 152: 107–114, 1965.

28. KOSKENOJA, M.: Alloxan diabetes in the pregnant mouse. Acta Ophthal. (Kobenhavn), Suppl. 68: 1–92, 1961.

29. KREMENTZ, E.T., HOOPER, R.G. and KEMPSON, R.L.: The effect on the rabbit fetus of the maternal administration of propylthiouracil. Surgery 41: 619–631, 1957.

30. KUČERA, J., LENZ, W. and MAIER, W.: Missbildungen der Beine und der kaudalen Wirbelsäule bei Kindern diabetischer Mutter. Deutsch. Med. Wschr. 90: 901–905, 1965.

31. LAZARUS, S.S. and VOLK, B.W.: Absence of teratogenic effect of tolbutamide in rabbits. J. Clin. Endocr. 23: 597–599, 1963.

32. LENZ, W. and MAIER, W: Congenital malformations and maternal diabetes. Lancet 2: 1124–1125, 1964.

33. LICHTENSTEIN, H., GUEST, G.M. and WARKANY, J.: Abnormalities in offspring of white rats given protamine zinc insulin during prenancy. Proc. Soc. Exp. Biol. Med. 78: 398–402, 1951.

34. LOVE, E.J., KINCH, R.A.H. and STEVENSON, J.A.F.: The effect of protamine zinc insulin on the outcome of pregnancy in the normal rat. Diabetes 13: 44–48, 1964.

35. LUTWAK-MANN, C.: A discussion presented in the paper of HOET et al.[24] In: Ciba Foundation Symposium on Congenital Malformations, edited by G.E.W. WOLSTENHOLME and C.M. O'CONNOR. pp. 238–239. J. & A. Churchill Ltd., London, 1960.

36. MALINS, J.M., COOKE, A.M., PYKE, D.A. and FITZGERALD, M.G.: Sulphonylurea drugs in pregnancy. Brit. Med. J. 2: 187, 1964.

37. MARTIN, M.M. and MATUS, R.N.: Neonatal exophthalmos with maternal thyrotoxicosis. Am. J. Dis. Child. 111: 545–547, 1966.

38. MCKENZIE, J.M.: Neonatal Graves' disease. J. Clin. Endocr. 24: 660–668, 1964.

39. MIYAMOTO, S.: Association of thyroid drugs with teratogenic actions of ethylurethan in mice. Acta Anat. Nippon. 42: 92–93, 1967. (Japanese)

40. NICHOLSON, J. and DEMARIA, F.J.: Pregnancy and diabetes. Brit. Columbia Med. J. 5: 356–359, 1963.

41. NISHIMURA, H., TERADA, M. and YASUDA, M.: Mitigated teratogenicity of thio-TEPA in goldthioglucose obese mice. Proc. Soc. Exp. Biol. Med. 124: 1190–1193, 1967.

42. OPPENHEIMER, E.H. and ESTERLY, J.R.: Thrombosis in the newborn: Comparison between infants of diabetic and nondiabetic mothers. J. Pediat. 67: 549–556, 1965.

43. ORLOVA, O.I.: The health and development of children born of mothers with thyrotoxicosis. Akush. I. Ginek. 4: 61–65, 1965. (Cited from Excerpta Medica, Section 21, 6: 609, No. 2749, 1966)

44. PASSARGE, E.: Congenital malformations and maternal diabetes. Lancet 1: 324–325, 1965.

45. PEDERSEN, L. M., TYGSTRUP, I. and PEDERSEN, J.: Congenital malformations in newborn infants of diabetic women: Correlation with maternal diabetic vascular complications. Lancet 1: 1124–1126, 1964.

46. PETERSON, R.R. and YOUNG, W.C.: The problem of placental permeability for thyrotrophin, propylthiouracil and thyroxin in the guinea pig. Endocrinol. 50: 218–225, 1952.

47. RATH, F. and THALHAMMER, O.: Diabetogene Fetalkrankheit: Klinik und Prophylaxe. Geburtsh. Frauenheilk. 24: 1115–1123, 1964.

48. ROSS, O.A. and SPECTOR, S.: Production of congenital abnormalities in mice by alloxan. Am. J. Dis. Child. 84: 647–648, 1952.

49. RUBIN, A. and MURPHY, D.P.: Studies in human reproduction. III. The frequency of congenital malformations in the offspring of nondiabetic and diabetic individuals. J. Pediat. 53: 579–585, 1958

50. SAVITSKII, G.A.: The effect of insulin-induced hypoglycemia of the pregnant woman on the fetus. Vop. Okhr. Materrin. Dets. 8: 67–71, 1966. (Cited from Excerpta Medica, Section 21, 7: 386, No. 2695, 1967)

51. SMITHBERG, M.: Teratogenic effects of tolbutamide on the early development of the fish, Oryzias latipes. Am. J. Anat. 111: 205–213, 1962.

52. SMITHBERG, M. and RUNNER, M.N.: Teratogenic effects of hypoglycemic treatments in inbred strains of mice. Am. J. Anat. 113: 479–489, 1963.

53. SOBEL, D.E.: Fetal damage due to ECT, insulin coma, chlorpromazine or reserpine. A.M.A. Arch. Gen. Psychiat. 2: 606–611, 1960.

54. STENGER, V., HENRY, J., CESTARIC, E., EITZMAN, D. and PRYSTOWSKY, H.: Movements of glucose in the human pregnant uterus. Am. J. Obst. Gynec. 94: 261–267, 1966.

55. STERN, L., RAMOS, A. and LIGHT, I.: Congenital malformations and diabetes. Lancet 1: 1393–1394, 1965.

56. STERNE, J.: Antidiabetic drugs and teratogenicity. Lancet 1: 1165, 1963.

57. SUTHERLAND, J.M., ESSELBORN, V.M., BURKET, R.L., SKILLMAN, T.B. and BENSON, J.T.: Familial nongoitrous cretinism apparently due to maternal antithyroid antibody. New Eng. J. Med. 263: 336–341, 1960.

58. TAKANO, K., TANIMURA, T. and NISHIMURA, H.: The susceptibility of the offspring of alloxan-diabetic mice to a teratogen. J. Embryol. Exp. Morph. 14: 63–73, 1965.

59. TAKANO, K. and NISHIMURA, H.: Congenital malformations induced by alloxan diabetes in mice and rats. Anat. Rec. 158: 303–312, 1967.

60. TAKEKOSHI, S.: The mechanism of vitamin A induced teratogenesis. J. Embryol. Exp. Morph. 12: 263–271, 1964.

61. TANIMURA, T., TAKINO, T. and NISHIMURA, H.: Modification of the teratogenic effect of thio-TEPA on the mouse offspring by successive maternal treatment with tolbutamide. Okajimas Fol. Anat. Jap. 42: 51–62, 1966.

62. TUCHMANN-DUPLESSIS, H. and MERCIER-PAROT, L.: Influence of three hypoglycemic sulfamides, carbutamide BZ55, tolbutamide D860, and chlorpropamide on pregnancy and prenatal development of the rat. Anat. Rec. 136: 294, 1960.

63. ...... : Oral antidiabetic drugs and teratogenicity. Lancet 2: 408, 1963.

64. VALLANCE-OWEN, J., BRAITHWAITE, F. and WILSON, J.S.P.: Cleft lip and palate deformities and insulin antagonism. Lancet 2: 912–914, 1967.

65. WATANABE, G. and INGALLS, T.H.: Congenital malformations in the offspring of alloxan-diabetic mice. Diabetes 12: 66–72, 1963.

66. WILSON, J.G.: Methods for administering agents and detecting malformations in

experimental animals. In: Teratology: Principles and Techniques, edited by J.G. WILSON and J. WARKANY, pp. 262–277, University of Chicago Press, Chicago, 1965.

67. WILSON, J.S.P. and VALLANCE-OWEN, J.: Congenital deformities and insulin antagonism. Lancet 2: 940–942, 1966.

68. WOOLLAM, D.H.M. and MILLEN, J.W.: The modification of the activity of certain agents exerting a deleterious effect on the development of the mammalian embryo. In: Ciba Foundation Symposium on Congenital Malformations, edited by G.E.W. WOLSTENHOLME and C.M. O'CONNOR. pp. 158–177. J. & A. Churchill Ltd., London, 1960.

69. YASUDA, M., ARIYUKI, F. and NISHIMURA, H.: Effect of amphetamine on pregnancy in ICR-JCL mice. Okajimas Fol. Anat. Jap. 41: 227–231, 1965.

70. YASUDA, M. and OOWAKI, Y.: Mitigated teratogenicity of thio-TEPA by successive administration of methylthiouracil to pregnant mice. Proc. Cong. Anom. Res. Assoc. Japan 6: 21–22, 1966.

DISCUSSION

KIMBEL (Germany)

Did you try to compensate for the alloxan effect by insulin?

TAKANO

I did not myself. But there is a report of Dr. WATANABE, University of Niigata, Japan, stating that a certain amount of insulin completely prevented the occurrence of malformed offspring from alloxan-induced diabetic mothers in mice.

McBRIDE (Australia)

The varying incidence of congenital abnormalities amongst the offspring of diabetic mother reported by various workers would most likely be due to how well the diabetes is controlled during the pregnancy.

Similar to the variation in perinatal mortality of the new born of diabetic mothers reported by various centers.

TAKANO

It may be so. However, it is almost impossible to obtain a definite conclusion in that regard, because in only few clinical reports do the authors mention how well the diabetes of the mother has been controlled.

COMPARATIVE ASPECTS OF THE PLACENTAL BARRIER

EDWARD W. DEMPSEY

Professor, Department of Anatomy, Columbia University,
College of Physicians and Surgeons, New York, U.S.A.

Since the publication of GROSSER's monograph[3], there has been widespread acceptance of an anthropocentric concept of the placental barrier. It is ordinarily believed that the barrier separating fetal from maternal blood becomes progressively thinner, simpler and more efficient both ontogenetically and phylogenetically. That is, a more tenuous barrier is present at term than earlier in gestation and the barrier is composed of fewer layers, in the hemochorial placenta characteristic of primates, than is the case in the syndesmochorial placentas of carnivores and both are simpler than are the epitheliochorial placentas of ungulates.

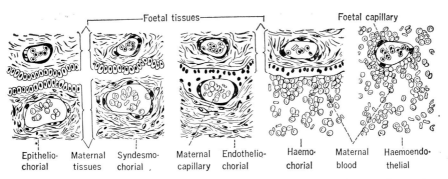

Fig. 1 Diagram illustrating MOSSMAN's hemoendothelial type, in addition to GROSSER's four original types. It was designed to show the progressive phylogenetic reduction in the number of layers and the diminution in width of the placental barrier. From MARSHALL's Physiology of Reproduction, Vol. II, p. 150, Third Edition. LONGMANS GREEN and Company, London, 1952.

In recent years, evidence has been accumulating from many sources indicating that the GROSSER concept is oversimplified. Indeed, so deceptively persuasive has it seemed that it has probably delayed progress by drawing attention away from, not toward, critical facts. We intend to draw attention to some of these situations in this presentation.

We now believe the GROSSER concept to be seriously deficient in at least three ways. It fails to consider the important aspects of placental transfer accomplished by the yolk sac or choriovitelline placenta. By its emphasis upon simple thickness of the barrier, it fails to draw attention to the active processes of placental transfer. Finally, species low in the phylogenetic scale are now known to possess an "advanced" placenta. Similarly, closely related species can exhibit wide differences in their placental types.

BRAMBELL[2] has made extensive studies of the route through which maternal antibodies cross the placenta in the rabbit, thereby conferring a passive, temporary immunity to the newborn. A fortunate anatomical disposition of the vitelline vessels in this species has permitted an elegant series of experiments which prove that antibodies present in the maternal blood reach the fetal circulation only by traversing the yolk-sac epithelium. That this pathway is indeed a likely route for transfer of large molecules was shown in our laboratory in experiments demonstrating that proteins, lipids and colloidal particulates were readily ingested by process of pinocytosis into the yolk sac cells. Taken together, these experiments suggest strongly that antibodies and other maternal substances are transferred to the yolk sac cavity through uterine secretions, and that these products are in turn transferred to the fetus by absorption through the yolk sac cells.

The pathways through which iron crosses the placenta to become available for fetal erythropoiesis have long been the subjects of active interest. The early appearance of erythropoietic islands in the chorion and yolk sacs of many animals has whetted curiosity. In carnivores, a zonular placenta is accompanied, on its margins, by paraplacental extensions of chorionic cytotrophoblast, which are apposed to the uterine epithelium. In the cat and dog, these paraplacental regions are colored brown and green, respectively, by the accumulation in the chorionic cells of bile pigments derived from the breakdown of maternal erythrocytes which have leaked into the uterine cavity and have been absorbed by the chorion. Iron abounds in these regions, derived presumably from the maternal hemoglobin. In other species, similar ingestion and breakdown of maternal red cells has been observed in chorionic syncytiotrophoblast. In none of these instances does the simple thickness of the placental barrier play a part in the active physiological process of transfer; indeed, the highly complex processes of red cell lysis, the breakdown of hemoglobin with absorption of its iron and retention of its bile pigments bespeaks mechanisms requiring all of the metabolic machinery of robust cells.

The larger the number of species the placentas of which have been examined, the less exact has been the correspondence between place in the phylogenetic scale and type of placenta. Only a few such instances will be cited here, for the reason that we now know that the observations made with light microscopes can sometimes be misleading, and as yet only a relatively small number of species has been examined critically by electron microscopy. Nevertheless, the evidence, though scanty, is enough to prove the point.

In the higher primates, as typified by the monkey and man, complete destruction of the maternal endometrium is accomplished so that placental villi are exposed directly to maternal blood. These villi, at term, exhibit an attenuated layer of syncytial trophoblast covering the fetal capillary and its attendant connective tissue sheath. This situation typifies the hemochorial placenta characteristic of primates in the GROSSER scheme. However, not all primates display such an arrangement. In Galago, the African bush-baby, an epitheliochorial placenta occurs. Maternal capillaries, surrounded by connective tissue sheaths,

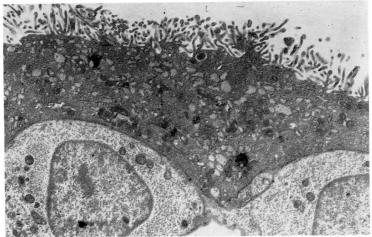

Fig. 2 Electron micrograph of an early human placenta showing the syncytial trophoblast lining the maternal blood space at the top of the picture. Portions of two cytotrophoblastic cells of Langhans, resting on a thin basement membrane, are at the bottom.

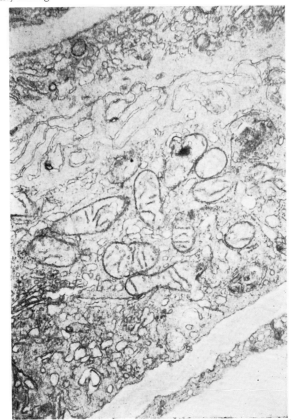

Fig. 3 Electron micrograph of a Galago placenta. The interdigitating processes of the maternal epithelium and of the fetal chorion can be seen.

course immediately beneath the uterine epithelium. On the fetal side, chorion is apposed to the epithelium and fetal vessels with their sheaths lie under or embedded into it. The zone of apposition between fetal and maternal cells is complex; extensive, finger-like extensions of the epithelium penetrate deeply into the chorion in a fashion entirely similar to the mode of apposition in the epitheliochorial placentas of Ungulates. Thus, within the Primates, radically different types of placentas may be found.

Differences less extensive, but in some ways more informative, have also been seen in Carnivora. Typically, this order exhibits a syndesmochorial or vasochorial placenta in which maternal vessels are surrounded by an investment of trophoblast separating them from the fetal capillaries and their sheaths. The maternal elements often are altered in an interesting manner: the endothelial cells in some forms become greatly enlarged, appearing cuboidal or even columnar, thecapillary basement membranes are often much thickened and, again in some species, notably the domestic cat, occasional decidual cells accompany the maternal vessels and become greatly hypertrophied into a characteristic type of giant cell.

In the cat and dog, the hypertrophied maternal basement membrane is fenestrated in some locations. In the cat, the margin toward the trophoblast is often indented so that bays filled with trophoblast are common. Here and there the layer is interrupted so that trophoblast and endothelium are directly in contact. A similar situation exists in the dog, except that here the endothelial cells often push through the fenestrae, and project into the subjacent zone normally occupied by the syncytiotrophoblast. Thus, in both species, the maternal

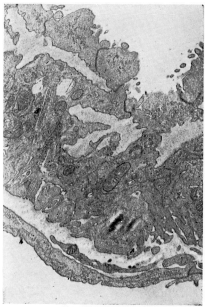

Fig. 4 Electron micrograph of a hyaena placenta. The amorphous gray masses represent remnants of the thickened basement membrane originally associated with the maternal endothelium and now surrounded by trophoblast.

connective tissue first becomes hypertrophied and later is broken into islands or peninsulas partially surrounded by trophoblast.

In the hyaena, this process has gone even further. This species exhibits the same well-defined and thickened maternal basement membranes as do the other Carnivora but a conspicuous difference is that the maternal endothelium is totally lacking. The maternal blood space is lined by trophoblastic elements the nuclei of which lie beneath the now isolated island of basement membrane. The placenta of this species must therefore be classified as hemochorial, but the persistent remnants of maternal connective tissue testify to its syndesmochorial origin.

SUMMARY

A simple concept of the placental barrier, involving only the distance across which diffusion must take place, has dominated research in this field for many years. It is now apparent that a more sophisticated concept must be derived, based upon considerations of active transport and of cellular biology. Similarly, facts now obtrude which force examination of the yolk-sac and paraplacental chorion, formerly largely ignored as regions involved in important transfer. Finally, currently prevailing schemas on the phylogenetic relationships of placental types are seriously oversimpled. Improved understanding of these concepts must await study by electron microscopy of additional species.

REFERENCES

1. AMOROSO, E.C.: Placentation. In: MARSHALL's Physiology of Reproduction. 3rd Ed, edited by A.S. PARKES. p. 127, Longmans, Green & Co. Inc. London, 1952.

2. BRAMBELL, F.W. R.: The Development of Fetal Immunity. Fourth Conference on Gestation, p. 143, The Josiah Macy Jr. Foundation, New York, 1957.

3. GROSSER, O.: Frühentwicklung, Eihautbildung und Placentation des Menschen und der Säugetiere. Deutsche Frauenheilkunde Bd. 5, S. 1–454, Bergmann, München, 1927.

DISCUSSION

FUJIKURA (U.S.A.)

Could you tell us about the placental barrier changes which occur in relation to placental development?

DEMPSEY

I believe little is known on this subject. Dr. SEVER's data seemed to show that rubella crossed the placenta more completely in early stages than in later. I believe this subject should be studied much more extensively.

MILLER, R.W. (U.S.A.)

Why are there so many gaps in our knowledge of the placenta?

DEMPSEY

Simply because so few people have chosen seriously to investigate the placenta. Only a small group of placentologists exists today. I would hope that meetings such as this would stimulate greater interest in placental research in the future.

MURAKAMI (Japan)

I think that Dr. FUJIKURA pointed out one of the most important problems. Studies on placental barrier have been carried out by many groups. However, they usually pay attention only to the placenta complete in its structure.

I am convinced that major attention should be directed to the early stage of development, i.e., the period of organogenesis, when the form of the placenta is not yet completed.

DEMPSEY

I agree completely with Dr. MURAKAMI's comment.

SISODIA (India)

Did you mention that the mechanism of transport across other cell membranes may not hold good for the placenta?

DEMPSEY

No, the placental barrier has not been well enough studied to elucidate the mechanism of membrane transport.

SISODIA

Do you think the methods and techniques employed to study membrane transport at other sites may also be fruitfully employed to study the placental barrier?

DEMPSEY

Yes.

LOO (Malaysia)

What is the mechanism by which the foetal red blood cells enter the maternal circulation to induce antibodies to produce erythroblastosis foetalis.

DEMPSEY

Probably by breaking of the placental villi with a consequent leakage of fetal red cells into the maternal intervillous space.

SEVER (U.S.A.)

Would you describe further the development and changes of the yolk sac in primates and man?

DEMPSEY

The yolk sac is ordinarily described as rudimentary and vestigeal in man. Yet, in about a third of placentas, a small vesicular yolk-sac is observable at term. It seems unlikely to me that the structure concerned so importantly in the uptake of antibodies in the rabbit has had its function completely annexed in man. I believe the fate of the yolk-sac in man warrants further study.

TAKANO (Japan)

Although I do not know whether or not Dr. DEMPSEY has much interest in experimental teratology, I would like to hear his opinion about the role of the yolk sac epithelium in the teratogenesis of the rat embryo. Recently, BECK, et al. (Science, 157: 1180–1182, 1967) reported that trypan blue may induce a dysfunction in the yolk sac epithelium of rats and that dysfunction is a direct cause of the teratogenesis of the embryo. What do you think about this report?

DEMPSEY

Dr. JOHN EVERETT showed many years ago that trypan blue was concentrated in the Golgi region of yolk sac cells. The older literature abounds with reference to "reticulo-endothelial blockade" by trypan blue. An unmetabolizable substance such as trypan blue conceivably could saturate a cellular mechanism located in an organelle such as the Golgi apparatus or a lysosome and thus block the transport of other materials ordinarily handled by these structures. I must hasten to say, however, that this explanation is entirely speculative, as I have no direct experience on the subject.

SPECTROPHOTOMETRIC ASSAY OF DRUGS
IN TISSUES

Toyozo Uno

Professor, Department of Analytical Chemistry, Faculty of Pharmaceutical Sciences, Kyoto University, Kyoto, Japan.

The most popular spectrophotometric methods for the determination of drugs in tissues are absorptimetry and fluorometry. In absorptimetry, the absorption in visible, ultraviolet and infrared regions is utilized. The first two are due to the transition of electronic energy and generally consist of a few broad bands for polyatomic molecules. The absorption in the infrared region, however, is due to the transition of vibrational energy and consists of many narrow bands. To the assay of drugs in biological material, the infrared spectrophotometric method is not usually applied, because suitable solvents for the infrared spectrometry are limited. Although water is a suitable solvent for biological material, it is difficult to use as a solvent for infrared spectroscopy.

Fluorometry belongs to emission spectrometry, and is a more sensitive method than ultraviolet and visible absorptimetries. It is frequently applied to the assay of trace substances. The choice of experimental conditions of analysis in fluorometric assay is, however, more complicated than that in absorptimetry. Moreover, the precision in fluorometry is less than that in absorptimetry.

I would like to talk about: 1) fundamental points in the technique in the ultraviolet and visible absorptimetric assays of drugs in tissues, 2) placental transfer of thiopental, and 3) assay of metabolites of sulfa drugs, as examples of spectrophotometric assay.

FUNDAMENTAL POINTS IN THE TECHNIQUE IN ABSORPTIMETRY

a. Selection of the wavelength

The measurement of absorbance in absorptimetry is made at the wavelength where the absorption of the sample is as strong and stable as possible. For this purpose we usually choose the wavelength of an absorption maximum. If we choose a wavelength where the absorption curve has a large gradient, any small deviations in the wavelength and the slit width often give rise to a big error. In the case when the sample shows two absorption maxima as shown in Figure 1, the wavelength with the smaller blank absorption is recommended. If we use the wavelength with a large blank absorption, the result of the assay is affected seriously by deviations in the blank absorption.

The wavelength of the absorption maximum varies with the change in the solvent and pH, because of the interaction between the sample material and the solvent. In any report of results of an absorptimetric assay, we must therefore describe the solvent and pH. There are many cases when quite different absorption

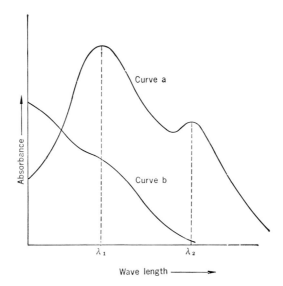

Fig. 1 The selection of wave length

spectra are shown by the same substance on a change in pH.

b. Selection of solvents

For the solvents used in the ultraviolet and visible absorptimetry, it is essential that the sample material is soluble in the solvent in the necessary concentration and that the solvent shows no absorption at the wavelength used for the measurement. Water may be regarded as the best solvent in this sense. Acidic and basic substances undergo, however, a spectral change on the formation of salts, and the observed spectrum of an aqueous solution of salts is sometimes the superposition of its own spectrum and the spectrum of the acid or the base formed by the hydrolysis of the salt. In such a case, it is recommended to carry out the measurement under a strongly acidic or a strongly basic condition if possible. Amphoteric substances may be treated similarly.

Ethanol is the solvent most frequently used in the absorptimetry. Absolute ethanol prepared from the azeotrope with benzene shows absorption in the ultraviolet spectrum and is not appropriate for the ultraviolet absorptimetry. Hydrocarbons are good solvents for non-polar materials. Usually they contain, however, trace aromatic and olefinic substances and these must be removed by silica gel before use. Chloroform is a good solvent but can not be used for the wavelength below 245 mμ.

In usual absorptimetry the amount of solutes is very small (M/1,000–M/20,000) in comparison with that of solvents. Accordingly, the amount of impurities in the solvent may exceed that of the solute even if the solvent contains only a trace impurity. We must be very careful in purifying the solvent, because the impurities often obstruct the measurement by absorbing at the wavelength under investigation or by reacting chemically with the solute.

c. Preparation of samples

Most commonly encountered biological samples are blood, urine and tissues.

In determining how to treat and preserve these samples, we must take into account the effect of pH, enzyme and air oxidation according to the nature of drugs to be assayed.   For the assay of N-glucuronides of sulfa drugs in urine, for example, it is necessary to maintain the collected urine at pH 8.   For this purpose, we must adjust the pH of the sample urine immediately after taking it, because the decomposition of N-glucuronides occurs when the urine is acidic. Sometimes drugs in tissues are metabolized by enzymes.   In order to prevent such decomposition of drugs during the course of the sample preservation, we must decompose enzymes or suppress the activity of enzymes by regulating the temperature and pH of the sample.   For example, the amount of thiopental contained in an embryo remains constant for at least 60 days when the embryo is preserved frozen.

d.   Extraction

In order to determine drugs in tissues, we must first remove the drug from the tissue.   Different solvents are used for different samples.   It is not recommended to extract only once by using a large amount of the solvent.   The same amount of the solvent is used more effectively by dividing in to several portions and repeating the extraction.   Continuous extraction may be applicable when the sample is not affected by heating.   Since the efficiency of the extraction depends appreciable on the pH, we must check optimum pH in the extraction by using samples containing known amounts of the drug under investigation.

In the case when the method of determination includes deproteinization, we often observe that the drugs are trapped in the precipitates of the denatured proteins and the concentration of the drugs in the filtrate is accordingly reduced. For such a method of determination, it is necessary to use the calibration curve obtained from the standard samples subjected to the same procedure of deproteinization as the samples to be determined.   Similarly, for the methods of determination including the separation of drugs by chromatography, we must estimate the recovery for the standard sample in advance.

e.   Procedures which involve chemical reactions

In the methods of determination which involve chemical reactions, usually a large excess of the reagent over the amount of the sample is added in order that the reaction proceeds quantitatively, and the absorbance is measured after the reaction proceeds under a constant condition.   In such procedures, the excess of the reagent sometimes reacts with the reaction product to reduce the absorbance, or is often oxidized to give colored substances which interferes with the determination.   In these cases we extract either the reaction product or the reagent.   Otherwise, some device is necessary to separate the reaction product from the excess of the reagent.   It is essential, of coures, to select the most suitable pH and a solvent for this purpose.

f.   Blank

The most difficult problem in the spectrophotometric assay of biological samples is how to estimate the blank absorption.   Since the blank absorbance is different for different samples, it must be subtracted from the measured absorbance for each measurement.   If the blank absorbance is large and the sample absorbance is small, the deviation in the former gives rise to a large error seriously reducing the reliability of the data obtained.   It is essential to find out such an experimental condition that the blank absorbance is as small as possible.

i) Reagent blank

The blank absorbance due to the excess of the reagent is estimated from the experiment in which the sample containing none of the drugs under investigation is treated according to the procedure of the determination.

ii) Blank due to biological substances

Besides the excess of the reagent, the biological samples usually contain miscellaneous components which often give rise to the blank absorptions. Even the shape of the absorption curve itself is sometimes distorted by the interference of these components. A frequently used method for such cases involves the estimation of the blank absorbance from the data for the biological sample taken without the administration of the drug under investigation. In this method

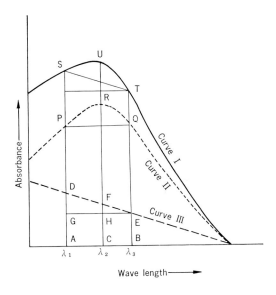

Fig. 2 Morton Stubbs' correction

however, there is no assurance that the absorbance before the administration of the drug is the same as the blank absorbance after the administration.

One of the most frequently used method to estimate the blank absorbance is Morton-Stubbs' correction[13]. In Figure 2, I is the absorption curve of the sample, II is the absorption curve of the pure drug to be determined, and III is the blank absorption curve. Let λ_2 be the wavelength of the absorption maximum of the pure drug, and λ_1 and λ_3 be the wavelength at which the absorbance is 6/7 of that at λ_2. The absorbances at λ_1, λ_2 and λ_3 are denoted by A_1, A_2 and A_3, respectively.

$$CR = CU - (CH + HF) \dots\dots\dots\dots\dots\dots\dots\dots\dots\dots\dots\dots\dots\dots\dots(1)$$

$$HF = GD \times \frac{HE}{GE} = (AD - BE) \times \frac{HE}{GE} = [(AS - AP) - (BT - BQ)] \times \frac{HE}{GE}$$

$$= (AS - BT) \times \frac{HE}{GE} = (AS - BT) \times \frac{\lambda_3 - \lambda_2}{\lambda_3 - \lambda_1} \quad \dots\dots\dots\dots\dots\dots\dots\dots\dots (2)$$

$$\frac{7}{6} = \frac{CR}{BQ} = \frac{CU - CH - HF}{BT - CH},$$

therefore

$$CH = 7BT - 6CU + 6HF \quad \dots\dots\dots\dots\dots\dots\dots\dots\dots\dots\dots\dots\dots (3)$$

Combining Eqs. (2), (3) and (1) gives

$$A = CR = CU - (7BT - 6CU + 7HF)$$

$$= CU - \left[7BT - 6CU + 7(AS - BT) \times \frac{\lambda_3 - \lambda_2}{\lambda_3 - \lambda_1} \right]$$

$$= A_2 - \left[7A_3 - 6A_2 + 7(A_1 - A_3) \times \frac{\lambda_3 - \lambda_2}{\lambda_3 - \lambda_1} \right],$$

$$7A_2 - 7A_3 - 7(A_1 - A_3) \times \frac{\lambda_3 - \lambda_2}{\lambda_3 - \lambda_1}$$

(where, $AS = A_1$; $CU = A_2$; $BT = A_3$)

For the preparation of the reference solution for biological materials, we may decompose the drug in the sample by adding the enzyme which reacts specifically with the drug. This method is often used in the determination of antibiotics[8].

PLACENTAL TRANSFER OF THIOPENTAL

As an example of the spectrophotometric assay of drugs in tissues, I would like to talk about the determination of thiopental in embryos. In cooperation with Prof. NISHIMURA of Faculty of Medicine, Kyoto University, we have been studying its placental transfer for a few years. Thiopental is widely used as an ultrashort acting anesthetic and there have been many reports on its metabolites[1,2,4,15,23] and placental transfer[5-7,10,14]. Usually thiopental in high dosage, 6 mg/kg, is used in the operation of inducing abortion. Therefore, it is considered to be a suitable substance to investigate drug transfer from the mother to the embryo in the early stage of pregnancy.

a. Material and its treatment

Embryos of colony bred ICR-JCL mice were removed from the uterus at day 11 of pregnancy, washed with physiological sodium chloride solution and weighed. Human embryos obtained by curettage were collected by Prof. NISHIMURA. They were sent to him under frozen conditions. The amount of thiopental in an embryo measured shortly after the operation was found to be the same as that observed in the same embryo after being kept frozen at $-20°C$ for 2 months. Therefore, it is supposed that thiopental is not metabolized in a frozen embryo. The materials were returned to the anatomy laboratory after the determination of thiopental.

b. Assay

An assay method of thiopental in biological material has been reported by BRODIE et al.[1] They extracted thiopental from urine with petroleum ether containing 1.5 % isoamyl alcohol and determined its absorption at 305 mμ as shown in Chart 1. However, when their method is directly applied to the determination of a trace amount of thiopental in embryos, the absorption maximum of thiopental overlaps with the blank absorption. Moreover, the variation in the blank

126   Toyozo Uno

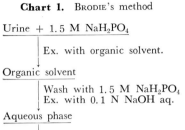

Chart 1. Brodie's method

Urine + 1.5 M NaH₂PO₄

    │ Ex. with organic solvent.

Organic solvent

    │ Wash with 1.5 M NaH₂PO₄
    │ Ex. with 0.1 N NaOH aq.

Aqueous phase

Measured O.D. at 305 mμ

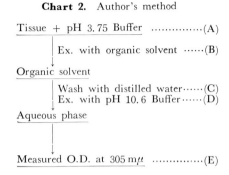

Chart 2. Author's method

Tissue + pH 3.75 Buffer ....(A)

    │ Ex. with organic solvent ......(B)

Organic solvent

    │ Wash with distilled water......(C)
    │ Ex. with pH 10.6 Buffer......(D)

Aqueous phase

Measured O.D. at 305 mμ ....(E)

absorption is considerably large, therefore we could not obtain any reproducible results. We investigated the experimental conditions such as pH of extraction and composition of buffer solutions, and improved their method as shown in Chart 2. According to this modified method, we obtained a quite reproducible concentration-absorption curve shown in Figure 3, with the recovery of 85 per cent in the case of mouse and human embryos.

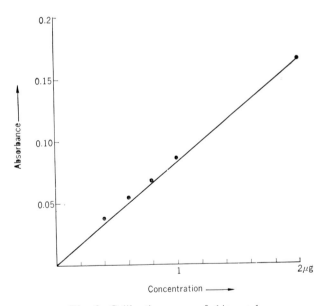

Fig. 3 Calibration curve of thiopental

The difference between the absorbance at 305 mμ (E_{305}) and that at 340 mμ (E_{340}) corresponds to the unchanged thiopental. The absorption curve obtained by this procedure is shown in Figure 4. It is clear that the blank absorbance at 340 mμ is far less than that which is observed by Brodie's method, and the absorption due to other metabolites does not overlap with that of thiopental at 305 mμ.

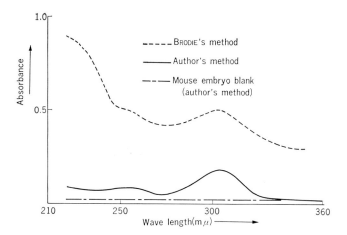

Fig. 4 Absorption curves of thiopental

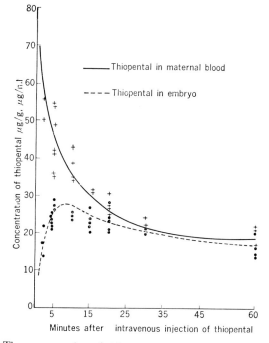

Fig. 5 The concentration of thiopental in maternal blood and embryo

c. Results in mouse embryos

After 75 mg/kg of thiopental was administered intravenously or intraperitone-ally to a mouse at day 11 of pregnancy, the embryos were removed after specific time intervals, and the amount of thiopental was determined. The maximum amount of thiopental in embryos was 20–30 μg/g, and reached about ten and five to ten minutes after intraperitoneal and intravenous injection, respectively.

The concentration of thiopental in blood of the dam was higher than that in the embryo in 5–10 minutes, but the former became comparable to the latter in 15 minutes, and reached an equilibrium in about 20 minutes (Fig. 5).

d. Results in human embryos

Three hundred or 500 mg of thiopental was administered to mothers intravenously before the operation of termination of pregnancy, and after 3–10 minutes the embryos (STREETER's horizon 14–23) were removed. To determine thiopental, several embryos up to horizon 15 were used together in a single procedure, and larger embryos were used separately.

With a 300 mg dose, the thiopental content in embryos, 5 minutes after injection, was found to be 3–4 $\mu g/g$, and with a 500 mg dose, 5–6 $\mu g/g$. The concentration in the mother's blood after 10 minutes, was 7 $\mu g/g$. No significant difference in the thiopental content per gram was found among embryos with different weights (Table 1).

e. Metabolites of thiopental in embryo

Three metabolites of thiopental have been reported (Table 2). BRODIE et

Table 1   Thiopental concentration in human embryos

300 mg/body

Horizon 15–16		Horizon 17–18		Horizon 19–20		Horizon 21–23	
No.	$\mu g/g$	No	$\mu g/g$	No.	$\mu g/g$	No.	$\mu g/g$
1	2.6	1	3.5	1	3.0	1	3.4
2*	2.4	2	3.5	2	1.8	2	3.4
3*	2.3	3	3.1	3	1.8	3	3.4
4*	3.4	4	2.7	4	3.0	4	5.4
5*	3.3	5	3.1	5	2.1	5	2.1
6	2.1	6	2.4	6	3.7	6	3.8
7	3.4	7	2.4	7	2.7	7*	3.3
8	4.2	8	2.7	8	2.9	8	2.9
		9	3.3	9	4.3	9	2.4
		10	2.5	10	1.8	10	3.2
		11	3.2	11	2.2		
		12	2.5	12	3.0		
		13	3.4	13	2.8		
		14	3.0	14	3.1		
		15	3.4				
		16	2.3				
		17	2.9				
		18	3.3				
		19	3.2				
		20	2.0				
Average 3.0		2.9		2.7		3.3	

* The mother had genital bleeding during pregnancy.

500 mg/body

Horizon 15–16		Horizon 17–18		Horizon 19–20		Horizon 21–23	
No.	μg/g	No.	μg/g	No.	μg/g	No.	μg/g
1	6.1	1	6.0	1	4.4	1	5.0
2	5.6	2	4.4	2	8.1	2	2.7
3	6.7	3	2.6	3	4.8	3	8.3
4	6.7	4	4.2	4	5.4	4	8.0
5	3.4	5	6.2	5	2.8		
		6	5.4				
		7	3.7				
		8	4.5				
		9	4.5				
		10	6.3				
		11	9.7				
		12	3.4				
		13	4.3				
		14	3.7				
		15	5.1				
Average	5.7		5.0		5.1		6.0

al.[1] considered that the main metabolites in human urine (adult) and rabbit liver[3] (*in vitro*) were thiopental-(ω)-carboxylic acid (I) and thiopental-(ω-1) OH (II). According to the radio isotopic investigation by WINTER[23], pentobarbital was supposed to be the main metabolite. In order to determine thiopental content in embryos, it was necessary to investigate the metabolites of thiopental in detail. For this purpose, we carried out thin layer chromatography of the petroleum ether extract of mouse and human embryos which were treated according to the procedure from A to C described in Chart 2.

Table 2 Expected metabolites of thiopental

(I) Thiopental carboxylic acid

(II) Thiopental alcohol

(III) Pentobarbital

The thin-layer-chromatogram of human and mouse embryos agreed with each other (Fig. 6).

Three spots other than thiopental were obtained. Spot "a" was identified as thiopental, and "c" as pentobarbital, by comparing Rf values with those of authentic samples and ultraviolet spectra of the spot's extracts. Chemical structures of the substances corresponding to spots "b" and "d" still remain unexplained. Spot "b" was not extracted from the petroleum ether layer to alkaline solution. Substance "b", therefore, is considered to be a neutral compound.

With the purpose of searching for thiopental-carboxylic acid, we attempted T. L. C. on the ethylene dichloride extract obtained by BRODIE's method. We could not find, however, any spot corresponding to the acid. It may be expected that sufficient metabolism did not take place because embryos were removed

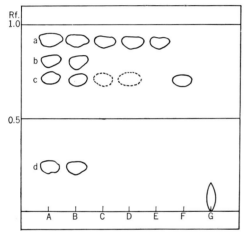

A: Mouse embryo (thiopental inj.)
B: Human embryo (thiopental inj.)
C: Mouse blood (thiopental inj.)
D: Human blood (thiopental inj.)
E: Thiopental
F: Pentobarbital
G: Thiopental carboxylic acid
Developing solvent:
        chloroform-acetone 9 : 1
Coloring reagent: $HgNO_3$ aq. and GROTE
        reagent

Fig. 6 Thin-layer-chromatogram (Sillica gel)

several minutes after the administration of the thiopental to the mother. However, thiopental-carboxylic acid was not found in mouse embryos removed one hour after the injection in our experiment, either. Therefore it may be concluded that the main metabolite of thiopental is pentobarbital.

On the other hand, it was found by FURANO[9] that the concentration of pentobarbital in blood was very low after the administration of thiopental. The result of our investigation by T.L.C. led to the same conclusion. An interesting result of the present investigation is that embryos contain larger amounts of pentobarbital as a metabolite of thiopental than does the mother's blood. It seems desirable to make further investigation on this point.

DETERMINATION OF METABOLITES OF SULFA DRUGS

As an example of the assay of drugs in urine and blood, I would like to speak about the separation and determination of the metabolites of sulfisoxazole[16,17,18],

a. Metabolites in urine

We had synthesized compounds expected to be metabolites of sulfisoxazole and compared them with the metabolites obtained from urine. Human urine was collected for 24 hrs after oral administration of 2 g of sulfisoxazole and was concentrated to a volume of about 1/25 under reduced pressure at temperature below 37°C. Precipitated salt was removed by centrifuging after adding twice the amount by volume of ethanol. The supernatant solution was used for paper chromatography and paper electrophoresis. On the examination of N-glucuronide, freeze drying method was used. Metabolites shown in Table 3 were identified.

The chemical structure of (A) was identified to be ring N-glucuronide by means of infrared spectroscopy, ultraviolet spectroscopy, and chemical reactions. After chemical structures were identified, we attempted to determine each metabolite

Table 3 Rf values of metabolites in human urine after administration of sulfisoxazole[16]

Solvent / Spot No.	BuOH satd. with H_2O	BuOH·AcOH·H_2O (5 : 1 : 4)	BuOH satd. with 3% NH_4OH	BuOH·PrOH·H_2O (2 : 1 : 1)
1	0.88 (0.88)*	0.86 (0.86)	0.39 (0.40)	0.86 (0.86)
2	0.92 (0.91)	0.90 (0.90)	0.44 (0.44)	0.91 (0.92)
3	0.56 (0.56)	0.58 (0.58)	0.55 (0.55)	0.54 (0.54)
4	0.29 (0.30)	0.38 (0.39)	0.00 (0.00)	0.23 (0.23)
5	0.005 (0.005)	decomp. (decomp.)	0.002 (0.002)	0.06 (0.05)
6	0.01	0.26	0.03	0.15

Solvent / Spot No.	BuOH·PrOH·0.1N NH_4OH (2 : 1 : 1)	BuOH satd. with N HCl	Substance
1	0.50 (0.51)	0.66 (0.66)	Sulfisoxazole
2	—	—	Acetylsulfisoxazole
3	0.56 (0.56)	—	Sulfanilamide
4	0.20 (0.20)	decomp. (decomp.)	Sulfisoxazole-N-sulfonate
5	0.04 (0.05)	decomp. (decomp.)	Sulfisoxazole-N-glucuronide
6	0.17	0.03	A

* The values in the parentheses are Rf values of standard substances dissolved in the same sample-urine.

in urine. Separation of the metabolites of sulfisoxazole was carried out by means of paper chromatography using 0.4 ml urine (2 g, 24 hrs).

Portions corresponding to each metabolite were cut off and eluted with 0.1 N ammonium hydroxide by the descending method, and the initial 2 ml of eluate was collected for each elution. The solutions of sulfisoxazole, sulfanilamide and sulfisoxazole-2′-glucuronide (A) were used directly for determination. The other substances had to be hydrolyzed before determination. For this purpose, 0.5 ml of N hydrochloric acid was added to these eluates and the solutions were treated as follows.

N^4-glucuronide	room temperature	30 min.
N^4-sulfonate	100°C	20 min.
N^4-acetate	100°C	30 min.

After the above treatment, 0.5 N ammonium hydroxide solution was added.

Assay: The test solution obtained by the above separation method was concentrated to dryness under reduced pressure. To the residue were added 1 ml of a mixed solvent (n-butanol, n-propanol, water (2:1:1), diluted to 2.5 times in volume with ethanol), 0.3 ml of 2 N hydrochloric acid and 5 ml of 2% EHRLICH's reagent ethanol solution. This solution was allowed to stand for 5 minutes at 30°C, and was diluted to 10 ml with ethanol. The absorbance was measured at 453 mμ. The calibration curve for sulfanilamide was obtained by using authentic sulfanilamide, and those for the other substances by authentic sulfisoxazole. Using authentic samples dissolved in fixed amounts in normal urine, calibration curves were prepared according to the method of determination. The amounts of metabolites obtained in human urine, 24 hrs after oral administration of 2 g of sulfisoxazole, are shown in Table 4.

Table 4 Metabolites of sulfa drugs in human urine

Substance	Dose	% of dose in 24 hr.	% of metabolites						
			un-changed	N⁴-glu.	N⁴-acetyl	N⁴-sulfonate	N¹-glu.	Ring N-glu.	Sulfanil-amide
Sulfisoxazole[17]	2 g	81.2	69.2	4.2	22.2	1.2	—	2.6	0.6
Sulfadiazine[20]	2 g (2 g)*	61.3 (81.6)*	54.7 (53.2)*	0.9 (0.7)*	43.1 (45.0)*	1.0 (0.8)*	— —	— —	0.3 (0.3)*
Sulfathiazole[19]	1 g	89.2	67.3	0.8	27.9	0.4	3.6	—	—
Sulfa-dimethoxine[21]	1 g (1 g)**	30.1 (83.3)**	5.5 (4.9)**	0.8 (0.9)**	12.8 (17.1)**	—	80.9 (77.1)**	— —	— —

( )*   72 hr.
( )** 168 hr.

b. Determination of sulfisoxazole in blood

The most popular method of determination of sulfisoxazole in blood seems to be BRATTON-MARSHALL's method[11,12]. The metabolites other than N⁴-acetyl derivative, however, are not taken into account in this method. We attempted to determine only the unchanged sulfisoxazole.

Separation: A chromatographic column was prepared with 1 g of cellulose powder filled in a glass tube (5.5×200 mm) with a developer [BuOH: PrOH (1:1)] and was allowed to stand overnight. To one ml of sample blood containing 3.8% sodium citrate at the rate of 20%, 0.5 ml of 0.3% saponin solution was added. This solution was shaken vigorously, diluted with developer to 5 ml and centrifuged after shaking. A half ml of the supernatant solution was added to the column and developed with butanol-propanol mixture. Three and a half ml of the initial eluate was discarded and the next 2 ml of the effluent was collected in a 10 ml test tube.

Determination: To the above solution in the test tube were added 0.8 ml of 2 N hydrochloric acid and 5 ml of alcohol solution of 3% EHRLICH's reagent. This solution was allowed to stand at 30°C for 7 minutes and diluted with ethanol to 10 ml. The absorbance was measured at 453 mμ and the concentration was calculated from the calibration curve obtained in the same way as in urine. The reference solution was prepared from the normal blood which did not contain sulfisoxazole according to the method of determination. The results are shown in Figure 7.

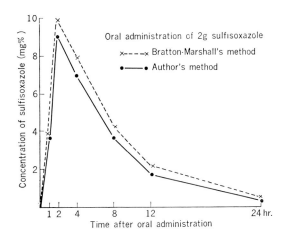

Fig. 7   The concentration of sulfisoxazole in blood

Table 5   Metabolism of sulfadimethoxine in various species

Species	% dose* of drug excreted in 24 hr.	% composition of 24 hr. excretion	
		N¹-glucuronide	N⁴-acetyl
Rat	9	7	46
Guinea pig	20	5	66
Rabbit	43(82)**	0 (9)**	94(55)**
Dog	23	19	0
Human	25(83)**	70(77)**	21(17)**
Rhesus monkey	25	70	21
Baboon	42	72	16
Squirrel monkey	9	51	37
Capuchin	8	48	15

* Dose 100 mg/kg orally
( )** Uno and Kushima[21], 168 hr.

c.   Conclusion

Sulfa drugs are administered to man. The amounts of metabolites excreted in urine are given in Table 4. R.T. Williams et al [22] determined N'-glucuronide and N⁴·acetate in urine, when sulfadimethoxine was administered to various species of mammals, and they obtained the results summarized in Table 5. Values in parentheses are the results obtained by the author in the urine collected for 168 hrs after administration. It seems difficult so far to tell briefly about the correlation between man and animals in the kind and the amount of metabolites of sulfa drugs.

REFERENCES

1. Brodie, B.B., Mark, L.C., Papper, E.M., Lief, P.A., Bernstein, E. and Rovenstein, E.A.: The fate of thiopental in man and a method for its estimation in biological material. J. Pharmacol. Exp. Ther. 98: 85–96, 1950.

2. Brodie, B.B., Burns, J.J., Mark, L.C., Lief, P.A., Bernstein, E. and Papper, E.M.: The fate of pentobarbital in man and dog and method for its estimation in biological material. J. Pharmacol. Exp. Ther. 109: 26–34, 1953.

3. Brodie, B.B. and Cooper, J.R.: Enzymatic oxidation of pentobarbital and thiopental. J. Pharmacol. Exp. Ther. 134: 75–83, 1957.

4. Bush, M.T., Mazel, P. and Chambers, J.: The metabolic fate of thiobarbital in man. J. Pharmacol. Exp. Ther. 134: 110–116, 1961.

5. Crawford, J.S.: Some aspects of obstetric anaesthesia. Brit. J. Anaesth. 28: 146–154, 1956.

6. Flowers, C.E. Jr.: The pracental transmission of barbiturates and thiobarbiturates and their pharmacological action on mother and infant. Amer. J. Obstet. Gynec. 78: 730–742, 1959.

7. Flowers, C.E. Jr.: Factors related to the placental transfer of thiopental in the hemochorial placenta. Amer. J. Obstet. Gynec. 85: 646–658, 1963.

8. Ford, J.H.: Hydroxylamine method of determining penicillines. Anal. Chem. 19: 1004–1005, 1947.

9. Furano, E.S. and Greene, N.M.: Metabolic breakdown of thiopental in man determined by gas chromatographic analysis of serum barbiturate levels. Anesthesiology 24: 796–800, 1963.

10. Makechnie, F.B. and Converse, J.G.: Placental transmission of thiopental. Amer. J. Obstet. Gynec. 70: 639–644, 1955.

11. Marshall, E.K. and Bratton, A.C.: A new coupling component for sulfanilamide determination. J. Biol. Chem. 128: 537–550, 1939.

12. Marshall, E.K. Jr.: Determination of sulfanilamide in blood and urine. J. Biol. Chem. 122: 263–273, 1937.

13. Morton, R.A. and Stubbs, A.L.: Photometric spectrometry applied to the analysis of mixtures and vitamine A oils. Analist 71: 348–356, 1946.

14. Moya, F. and Smith, B.E.: Uptake, distribution and placental transport of drugs and anesthetics. Anesthesiology 26: 465–475, 1965.

15. Tayler, J.D. and Richard, R.K.: Metabolism of S^{35} thiopental. J. Pharmacol. Exp. Ther. 104: 93–102, 1952.

16. Uno, T. and Kono, M.: Studies on the metabolism of sulfisoxazole I. On the excrements in the human urine after administration of sulfisoxazole. Yakugaku Zasshi 80: 201–204, 1960. (Japanese)

17. Uno, T. and Kono, M.: Studies on the metabolism of sulfisoxazole III. Determination of sulfisoxazole in urine and its excretion. Yakugaku Zasshi 81: 192–194, 1961. (Japanese)

18. Uno, T. and Kono, M.: Studies on the metabolism of sulfisoxazole VI. Determination of sulfisoxazole in blood and its absorption. Yakugaku Zasshi 81: 1509–1511, 1961. (Japanese)

19. Uno, T. and Ueda, M.: Studies on the metabolism of sulfathiazole II. Quantitative separation of excrements in the human urine after administration of sulfathiazole.

Yakugaku Zasshi 82: 759–762, 1962. (Japanese)

20. UNO, T. and SEKINE, Y.: Studies on the metabolism of sulfadiazine II. Quantitative separation of excrements in the human urine after administration of sulfadiazine. Chem. Pharm. Bull. (Tokyo) 14: 687–691, 1966.

21. UNO, T. and KUSHIMA, T.: Studies on the metabolism of sulfadimethoxine II. Determinations of metabolites in human and rabbit urine after oral administration of sulfadimethoxine. Chem. Pharm. Bull. 15: 1272–1276, 1967.

22. WILLIAMS, R.T.: Comparative patterns of drug metabolism. Fed. Proc. 26: 1029–1039, 1967.

23. WINTER, W.D., SPECTOR, F., WALLACH, D.P. and SHIDEMAN, F.E.: Metabolism of thiopental-S^{35} and thiopental-2-C^{14} by a rat liver mince and identification of pentobarbital as a major metabolite. J. Pharmacol. Exp. Ther. 114: 343–357, 1955.

COMPARATIVE PATHOLOGICAL DEVELOPMENT
ON THE CENTRAL NERVOUS SYSTEM

UJIHIRO MURAKAMI

Professor, Department of Pathology and Embryology, The Research Institute of
Environmental Medicine, Nagoya University, Nagoya, Japan.

The formation of the central nervous system compared with other organ systems is initiated at a very early stage of development. The process of development of this system is very rapid and complicated. Therefore, it tends to have various kinds of developmental disturbances. Here, I will discuss the relationship between developmental disturbances in the central nervous system in human beings and the corresponding situation in laboratory animals. Congenital malformations of the central nervous system are commonly seen both in human beings and laboratory animals.

It is said that the causes of maldevelopment in human beings, and also in laboratory animals, can be divided into four groups: genetic factors, environmental influences, interaction of genetic and environmental factors, and certain physiological and pathological conditions of the mother.

The differentiation of the nervous system occurs not only in the intrauterine period but extends into postnatal life. Therefore, developmental disturbances of the central nervous system are divided into three categories:

I. Malformations manifesting themselves in the stage when closure of the neural tube takes place.

II. Malformations due to disturbances in differentiation after the closure of the neural tube.

III. Malformations caused by disturbances in migrations of neural cells and differentiation of the cortex.

Here, the major emphasis will be limited to those disturbances originating in the embryonic period, i. e., cases corresponding to items 1 and 2. There are many instances in which the same pattern of congenital malformations is caused by either genetic or environmental factors. In such instances the defects caused by the environmental factors are called phenocopies. Many such congenital malformations due to environmental factors can be produced in laboratory animals. Dynamic observations on the morphogenesis of congenital malformations of the central nervous system are difficult in human beings. Therefore, comparative developmental pathology employing laboratory animals is useful.

MALFORMATIONS MANIFESTING THEMSELVES AT THE STAGE
WHEN CLOSURE OF THE NEURAL TUBE TAKES PLACE

Closure of the neural tube has definitive significance in the formation of

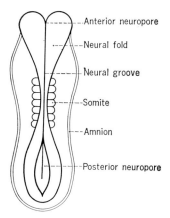

Fig. 1   Schematic drawing of a young mammal embryo.
Dorsal view showing neural tube development.

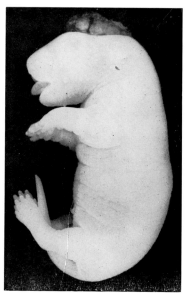

Fig. 2   Exencephalia of a rat fetus on day 20 due to
injection of vincristine on day 8.

anomalies of the central nervous system.   The location at which failure in closure
of the neural tube takes place determines the characteristics of the malformation
manifested (Fig. 1).

A. Anencephalia

It has been believed that certain types of exencephalias in laboratory animals
have a similarity in morphogenesis to human anencephalia (Fig. 2).   When
laboratory animals were treated with some teratogens at a certain stage of their
pregnancy, a spectrum of malformations similar to exencephalia resulted in the

offspring. In fact, exencephalia is one of the most common congenital malformations in laboratory animals produced by various kinds of teratogens. GIROUD[4]
and other investigators have explained the morphogenesis of exencephalia in
laboratory animals in term of a failure in the closure of the neural tube especially
in the rostral part.

Commonly the thalamic area had failed to close and was exposed. Therefore,
the surface of the exposed brain is the internal surface of ventricles. Whereas,
WARKANY[10] points out another type of exencephalia, the morphogenesis of which
is different. In this type, the nervous tissue protruding to the surface of the
head is convoluted and much overdeveloped. Further, in many such cases of
exencephalia the rostral part of the brain, though abnormal, is entirely closed,
while in the area of the midbrain, defects of closure are found. WARKANY
believes it to be of considerable importance that in such cases the rostral portion
of the brain, represented by fairly normal hemispheres, is not covered by an
osseous skull and, therefore, is exposed to amniotic fluid and probably destined
to be destroyed in the same way as those portions of the central nervous system
in which closure of the neural tube did not occur. Therefore, the morphogenesis
of exencephalia does not seem to be simple.

We often observe hemorrhages and degenerations of the exposed brain. Such
changes suggest that sequentially, the type of exencephalia in laboratory

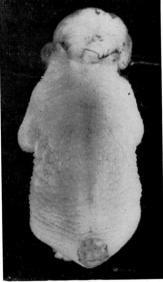

Fig. 3 A mouse fetus on day 18 with exencephalia and myeloschisis
due to hypervitaminosis-A of the mother on day 7.

animals is the forerunner of the type of anencephalia in man. In human
beings, sequential results of such degenerative change will be shown as area
cerebrovasculosa.

B. **Myeloschisis and its allied conditions**

1. Myeloschisis: Myeloschisis, i. e., spina bifida aperta, is also a common
malformation which is said to have a similar morphogenesis to anencephalia

(Fig. 3). In human beings, the exposed part of the neural tissue is involved in a condition called zona medullovasculosa. WARKANY[10] also suggests that it seems myeloschisis is the developmental precursor of the common type of myelomeningocele, but it should be emphasized that there exist many other forms of spina bifida which are not derived from a myeloschisis. At present, we are carrying out experiments subjecting pregnant rats to trypan blue solution, the teratogenicity of which is well known. We observed many cases of slight myeloschisis with various degree of myelocystocele on day 11 and 12. However, it is very interesting that after day 13 we can see only obvious myeloschisis without the above myelocystocele. Such myelocystocele seems to be a temporary one. Therefore, we also agree with the opinion of WARKANY who suggested that the morphogenesis of myeloschisis is not simple.

2. Spina bifida occulta: INGRAHAM and LOWREY[7] described that approximately 25 per cent of seemingly normal children have occult defects in the vertebral laminae, while BENDA[1] stated that the incidence indicated by INGRAHAM was too high. It is generally accepted that 10 to 15 per cent of seemingly normal children have this trait, with or without accompanying clinical handicaps. We can produce congenital malformations of this category by means of X-irradiation in mice (Fig. 4).

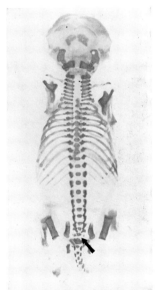

Fig. 4 Cleared specimen of a mouse fetus on day 18 with occult spina bifida (↘). The mother was exposed to X-irradiation on day 10.

3. Myelodysplasia: The above stated complete rachischisis and spina bifida occulta belong to the category of myelodysplasia in a broad sense. However, there are various kinds of this disorder. Such malformations are due to arrested development before the gray and white matters have completed their differentiation. Various types of this trait are also easily produced in laboratory animals by extrinsic factors such as injection of trypan blue solution or X-irradiation at a

certain critical period during embryogenesis.

C. Developmental disturbances of the cerebellum

Developmental disturbances of the cerebellum occur as isolated defects or also manifest themselves as a complication in the form of cerebellar rachischisis in the case of developmental disturbances of the upper spinal cord.

1. Agenesis of the cerebellar hemispheres.
2. Chiefly the formation of rachischisis in the vermis and hemisphere.
3. Dandy-Walker syndrome.
4. Arnold-Chiari syndrome.
5. Platybasia.
6. Klippel-Feil syndrome.

Those malformations are caused by myeloschisis of the spinal cord and the cerebellum or developmental disturbances in the occipital bone and cervical vertebrae. Developmental disturbances of the cerebellum are produced by X-irradiation upon pregnant animals. Detailed studies have been done by HICKS and his coworkers[6] using this technique. The Arnold-Chiari syndrome has been produced in rats by GUNBERG[5] and also by WARKANY, WILSON and GEIGER[11] by means of trypan blue solution. We could produce malformations in the occipital bone and cervical vertebrae in laboratory animals by X-irradiations.

MALFORMATIONS DUE TO DISTURBANCES IN DIFFERENTIATION AFTER THE CLOSURE OF THE NEURAL TUBE

Many congenital malformations which appear after the closure of the neural tube are divided into two types. One is the malformation that starts at the three brain vesicles stage and the other is the deformity that starts at the five brain vesicles stage (Figs. 5, 6 and 7).

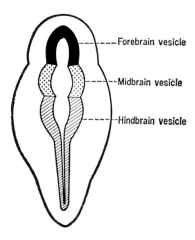

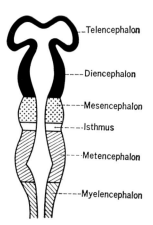

Fig. 5. Schematic drawing to show the neural tube in the three brain vesicle stage.

Fig. 6. Schematic drawing of the developing brain in the five brain vesicle stage.

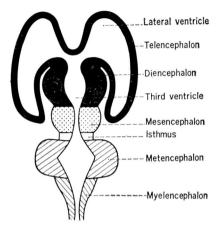

Fig. 7 Schematic drawing of the developing brain in further differentiation. (Figs. 6 and 7, adapted from Human Embryology, Hamilton, Boyd and Mossman, 1964)

A. Malformations belonging to univentricular telencephalon or holoprosencephaly

The malformations in this category include cyclopia and arrhinencephalia. Otocephalia is also closely related to these malformations. These three malformations present a spectrum. Combinations of these malformations are also found. The lateral ventricle are united in one cavity, though there are various degrees of transitions (Fig. 8).

1. Cyclopia or synophthalmia: There is a spectrum of this malformation. Above the eye, there is a peculiarly shaped protuberance called "proboscis" which corresponds to the nose. It looks like the spout of a cephalopod (Fig. 9). The opening of the mouth is also occasionally abnormal, representing an instance of transition to arrhinencephalia. This trait is occasionally found in domestic or laboratory animals, however, usually. it is difficult to produce by known teratogens in laboratory animals. However, there is an example of this trait produced by a naturally grown teratogen. In the Alpine meadows of the

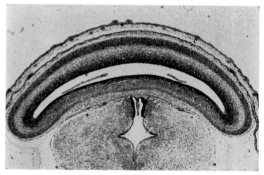

Fig. 8 Horizontal section through the telencephalon of a mouse fetus on day 16 with arrhinencephalia due to maternal X-irradiation on day 8. A univentricular telencephalon is shown.

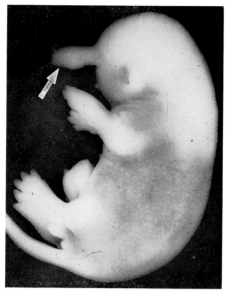

Fig. 9 Cyclopean rat fetus seen in a untreated group. Presumably deceased before day 18 and a little macerated. The proboscis is protruding in the head(↗).(Courtesy Kyo Kaziwara, M.D.)

Fig. 10. A mouse fetus with arrhinencephalia on day 18 due to X-irradiation of the mother on day 8. The shape of the snout is characteristic.

state of Idaho, U.S.A., sheep which ingested a range plant, *Veratrum californicum*, at a certain period of pregnancy, give birth to cyclopean lambs[2].

2. Arrhinencephalia: In arrhinencephalia, the rhinencephalon and olfactory nerve and their auxiliary organs are missing. Therefore, malformations of the olfactory organ such as a flat nose, union of the nostrils, a single nasal cavity or hypoplasia of the nasal cavity, etc. are characteristic features. We have produced this trait in mice by X-irradiation on day 8 of their pregnancy[9] (Fig. 10). DeMyer[3] also induced this pattern of malformation by the administration of vinca alkaloids to pregnant rats.

3. Otocephalias: In this condition the auricle is situated low. The jaw is also malformed, hypoplastic or even absent (Fig. 11). Associations with cyclopia

Fig. 11 A rat fetus with otocephalia and open eyelid on day 20 due to maternal injection of vincristine on day 8. The lower jaw is absent, the auricle is small sized and situated low. The palpebra is opened.

or arrhinencephalia have been observed. Otocephalia and its subgroup can be produced by some teratogens in laboratory animals.

B. Malformations started after the formation of the five brain vesicles

1. Hydrocephalus: This name only indicates the symptom and does not show the essence of the malformation. The following types are most common:

    (a) Excessive production of the cerebrospinal fluid.

    (b) Disturbances in the absorption of the fluid.

    (c) Disturbances in the circulation of the fluid.

These produce "symptomatic hydrocephalus". There is also another type which results from developmental disturbances of the brain itself and called "dysgenetic hydrocephalus". In animal experiments, there are many teratogens known to produce hydrocephalus. KALTER[8] described experimental hydrocephalus in detail. We also produced hydrocephalus in mice and rats employing some teratogens (Fig 12). However, these cases were all dysgenetic hydrocephaluses.

2. Microcephalia: One of the causes of this defect is genetic, i.e., microcephalia vera. Extrinsic factors also can produce this defect. In human beings, exposure to ionizing radiations such as X-irradiations and atomic bombs during intrauterine life are well known environmental factors. Even in a latter stage of pregnancy, ionizing irradiations are able to produce this trait. HICKS et al[6]. demonstrated this in rats. We also have produced microcephalias in mice fetuses by X-irradiations or by some chemicals. However, these were all hydromicrocephalias and were not comparable with those in human cases.

Fig. 12 A mouse fetus with internal hydrocephalus on day 18
due to maternal X-irradiation on day 11.

In summary, developmental disturbances in the central nervous system, which are the major congenital malformations in human beings, can be produced in laboratory animals by procedures of experimental teratology. Further, we can study their morphogenesis. Many congenital malformations produced by various kinds of teratogens exhibit a similar morphogenesis to those in human beings. However, differences may exist. A good example of the latter is the microcephalia produced in laboratory animals such as mice and rats. The fundamental difference between human beings and laboratory animals is the divergence in the differentiation of the telencehalon. However, I am convinced that such comparative developmental pathology on congenital malformations of the central nervous system is very helpful in understanding not only the morphogenesis of such malformations but also possible causes.

REFERENCES

1. BENDA, C.E.: Developmental Disorders of Mentation and Cerebral Palsies. Grune & Stratton, New York, 1952.
2. BINNS, W , JAMES, L.F., SHUPE, J.L. and EVERETT, G.: A congenital cyclopean-type malformation in lambs induced by maternal ingestion of a range plant, *Veratrum californicum.* Am. J. Vet. Res. 24: 1164-1175, 1963.
3. DEMYER, W.: Production of major cerebral malformations by drugs with special reference to the holoprosencephalies (cyclopia-arhinencephaly). Proc. V. Internat. Congr. Neuropathol., Zurich, 1965. Excerpta Medica, Amsterdam, 1966.
4. GIROUD, A.: Causes and Morphogenesis of Anencephaly. In: CIBA Foundation Symposium on Congenital Malformations, edited by G.E.W. WOLSTENHOLME and C.M. O'CONNOR. Churchill, London, 1960.
5. GUNBERG, D.L.: Spina bifida and the Arnold-Chiari malformation in the progeny of trypan blue injected rats. Anat. Rec. 126: 343-368, 1956.
6. HICKS, S.P., D'AMATO, C.J. and LOWE, M.J.: The development of the mammalian nervous system. J. Comp. Neurol. 113: 435-469, 1959.
7. INGRAHAM, F.D. and LOWREY, J.J.: Spina bifida and cranium bifidum; occult spinal disorders. N.E.J. Med. 228: 631-641, 1943.
8. KALTER, H.: Congenital malformations of the central nervous system. Am. J. Clin. Nutr. 12: 264-274, 1963.
9. MURAKAMI, U., KAMEYAMA, Y., MAJIMA, A. and SAKURAI, T.: Radiation malformations belonging to the cyclopia-arrhinencephalia-otocephalia group in the mouse foetus. J. Embryol. Exp. Morph. 10: 64-72, 1962.
10. WARKANY, J.: Experimental Production of Congenital Malformations of the Central Nervous System. In: Mental Retardation, edited by P.W. BOWMAN and H.V. MAUTNER. Grune & Stratton, New York, 1960.
11. WARKANY, J., WILSON, J.G. and GEIGER, J.F.: Myeloschisis and myelomeningocele produced experimentally in the rat. J. Comp. Neurol. 109: 35-64, 1958.

DISCUSSION

DENIZ (Turkey)

All of the cases involving anencephalia in The Women's and Children Hospital of Ankara in Turkey are female. Is this sex distribution normal or abnormal?

MURAKAMI

To my knowledge, the number of female anencephalias is dominant in every country. However, not all cases are females. I assume that male cases die during pregnancy. The number of cases of anencephalia in Japan is said to be about 1 in 1550 births. It is similar to that of European countries. However, in the U. K., and in some parts of New England in the U.S.A., the incidence is about 3 times more than in other countries.

FRASER (Canada)

Does the neural tube close later in female embryos than it dose in male embryos? If so, this would be a possible explanation of the fact that more females have anencephaly.

MURAKAMI

There is such a possibility. Unfortunately, I have not examined this point yet. However, there are divergencies in developmental potencies between strains of mice which cause a change of ratio of malformations of the eye. Such kinds of differences in the progression of development may exist between the sexes.

PATHOLOGY OF THE MALFORMED HUMAN
FETUS, WITH SPECIAL REFERENCE
TO THE ENDOCRINE GLANDS

Ichiro Hayashi

Professor of Pathology, Nagasaki University School of Medicine, Nagasaki, Japan.

At the autopsies of 3,676 human fetuses and newborns from 1946 to 1962, 496 malformed bodies (13.5 per cent) were found. Certain changes of the endocrine glands were detected quite frequently. These changes were of interest both in relation to the glands themselves and as they possibly relate to maldevelopment of other body systems. Some of these changes appear to be specifically related to certain anomalies. Major autopsy findings of the adrenal, hypophysis, thymus, pancreas, ovary and salivary gland will be discussed.

ADRENAL GLANDS

Cases with central-nervous system anomalies, particularly anencephalus, showed a remarkable reduction in the weight and size of the adrenal glands. Histological differentiation of the adrenal cortex was accelerated in central-nervous system anomalies, especially in anencephalus, even though the cortex was dysplastic, and the differentiation was retarded in cases with uro-genital anomalies (Figs. 1, 2). Measurement of the thickness of the permanent and fetal cortices disclosed that their growth patterns were characteristic for central-nervous, musculoskeletal and digestive system anomalies, but their variation in thickness was not always compatible with histological differentiation of the adrenal cortex[14]. In the malformed fetus and newborn formation of the lattice fibers appeared accelerated or complicated, and the presence of sudanophilia in the adrenal cortex through the fetal to the neonatal period varied considerably when compared with the controls, i.e., nonmalformed fetuses or newborns. Except for central-nervous system anomalies, ponceau-fuchsinophilia of the inner fetal cortex, was demonstrably greater, in general, in the malformed fetus and newborn than in the controls. In cases with central-nervous system anomalies fuchsinophilia of the fetal cortical cells was markedly reduced except in the adrenogenital syndrome, in which there was an increase[1,4].

Based upon the above autopsy findings of the adrenal glands in malformed human fetuses and newborns, the effects of maternal disorders, due to adrenalectomy or adrenocortical hormone injection, upon fetal development were studied experimentally using albino rats of an inbred strain[10,11]. In both experiments treated fetuses showed accelerated or retarded organogenesis, and also anomalous or retarded development of the brain, eyeball and skin. Further, in fetuses obtained from the adrenalectomized females there occurred bridge-formation,

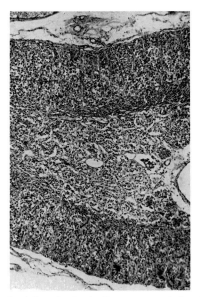

Fig. 1 Adrenal gland of an anencephaly. The cortex with the dysplastic internal zone is narrowed. The glomerular, fascicular and reticular zones are differentiated (adult type adrenal). There is found a rapid advance in physiologic involution of the fetal zone.

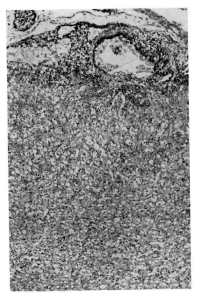

Fig. 2 Adrenal gland in a case with renal agenesis. Note irregular arrangement of the cortical cells and multiple space-formation in the permanent cortex. Physiologic involution of the fetal cortex is retarded.

adhesion and stickiness of the chromosomes at the metaphase of nuclear division, pyknosis and karyorrhexis of the cerebral cell nuclei, and an inversion of relative frequencies of the prophase and metaphase at the mitotic stage of the cerebral cells (Fig. 3)[12].

With regard to the relationship between maternal adrenal disorders and fetal development of the ectodermal organs, histological study of the zonation of the cerebral vesicle wall and microspectrophotometric measurement of nuclear DNA

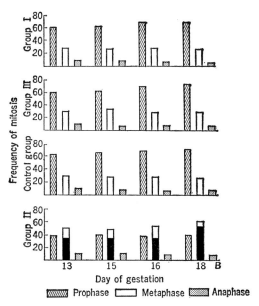

Fig. 3 Relative incidence of mitosis of cerebral cells in fetus obtained from control and adrenalectomized mother rat.

Group   I: One of the adrenal glands was removed 3 weeks before pregnancy.

Group   II: One of the adrenal glands was extirpated 3 weeks before pregnancy, and the remaining one removed on the 2nd day of gestation.

Group III: One of the adrenal glands was removed 3 weeks before pregnancy, and subjected to operative procedure but not adrenalectomized on the 2nd day of gestation.

Stickiness and adhesion of the chromosomes were detected only in Group II as shown by black bar.

content of the cerebral cells were made on fetuses obtained from adrenalectomized or cortisone-injected female rats[2,8]. Histologically, a retardation of zonation and a remarkable individual variation of thickness of the cerebral vesicle wall were found in treated fetuses. The nuclear DNA content of the cerebral cell, expressed in relative values had a normal distribution in untreated fetuses, with a peak between 350 to 400. However, such uniform results were not obtained from treated fetuses, in which there occurred, a) the absence of a peak associated with a decrease in the level, and b) several peaks which were dispersed and shifted toward higher relative values of DNA. It is considered that these phenomena resulted from certain disturbances of the rhythm of DNA synthesis in the mitotic cycle of the cerebral cell nuclei of treated fetuses.

Further, atrophic changes and disarrangement of the adreno-cortical cells were experimentally produced in irradiated rat fetuses, particularly in those which were malformed. The scanty presence of sudanophilia in the adreno-cortical cells associated with marked atrophic changes seems to indicate disorders of the adrenal function in malformed fetuses. Also the appearance of fuchsinophilic cells in the adrenal cortex was distinctly reduced in irradiated malformed fetuses, particularly in those with cephalic anomalies (Tables 1, 2)[6]. It should be pointed out that there is a similar reduction of fuchsinophilia of the adrenocortical cells in human fetuses with central-nervous system anomalies mentioned above. These

Table 1 The average number of fuchsinophilic cells in the adrenal cortex of rat fetuses irradiated with 130r of X-rays

Untreated	Treated			
	Non-malformed (29)		Malformed (20)	
	Irradiated on the 10th day	Irradiated on the 10th and 13th days	Irradiated on the 10th day	Irradiated on the 10th and 13th days
20.3 (10)	10.3 (16)	15.4 (13)	9.7 (10)	5.9 (10)

The figure in parentheses shows the number of rat fetuses examined.

Table 2 The average number of fuchsinophilic cells in the adrenal cortex of malformed fetuses irradiated with 130r of X-rays

Malformed fetus	Irradiated on the 10th day	Irradiated on the 10th and 13th days
Cephalic anomalies (7)	2.0 (2)	2.8 (5)
Non-cephalic anomalies (13)	11.4 (8)	8.0 (5)

The figure in parentheses shows the number of malformed fetuses examined.

histological changes of the fetal adrenal glands occurring most severely in malformed fetuses suggest some relationships, whether direct or indirect, between the lesions of the adrenal glands during the fetal period and the pathogenesis of developmental anomalies.

HYPOPHYSIS

In anencephalics, abnormalities of shape, size and location of the hypophysis were noted (Fig. 4). The weight of the hypophysis was reduced in some cases with central-nervous system anomalies, except anencephalus. The hypophysis in female cases with genital anomalies was reduced or increased in weight compared with the controls. No difference in weight was proved in cases with anomalies of other systems.

In the controls the acidophile and basophile cells were scattered sparsely or were barely identified at 5 months of fetal age.   With advance of fetal age, however, such chromophile cells appeared to be increased in number and stainability.   Cases with anencephalus showed marked distension of the sinusoid associated with compression atrophy of the gland cells.   Most of the gland cells were regarded as undifferentiated chromophobe cells.   The acidophile cells were remarkably scanty and no typical basophile cells were recognized.   In cases of central-nervous system anomalies, except anencephalus, no definite changes were seen histologically.   An increase of the acidophile cells in chondrodystrophia fetalis and a reduction of the acidophile cells in diaphragmatic hernia were detected.   Female cases with genital anomalies revealed a tendency for reduction in the basophile cells.   The hypophysis in cases of cardio-vascular, digestive and respiratory system anomalies showed no definite changes[9],[16].

Anencephalic fetuses

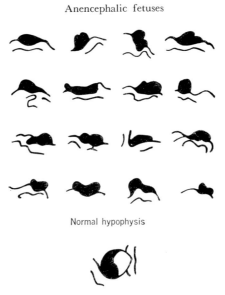

Normal hypophysis

Fig. 4   Diagrams of variations in the gross appearance of hypophysis in cases of anencephaly

THYMUS

Cases with central-nervous system and uro-genital system anomalies showed the most characteristic picture in relation to variation in weight and histological changes of the thymus[17].   The thymus in cases with central-nervous system anomalies generally weighed more than that of the controls, and histologically showed a remarkably distinct demarcation between the cortex and medulla, thickening of the cortex and an abundance of the lymphocytic cells (Fig. 5).   On the contrary, the thymus in cases with uro-genital anomalies generally weighed less than that of the controls, and histologically the demarcation between the cortex and medulla was indistinct with reduction of the cortical

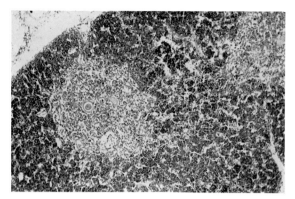

Fig. 5 Thymus of a case with anencephalus. Note the remarkable thickening of the cortex and the clear demarcation between the cortex and medulla. The lymphocytic cells in the cortex are abundant.

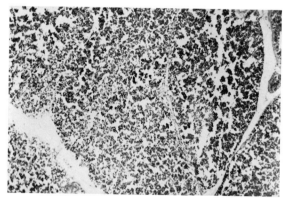

Fig. 6 Thymus in a case with cystic kidney. Note the thinning of the cortex and indistinct demarcation between the cortex and medulla. The lymphocytic cells in the cortex are arranged less densely.

thickness and scarcity of lymphocytic cells (Fig. 6). The most characteristic changes in weight and histological features of the thymus were found in cases of anencephalus. In relation to histological changes of the thymus in anomalies of single body system, it was ascertained that central nervous anomalies, particularly anencephalus, and uro-genital system anomalies were situated opposite each other, the control being placed in the middle, and that all anomalies in other body systems than central nervous and uro-genital systems were located between uro-genital anomalies and the control (Figs. 7, 8). Variation in weight and histological changes of the thymus associated with central-nervous system anomalies were regarded to be caused by developmental or functional differences of the hypophysis.

Histological changes of the thymus in cases with anomalies of a single body system, other than the central-nervous system or uro-genital system, were observed

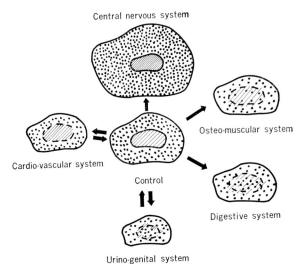

Fig. 7 Schema of histological findings of the thymus in the malformed fetus and newborn associated with developmental anomalies in various body systems.

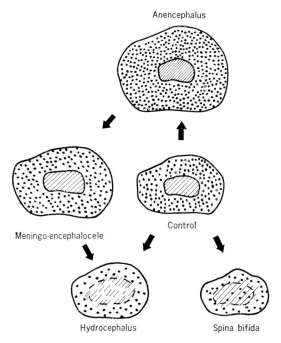

Fig. 8 Schema of histological findings of the thymus in the fetus and newborn with general type of central nervous system anomalies.

to be similar, in general, to those noted in cases of the latter, but were not as extreme. Variation in the weight and histological changes of the thymus in cases involving anomalies of two or more body systems were to some extent specific to those observed in cases of either central-nervous or uro-genital system anomalies respectively when complicated with either one or the other. It was observed that more or less characteristic changes in weight and of the histological picture of the thymus might occur in malformed human fetuses and newborns according to the body systems involved in maldevelopment.

PANCREAS

Histological changes of the pancreas peculiar to central-nervous system and digestive system anomalies were found[5]. In cases with central-nervous system anomalies, especially anencephalus, there was a tendency for the islet of Langerhans to be reduced in number and size. No remarkable changes, however, were noted in the acinar cells and interstitial tissue. In cases of digestive system anomalies a marked proliferation of the interstitial connective tissue and a reduction in number and size of the islets of Langerhans, although slight, were detected, in addition to atrophy of the acinar cells and unequal size of the lobuli.

In cases of developmental anomalies of almost all body systems the ratio of the A cells to the B cells counted in the islets of Langerhans proved to be significantly larger than the control. It was because a definite reduction in number of the A cells occurred in these malformed fetuses and newborns. Particularly, in cases of central-nervous system and digestive system anomalies a higher ratio of the A cells to the B cells was frequently noted, and also a distinct decrease in number of the A cells was observed histologically (Tables 3, 4)[5].

OVARY

Few or no remarkable histological changes of the ovary, in general, were seen. It was noted, however, that the most characteristic findings arose in 29 out of 34 cases of fetal coarctation of the aorta showing seminoma-like features in 16 cases (47 per cent) and further dysgerminoma-like pattern in 13 cases (38

Table 3 Confidence limit of ratio of number of A to B cells in Langerhans islet of control fetus and newborn ($\alpha = 0.05$)

Fetal month		Number of cases	Confidence limit
Stillbirth	VI	7	$0.623 \leq 0.736 \leq 0.849$
	VII	10	$0.803 \leq 0.823 \leq 0.843$
	VIII	7	$0.778 \leq 0.924 \leq 1.070$
	IX	4	$0.740 \leq 0.849 \leq 0.958$
	X	6	$0.928 \leq 1.169 \leq 1.410$
Neonatal death	X	8	$1.039 \leq 1.173 \leq 1.307$

Table 4 Confidence limit of ratio of number of A to B cells in Langerhans islet of malformed fetus and newborn

Malformation in body system	Fetal month	B/A	Malformation in body system	Fetal month	B/A
Central-nervous system anomaly (8 cases)	VI	0. 977	Cardio-vascular system anomaly (10 cases)	VI	1. 889
	VII	1. 670		VII	0. 765
	VIII	2. 020		VII	0. 853
	VIII	2. 836		IX	1. 506
	VIII	3. 204		X	2. 600
	VIII	**0. 966**		X	**1. 264**
	X	1. 669		X	0. 796
	X	2. 145		X	**1. 274**
Osteo-muscular system anomaly (12 cases)	VII	1. 434		X	1. 421
	VIII	1. 556		X	**1. 310**
	IX	1. 082	Digestive system anomaly (8 cases)	VIII	1. 603
	IX	1. 659		IX	1. 613
	IX	1. 578		X	1. 765
	IX	0. 993		X	**1. 169**
	IX	1. 074		X	2. 749
	X	1. 628		X	1. 596
	X	1. 748		X	1. 481
	X	**1. 159**		X	1. 755
	X	1. 524	Urino-genital system anomaly (3 cases)	VIII	1. 577
	X	0. 979		IX	1. 491
				X	**1. 306**

Gothic numerals: within confidence limit of control $(\alpha = 0.05)$

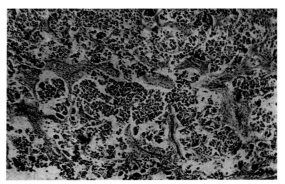

Fig. 9 Ovary of a case with fetal coarctation of aorta. Tubular or solid nests are composed of various-sized round or oval cells with chromatin-poor nuclei. Note a close resemblance to histologic features of seminoma.

Fig. 10 Ovary of a case with fetal coarctation of aorta. Irregularly-shaped cell groups in part complicated with fascicular proliferation of immature fibroblasts in the interstitium show microscopic appearance of dysgerminoma.

per cent) (Figs. 9, 10)[18]. In relation to these histological changes of the ovary associated with fetal coarctation of the aorta, an examination was made on the appearance of sex chromatin in the adrenocortical cells in human fetuses and newborns. The average of sex chromatin count was lower in female fetuses with seminoma-like changes in the ovary, but was higher in those showing dysgerminoma-like changes[7]. On the basis of these results, certain histological changes of the ovary and abnormalities of sex chromatin are presumed to be associated with aortic coarctation in the fetal period.

SALIVARY GLANDS

It has been suggested that the endocrine function of the salivary glands is closely related to the proliferation of mesenchymal tissues, and that chondrodystrophia fetalis seems to be caused by retardation of functional development of the salivary glands during the fetal and neonatal period[15]. Atrophic or more regressive changes of the epithelium of the striated tubules and the acinar cells were observed in the parotid and submaxillary glands characteristically in cases of chondrodystrophia fetalis. On the other hand, no change or simple hypertrophy of the epithelium of the striated tubules was detected in osteogenesis imperfecta. These results suggest different pathogenetic mechanisms in these two developmental anomalies of the bone system.

In order to observe influences of maternal salivary glands upon embryonic development experimentally, the parotid and submaxillary glands of female rats were removed bilaterally before pregnancy. Fetuses derived from these mother rats showed developmental retardation or hypoplasia of the endocrine glands, and further, less developed hematopoietic foci. However, neither the salivary glands nor the bones showed remarkable changes[13]. The prenatal developmental retardation of the endocrine glands and hematopoietic foci is considered to affect the postnatal function of the endocrine glands, and to result in formation of predisposition to diseases.

COMMENT

Generally speaking, it still remains unclear whether or not, and also to what extent if any, these autopsy findings of the endocrine glands in malformed human fetuses and newborns are related to the production of the congenital anomalies observed. However, if the above mentioned changes of the endocrine glands are interpreted as basic or concomitant indications of latent and unknown mechanisms of developmental anomalies through the fetal period, then they may suggest an approach in the exploration of some causative and diathetic factors in developmental anomalies.

REFERENCES

1. AKASHI, M.: Fetal-histological study on fuchsinophilia of adrenal cortex of human fetus and newborn. Nagasaki Med. J. 41: 112–123, 1966.
2. FURUKAWA, T.: Experimental study on the influence of abnormal maternal environment due to cortisone-treatment on the nuclear desoxyribonucleic acid content of the cerebral cells of rat fetus by means of microspectrophotometry. Nagasaki Med. J. 39: 123–135, 1964.
3. HARA, H.: Fetal-pathological studies on the salivary glands of malformed human fetuses and newborns. Nagasaki Med. J. 34: 548–551, 1959.
4. HAYASHI, A.: Fetal-pathological study on fuchsinophilia of adrenal cortex in malformed human fetus and newborn. Nagasaki Med. J. 41: 313–331, 1966.
5. HAYASHIDA, M.: Fetal-pathological studies on the pancreas of malformed human fetus and newborn. Nagasaki Med. J. 34: 945–961, 1959.
6. HONDA, Y.: Histological appearance of fetal adrenal glands in experimental production of developmental anomalies. Nagasaki Med. J. 39: 730–744, 1964.
7. IKEDA, T.: On the sex chromatin in fetal coarctation of the aorta. Jap. J. Human Genet. 8: 241–254, 1963.
8. KANEKO, M.: Experimental study of the effect of abnormal maternal environment due to adrenalectomy on the nuclear desoxyribonucleic acid content of the cerebral cells of rat fetus by means of microspectrophotometry. Nagasaki Med. J. 38: 909–919, 1963.
9. MORI, Y.: Fetal-pathological studies on the pituitary gland of malformed human fetus and newborn. Nagasaki Med. J. 33: 1639–1677, 1958.
10. NAKAMURA, K.: Experimental studies on the influence of abnormal maternal environment (Removal of the adrenal glands) upon fetal development. Nagasaki Med. J. 32: 783–815, 1957.
11. NAKAZATO, Y.: Experimental investigation on the influence of abnormal maternal environment (Excess of adrenal cortex hormone) upon organ development during the embryonic period. Nagasaki Med. J. 28: 825–844, 1953.
12. OGATA, Y.: The influence of abnormal maternal environment due to experimental adrenalectomy upon mitosis of the cerebral cell in fetus. Nagasaki Med. J. 35: 255–273, 1960.
13. SATO, T.: Experimental studies on the influence of abnormal maternal environment induced by removal of salivary glands upon fetal development. Nagasaki Med. J. 34: 932–944, 1959.
14. TAKEHARA, N.: Fetal-pathological studies on the adrenal galnd of malformed human

fetus and newborn. Nagasaki Med. J. 32: 1162–1210, 1957.

15. TAKIZAWA, N.: A pathological research on the internal secretion of the salivary glands. Acta Path. Jap. 4: 229–266, 1954.

16. TSUCHIYAMA, H.: Pathological studies on the endocrine glands in anencephalic fetuses. Report I. Introduction. Nagasaki Med. J. 31: 1062–1065, 1956.

17. URANO, K.: Fetal-pathological studies on the thymus of human fetus and newborn. Nagasaki Med. J. 33: 85–127, 1958.

18. YAMABE, I.: Fetal-pathological studies on the sex glands of malformed human fetus and newborn. Nagasaki Med. J. 33: 1445–1469, 1958.

EPIDEMIOLOGIC STUDIES OF CONGENITAL DEFECTS

Robert W. Miller

Chief, Epidemiology Branch, National Cancer Institute,
National Institutes of Health, Bethesda, U.S.A.

The story of the discovery of German measles as a cause of congenital defects in man is now well known. It is not generally appreciated, however, that this most important finding was made through an epidemiologic study. By looking backwards into the histories of mothers whose children had congenital cataracts, Gregg[7] identified rubella infection during pregnancy as the cause. This discovery had a very large impact on human teratology and on chronic-disease epidemiology.

NATURE OF EPIDEMIOLOGIC STUDIES

Generally, epidemiology can be classified as descriptive or analytical. Descriptive epidemiology is concerned with the distribution of disease by such variables as age, sex, race and socioeconomic status. While these studies may seem tedious to non-epidemiologists, they can provide interesting clues to the origins of disease. Of particular value with regard to the etiology of congenital defects are studies of case-clustering in time or space (geography), and changing risks with maternal age or parity.

Analytical epidemiology is often underestimated. It is just as much concerned with testing hypotheses as laboratory research is, but the epidemiologist must take things as they are, not as he might want them ideally. He must try to recognize in natural occurrences the factors that influence development of disease.

MATERNAL AGE EFFECT

Let us consider an example of how one moves from descriptive to analytical epidemiologic studies. Down's syndrome was first recognized to be associated with maternal age in 1909[22], long before the era of big grants. In fact it did not require any money at all to recognize the relationship, since 20 case-histories which gave maternal age would be sufficient. The risk of having a child with Down's syndrome has subsequently been shown to be about 20 times greater among pregnant women over 40 years of age than it is among women 20-24 years of age[24].

Obstetricians have known for decades that the risk of miscarriage also increases with maternal age, but no one quantitated or documented the relationship until 1962; and then the study was done not by an obstetrician, but by a statistician through the use of the records of the Hospital Insurance Plan of Greater New York[20]. Spontaneous abortion in women over 40 is about twice as common as it is among women 20 years younger.

The risk of childhood leukemia is also related to maternal age, the probability being 40% greater if the mother is over 40 years of age than if she is 20–24 years old at the time the child is born[14].

THE DEVELOPMENT OF A HYPOTHESIS

The relatioship of maternal age to Down's syndrome, miscarriage and childhood leukemia suggests a hypothesis: this characteristic in common has an explanation in common. One possibility pertains to cytogenetic abnormality, for it has been observed that meiotic non-disjunction is related to maternal age. In Down's syndrome there is usually an extra chromosome present from conception or soon thereafter. Among early spontaneous abortions, about 22% have chromosomal abnormalities[2]. Down's syndrome is associated with childhood leukemia, as may also prove true of other congenital defects characterized by errors in meiosis[5]. It is possible that errors in chromosomal division are the factor in common that relates Down's syndrome, abortions and childhood leukemia to one another and to maternal age.

TIME-SPACE CLUSTERING

The next question is, what causes meiotic non-disjunction? Some people have suggested that infection does. In particular, STOLLER and COLLMAN[27] in Australia have claimed that peaks in infectious hepatitis are followed in 9 months by peaks in the births of children with Down's syndrome. The number of cases of Down's syndrome in their study was small, the average each year being only 13. The range was from 6 to 20. With such a small sample size, there is a large random error. It is entirely possible that the seeming peaks in Down's syndrome represent random fluctuations which by chance followed peaks in hepatitis occurrence. The hypothesis that the two diseases were related was tested further by STARK and FRAUMENI[23]. They studied the occurrence of Down's syndrome among children born in Michigan, 1950–64. The sample, exhaustively ascertained, consisted of about 2500 children with Down's syndrome. Information on the occurrence of hepatitis in the same area was obtained from the Communicable Disease Center of the Public Health Service. The results showed that there were two peaks in the occurrence of hepatitis, but there was no peak in the occurrence of Down's syndrome at any time during the 15-year interval. There were between 100 and 200 children with Down's syndrome in each year of the study. With a sample of this considerable size, the results of STOLLER and COLLMAN in Australia could not be substantiated in the United States. Similarly no correlation between the two diseases was found in Birmingham, England[13], Seattle, Washington[12], or Italy[3].

Several statistical techniques have been devised to determine if there is subtle clustering of rare events in time and space[15]. These methods are very valuable in studies of the distribution of specific congenital defects such as Down's syndrome. When Michigan is subdivided geographically over various intervals of time, one would expect a certain number of subdivisions by chance to contain

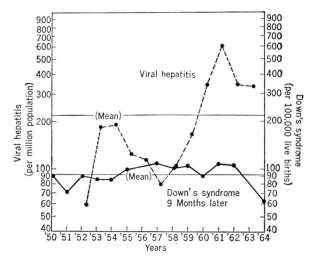

Fig. 1 Annual incidence of viral hepatitis at all ages, and annual incidence of Down's syndrome among children born 9 months later, Michigan, U.S., 1952–1964.

clusters of the syndrome.   Comparison of the expected number with the observed number of areas containing clusters will reveal whether or not Down's syndrome shows any excessive time-space aggregation.   When the observed and expected numbers of clusters in Michigan were compared through the use of χ^2 test, the value obtained was 0.26 (1 d.f.), a low figure which indicates no significant difference.   When the same technique was applied to infectious hepatitis, a known contagious disease, the χ^2 value was 6116.   Obviously the technique works when the disease to which it is applied really occurs in aggregates.   When applied to Down's syndrome, the test was negative not only with regard to clusters by units of a year but also by months or seasons[25].   Thus, even within small time-intervals there was no tendency to cluster.

OTHER RETROSPECTIVE STUDIES

Retrospective studies, often regarded with scorn by scientists inexperienced with them, have made important contributions to human teratology. Rubella has already been mentioned in this respect. In a similar fashion, by looking back into the maternal histories of children with small head circumference and mental retardation, it was possible, 40 years ago, to reveal that this anomaly was caused by therapeutic X-ray exposure during pregnancy.   Retrospective study also identified thalidomide as a teratogen.   The gross findings of retrospective studies were subsequently refined through prospective studies which provided more accurate estimates of the risks involved.   The prospective approach involves identification of a cohort of exposed persons, as, for example, women exposed to rubella infection during pregnancy.   Prospective studies can reveal the true risk of 1) fetal wastage, 2) congenital defects in the liveborn, 3) the interval of greatest susceptibility during pregnancy, and 4) the more subtle manifestations of fetal injury. Thus, it has only recently been established by this technique that rubella infection during pregnancy may cause only deafness in the child.

ASSOCIATION OF CANCER AND CONGENITAL DEFECTS

Mention has been made of retrospective studies in which one looks backward, and of prospective studies, in which one looks forward. It seems logical that there should also be "laterospective" studies. There is no such term in textbooks of epidemiology, but there is such an approach, which is extremely effective. It concerns looking sideways for associated diseases. In this way, leukemia was found to be excessively associated with Down's syndrome, the risk being about 20 times greater than usual[26]. The question then arose, are other specific congenital malformations excessively associated with specific childhood neoplasms? Wilms' tumor was a good prospect for study in this regard, and the results are the subject of the demonstration later in this Workshop (p. 259). The discovery of associations between congenital defects and other diseases may lead to new understanding of the etiology or mechanisms involved. Thus has it been learned, for example, that genetically induced diseases with immunologic deficiency (Wiskott-Aldrich syndrome, ataxia-telangiectasia, congenital agammaglobulinemia and Chediak-Higashi syndrome) predispose to lymphomas, but not to other neoplasia.

BEGINNING AT THE BEDSIDE

At present there is very little epidemiologic activity on hospital wards. Opportunities may be great, but are largely unexplored. The illness of the hospitalized person tends to be regarded as an isolated event rather than as perhaps one of a series of connected occurrences affecting the individual, his family or the community. It would be useful on ward rounds to attempt to put the medical history and physical findings into etiologic perspective, taking into account what is already known about the relationships among the findings, what new hypotheses are suggested by the present case, and how they might be tested epidemiologically. Let us consider a few examples.

NEUROBLASTOMA AND CLEFT LIP/PALATE

A child with cleft lip and palate is found to have a neuroblastoma. Is there a real association between these two disorders, or did they occur in the same person by chance? The first step in deciding between these two possibilities is, of course, to review the literature. Such a review would reveal that only two children have been described who had both diseases[19]. Obviously, no judgment can be made from these scant data. The second step involves study of hospital records for a series of children with neuroblastoma in the search for mention of cleft lip/palate or study of records for a series of children with cleft lip/palate for mention of neuroblastoma. It is more effective to start with cases having the less frequent disorder, in this case neuroblastoma, and to search for the more frequent disease.   One would start in the record room of his own hospital, and abstract information pertaining to congenital defects among hospital charts concerning neuroblastoma.   No single hospital will have sufficient cases on which to make a judgment whether or not cleft lip/palate occurs excessively with this neoplasm.   The series must therefore be extended to medical charts of other hospitals.   In our own experience[19] when this was done, among a total of 504 neuroblastoma records, cleft lip/palate was found in only 2 cases; the frequency was too low to indicate a real association between the neoplasm and the congenital defect.   In this instance, through the use of the epidemiologic method, one could avoid giving undue significance to the occurrence of the two diseases together.

CONGENITAL HEART DISEASE WITH HORSESHOE KIDNEY

With luck, an investigator may find the answer to his question in the literature, overlooked by the original authors.   Let us suppose that a child is found to have ventricular septal defect and horseshoe kidney.   Again the question arises, is this a chance or a real association?   The answer, in part at least, is available through an inexpensive survey procedure, the results of which have been described by HUMPHRY and MUNN[11].   Immediately after children with congenital heart disease were examined by angiocardiography, an X-ray film of the abdomen was obtained.   As the radio-opaque dye was excreted by the kidneys, it outlined the urinary tract in 400 of the 450 children so studied.   It was found that 22 of the 400 had renal anomalies, a frequency which did not differ significantly from that for the controls.   The controls, however, were selected from among other hospital patients, who may also have differed from normal.   In this instance they were children without heart disease who had had intravenous pyelography for the first time for some complaint thought not to be due to congenital defect. These children were, in consequence, not representative of the normal population.   Furthermore, inspection of the list of renal abnormalities found with congenital heart disease revealed that 6 of the 400 children had horseshoe kidney or crossed ectopia, a pair of anomalies which are closely related embryologically, and which appear to have occurred excessively among the children with cardiac defects.   No such renal anomaly has been recorded among hundreds of autopsied children with neoplasia other than Wilms' tumor[18] and, in a survey of about 12,000 newborn infants, only 4 were found with horseshoe or fused kidney[21]; that is, a frequency of about 1 in 3,000 as contrasted with 1 in 66 among children with congenital heart disease examined by angiocardiography.   The cardiac defects associated with these renal anomalies, though varied in type, included 2 ventricular septal defects.

PROGNOSTIC VALUE OF CAFE-AU-LAIT SPOTS

Cafe-au-lait spots, commonly seen in children, may be an early sign of multiple neurofibromatosis.   To what extent does this pigmentation predict the later occurrence of neurofibromatosis?   In an epidemiologic study, it has been found that among 149 patients with neurofibromatosis, 78% had six or more cafe-au-lait spots whose longest diameter was 1.5 centimeters or greater. Spots of this size and number were not seen among thousands of adults without neurofibromatosis and without a known family history of the disease[4]. In this instance, the epidemiologic technique was used to identify a predictive sign of a serious illness well in advance of clinical symptoms.

AN EPIDEMIC OF CEREBRAL PALSY

The epidemiologist must make the most of natural circumstances. In this way the rubella syndrome was discovered in Australia, phocomelia induced by thalidomide was found in West Germany and Great Britain, the effects of LSD are under observation in the U.S., and the teratogenic effects of pesticides can be evaluated in Mexico and Colombia where pregnant women are among those who ate bread prepared with contaminated flour. In Japan, at Minamata Bay, an epidemic of cerebral palsy was recognized about 10 years ago[17]. Twenty-two cases occurred between 1955 and 1962. Among 188 children born in adjacent villages 13 (6.9%) were affected, a frequency substantially above normal expectation. At the same time older children and adults were afflicted with a severe neurological disorder, often fatal, which was traced to organic mercury in industrial wastes from a factory engaged in the manufacture of vinyl chloride. As production of this chemical rose dramatically, the industrial waste increasingly contaminated the fish in the Bay. The persons affected were from families of fishermen, who sold their best catch and consumed the rest. The mothers of the children with cerebral palsy had eaten the fish but were not themselves affected. The children were severely handicapped; eight were unable to sit up at five or six years of age. When fishing in the Bay was banned, the epidemic promptly stopped. The disease occurred among cats and birds that ate the fish, and has been experimentally induced by feeding seafood caught in the Bay to cats and chickens. Lest one consider such an occurrence unlikely in Western countries, note should be taken that acrodynia took a heavy toll in the United States and Great Britain before WARKANY[29] discovered that its cause was inorganic mercury in teething powders and ointments. When mercury was eliminated from these preparations, acrodynia became a rarity in pediatric practice.

FRAGMENTARY SYNDROMES

Epidemiologic study may identify syndromes, the elements of which are scattered over several family members rather than concentrated in a single person. Thus, leukemia and Down's syndrome occur excessively not only within the same individual, but leukemia is apparently also more frequent than usual among sibs of persons with mongolism[16]. Again, a possible explanation for such sibship aggregation is a seeming excess of chromosomal anomalies among close relatives of persons with Down's syndrome[28].

Medulloblastoma has affected six young children in families with multiple basal cell nevus syndrome[1,6,8,9,10]. Two of these children later developed other manifestations of the syndrome[9,10]. Thus, the neoplasm was the first sign of the disorder. This experience indicates the importance of the family history not only with respect to the cancer found in the index case, but also to characteristics of syndromes in which such neoplasia may occur.

CONCLUSION

My purpose in this presentation has been to emphasize that epidemiologic research can present a variety of approaches to the origins of congenital defects; that it does not have to be boring or costly; that it can test hypotheses that are being developed in the laboratory or through clinical observations; that it can generate hypotheses; and that it can often perform these functions very quickly through the use of existing data if one knows where to look for suitable resources.

REFERENCES

1. ANDERSON, D.E., TAYLOR, W.B., FALLS, H.F., and DAVIDSON, R.T.: The nevoid basal cell carcinoma syndrome. Amer. J. Human Genet. 19: 12–22, 1967.
2. CARR, D.H.: Chromosome anomalies as a cause of spontaneous abortion. Amer. J. Obstet. Gynec. 97: 283–293, 1967.
3. CECCARELLI, G., and TORBIDONI, L.: Viral hepatitis and Down's syndrome. Lancet 1: 438, 1967.
4. CROWE, F.W., SCHULL, W.J., and NEEL, J.V.: A Clinical, Pathological and Genetic Study of Multiple Neurofibromatosis. Springfield, Illinois, Charles C. Thomas, 1956.
5. FRAUMENI, J.F., Jr., and MILLER, R.W.: Epidemiology of human leukemia: recent observations. J. Nat. Cancer Inst. 38: 593–605, 1967.
6. GORLIN, R.J., VICKERS, R.A., KELLN, E., and WILLIAMSON, J.J.: The multiple basal-cell nevi syndrome. Cancer 18: 89–104, 1965.
7. GREGG, N.M.: Congenital cataract following German measles in the mother. Tr. Ophth. Soc. Australia 3: 35–46, 1941.
8. HERMANS, E.H., GROSFIELD, J.C.M., and SPAAS, J.A.J.: The fifth phacomatosis. Dermatologica 130: 446–476, 1965.
9. HERZBERG, J.J., and WISKEMANN, A: Die fünfte Phakomatose: Basalzellnaevus mit familiärer Belastung und Medulloblastom. Dermatologica 126: 106–123, 1963.
10. HOWELL, J.B., ANDERSON, D.E., and McCLENDON, J.L.: Multiple cutaneous cancers in children: The nevoid basal cell carcinoma syndrome. J. Pediat. 69: 97–103, 1966.
11. HUMPHRY, A., and MUNN, J.D.: Abnormalities of the urinary tract in association with congenital cardiovascular disease. Canad. Med. Ass. J. 95: 143–145, 1966.
12. KOGAN, A., KRONMAL, R., and PETERSON, D.R.: The relationship between infectious hepatitis and Down's syndrome. Amer. J. Public Health 58: 305–311, 1968.
13. LECK, I.: Incidence and epidemicity of Down's syndrome. Lancet 2: 457–460, 1966.
14. MacMAHON, B., and NEWILL, V.A.: Birth characteristics of children dying of malignant neoplasms. J. Nat. Cancer Inst. 28: 231–244, 1962.
15. MANTEL, N.: The detection of disease clustering and a generalized regression approach. Cancer Res. 27: 209–220, 1967.
16. MILLER, R.W.: Relation between cancer and congenital defects in man. New Eng. J. Med. 275: 87–93, 1966.
17. MILLER, R.W.: Prenatal origins of mental retardation: Epidemiological approach. J. Pediat. 71: 455–458, 1967.
18. MILLER, R.W.: Unpublished data.

19. MILLER, R.W., FRAUMENI, J.F., JR., and HILL, J.A.: Neuroblastoma: Epidemiologic approach to its origins. Amer. J. Dis. Child. 115: 253–261, 1968.

20. SHAPIRO, S., JONES, E.W. and DENSEN, P.M.: A life table of pregnancy terminations and correlates of fetal loss. Milbank Mem. Fund. Quart. 40: 7–45, 1962.

21. SHERWOOD, D.W., SMITH, R.C., LEMMON, R.H., and VRABEL, I.: Abnormalities of the genitourinary tract discovered by palpation of the abdomen of the newborn. Pediatrics 18: 782–789, 1956.

22. SHUTTLEWORTH, G.E.: Mongolian imbecility. Brit. Med. J. 2: 661–665, 1909.

23. STARK, C.R., and FRAUMENI, J.F., JR.: Viral hepatitis and Down's syndrome. Lancet 1: 1036–1037, 1966.

24. STARK, C.R., and MANTEL, N.: Effects of maternal age and birth order on the risk of mongolism and leukemia. J. Nat. Cancer Inst. 37: 687–698, 1966.

25. STARK, C.R., and MANTEL, N.: Lack of seasonal- or temporal-spatial clustering of Down's syndrome birth in Michigan. Amer. J. Epid. 86: 199–213, 1967.

26. STEWART, A., WEBB, J., and HEWITT, D.: A survey of childhood malignancies. Brit. Med. J. 1: 1495–1508, 1958.

27. STOLLER, A., and COLLMANN, R.D.: Incidence of infective hepatitis followed by Down's syndrome nine months later. Lancet 2: 1221–1223, 1965.

28. UCHIDA, I.A., RAY, M., and URSEL, M.: Cytogenetic investigations of a random series of mongoloid families. [Abs.] Amer. Soc. Human Genet., Dec. 1–3, 1967, p. 30.

29. WARKANY, J.: Acrodynia—Postmortem of a disease. Amer. J. Dis. Child. 112: 147–156, 1966.

DISCUSSION

RUNNER (U.S.A.)

You reported a correlation between leukemia and chromosomal aberration. It is also known that viral infection is correlated with chromosomal abnormality. Are current epidemiologic approaches going to be able to untangle such three-cornered correlates?

MILLER

Yes, an attempt is being made. There are half a dozen human characteristics known to carry a very high risk of leukemia, greater than 1 : 100 within a few years. Each has a distinctive genetic or cytogenetic feature (MILLER, Cancer Research 1967). This suggests that agents known to produce long-lasting chromosomal abnormalities be studied for leukemogenic effects. Herpes-simplex virus is such an agent. We are determining the cancer experience of U.S. Army veterans who, during world War II, had severe or recurring herpes-simplex infection. Chemicals which break chromosomes are also suspect. Benzene, for example, produces long-lasting chromo-somal breaks and leukemia. The same is true of ionizing radiation. Thus, the agent producing such breakage may be inherited (as in Bloom's syndrome), physical (x-ray), chemical (benzene), or possibly viral (none yet known to cause leukemia; those which produce chromosomal breakage should perhaps be the most suspect).

DENIZ (Turkey)

You mentioned that some fishes contaminated with organic mercury were eaten by women who subsequently produced abnormal children. Has there been any study done on the fishes themselves?

MILLER

The affected fish swim erratically; birds and cats that ate the fish also suffered neurological abnomalities. I believe that concentration of mercury has been found in various organs at autopsy, as is also true of the affected human beings. The chain of evidence inplicating mercury is very strong. I do not know of teratologic evaluation of the agent (or the contaminated fish) in species other than man.

KLINGBERG (Israel)

This morning you asked Dr. SEVER, about his suggestions for studies on the correlation between viruses and congenital malformations that can be carried out in Asia. May I ask you the same question?

MILLER

From a conversation we have had, I know that you have some good ideas on one subject. Will you tell us about them?

KLINGBERG

I think that it is worthwhile studying any possible correlation between those virus diseases that are common in certain countries and their potential teratogenicity. Such epidemiological studies can be carried out in Asian countries. Two examples would be in Japan studies involving the Japanese B encephalitis virus and in Israel, studies with the West Nile fever virus.

MILLER

Yes, I agree. Emphasis should be placed on those diseases which are particularly prevalent in Asia including evaluation of various forms of parasitosis for teratogenic effects.

BRENT (U.S.A.)

What pitfalls have been found in erroneous epidemiological studies? How does the novice pick these errors out of the reports?

MILLER

Among specialists in epidemiology, there is too often an excessive fear of the many pitfalls in scientific design—imperfections which can affect the results obtained.

Problems are more common when the differences observed among comparison groups are small. There are many opportunities to discover large differences, however, which cannot be attributed to imperfections of scientific design. The pitfalls should not make one afraid to take a chance through this research approach. A causal relationship is supported by finding: 1) a response which is proportionate to the dose received (dose-response effect), 2) results consistent with previous observations in man or experimental animals, and 3) other confounding variables could not account for the findings.

In studies of the leukemogenic effect in man of small intrauterine exposures to diagnostic X-ray (about 2r), no dose-response effect can be demonstrated, leukemia following such low doses has not been observed in experimental animals, and one confounding variable, maternal illness for which the X-ray procedure was performed, has not been entirely excluded. Thus, I regard with suspicion the relationship between small doses of X-ray *in utero* and the occurrence of leukemia during childhood.

It is difficult to enumerate pitfalls to be considered in conducting or evaluating epidemiologic studies, but consideration of the above 3 characteristics can help greatly in recognizing shortcomings of studies in which the differences observed are relatively small.

CONGENITAL MALFORMATIONS IN PERINATAL, INFANT AND CHILD DEATHS

Luz A. Froehlich, *Associate Pathologist* and

Toshio Fujikura, *Associate Pathologist*

*Perinatal Research Branch, National Institute of
Neurological Diseases and Stroke, National
Institutes of Health, Bethesda, U.S.A.*

Reported incidences of malformations vary considerably[1,2,4,6,11,15-18] depending on the definition and classification of malformations, the source of the diagnosis, and the sampled population. All samples are necessarily biased to some degree and it is important to clearly define the bias of a study sample. Most malformation incidences are based on a combination of autopsy with clinical data. This seems unsatisfactory because of the relative inadequacy of clinical methods to diagnose hidden internal defects, notably those of the cardiovascular and genitourinary system during the neonatal period, with the result that these undiagnosed defects are precluded from such incidences. Mellin[11] showed that autopsies on 177 fetal and neonatal deaths increased the incidence of malformations by 10.3% over that based on clinical diagnoses. In Neel's series[15], postmortem examination of 264 stillbirths and neonatal deaths without the diagnosis of major defect revealed that 10.2% of them had internal defects of major proportions. Because of this, Neel separately analyzed and clearly defined his autopsy sample as distinguished from his clinical data. Admittedly, in deaths occurring during the perinatal and infancy period there is a greater proportion of lethal or major malformations than in the general population. At the same time deaths from other causes will affect the relative incidence of malformations as well as make available such cases for "more extensive", i.e., postmortem examinations. However in an analysis particularly of multiple malformations this seems to be a more acceptable bias than that created by pooled autopsy and clinical data.

The purpose of this paper is to report the analysis of malformations on autopsied stillbirths, neonatal, infant and child deaths in the Collaborative Study and to determine the underlying relationship of multiple and single malformations to sex, race, type of death, birth weight, gestational age, and maternal age.

MATERIAL AND METHODS

The present study was limited to autopsied deaths of Collaborative Project cases. The Collaborative Study required that, where permission was granted, a detailed autopsy was to be performed according to a standard protocol on all deaths, including consistent reporting of such minor malformations as single umbilical artery and accessory spleen. Copies of such protocols were submitted to the Perinatal Research Branch. This report was based on 43,127 consecutive single births delivered of randomly selected Collaborative Study registrants from

Table 1 Death rate* and autopsy rate according to race, sex, and type of death

	All races					White					Negro				
	Number of births	Stillbirth	Neonatal death	Infant and child death	Total deaths	Number of births	Stillbirth	Neonatal death	Infant and child death	Total deaths	Number of births	Stillbirth	Neonatal death	Infant and child death	Total deaths
Male	21926	1.5 (335)	1.6 (358)	1.0 (219)	4.2 (912)	9891	1.3 (125)	1.3 (131)	0.6 (58)	3.2 (314)	10324	1.8 (185)	2.0 (210)	1.3 (130)	5.1 (525)
Female	21201	1.4 (302)	1.3 (284)	0.6 (128)	3.4 (714)	9270	1.4 (134)	1.1 (102)	0.4 (41)	3.0 (277)	10288	1.4 (140)	1.6 (165)	0.7 (77)	3.7 (382)
Total death rate	43127	1.5 (637)	1.5 (642)	0.8 (347)	3.8 (1626)	19161	1.4 (259)	1.2 (233)	0.5 (99)	3.1 (591)	20612	1.6 (325)	1.8 (375)	1.0 (207)	4.4 (907)
Total autopsy rate (%)		93	89	76	88		94	91	60	85		92	93	82	90

* Based on autopsied cases per 100 single births.

January 1, 1959 to December 31, 1964. The children born to the latest registrants were about 2 years old at the time of this study whereas the oldest child
was about 8 years old. Abortions and multiple births were not included. The
bulk of the population consisted of roughly an equal number of whites and
Negroes, with a small percentage of Puerto Ricans and other races (Table 1).

The types of death analyzed with their corresponding definitions were as
follows:

> Stillbirth: non-liveborn termination of a fetus 16.5 cm crown-rump length
> or more.
> Neonatal death: death in liveborn infant up to 28 days of life.
> Infant and child death: death beyond 28 days of life.
> Only 29 of the child deaths were over 2 years old.

Malformations were classified into two groups. Group A malformations
included all uniformly reported macroscopic abnormalities of structure present
at birth and resulting from faulty embryological development[10] which normally
would have been completed by the end of the ninth week. Group B included
anomalies which were thought to be a secondary effect of Group A malformations or were felt not to be universally accepted as malformations, or where
uncertainty as to consistency of reporting existed in autopsied material. Excluded
from either group were inborn errors of metabolism, hereditary blood or neurological diseases, microscopic abnormalities, congenital tumors and leukemia.
Multiple malformations were defined as Group A malformations involving two
or more organ systems. Single malformations were those involving only one organ
system, regardless of the number of malformations within the system. Overall,
single and multiple malformation rates were based only on Group A malformations and were calculated using number of deaths as denominator. All attempts
were made not to overcount and therefore the resulting figures are conservative.
For instance, where a malformation always involved more than one organ system
such as anencephaly, which affects both the central nervous and skeletal systems,
this was counted as a single malformation. Multiple heart malformations
unassociated with other organ system malformations were counted as single
malformations. A patent ductus was only considered in a liveborn 14 days or
older. Hypoplasias of the left or right heart were listed under Group B for
consistency, since all other organ hypoplasias were listed in this Group. In two
tables (Tables 3 A and B) multiplicity of malformations within the system was
also evaluated for each specific malformation. Whenever possible all malformation rates were based on number of cases, rather than number of malformations,
so that a malformed case was counted only once in each table. Exceptions are
tables which deal with specific malformations.

RESULTS AND DISCUSSION

General characteristics of sampled population

At the risk of being redundant we feel it necessary to repeat some characteristics of this particular series as well as those of the general Collaborative
Study population, which to a large extent explain the differences and similarities
between our data and other malformation series. The analysis of malformations

was confined to the autopsied death population. Whenever rates were involved, the malformations considered were limited to gross structural defects uniformly accepted as malformations and presumably uniformly reported (Group A). Since the Collaborative Study is a prospective one and the mothers randomly selected, the proportion of "high-risk" cases such as maternal diabetes would be relatively low. All these factors tend to result in lower malformation rates compared to other series. Frequencies reported here are calculated on the basis of number of deaths within specified population groups. Thus conspicuous differences in mortality rates such as are noted in infant and child deaths could affect in inverse proportion the malformation rates in the groups analyzed. Although this is so, the "artifacts" created by this bias are relatively minor and where differences in malformation rates are clearly significant the high rates in certain groups truly reflect high frequencies of malformations within that group.

Inasmuch as analysis was limited to deaths, it is important to know the proportion of lethal malformations in this study. A lethal malformation was defined as a Group A malformation which would kill a liveborn infant without surgical intervention. Small isolated ventricular and atrial septal defects were not considered lethal nor was agenesis involving only one of bilateral vital organs. All but one of the multiply malformed cases and 61.9 % of those with single malformations had at least one lethal malformation, indicating that nearly three-quarters of the malformed cases (73.6 %) had lethal malformations.

Mortality rates and autopsy rates

Table 1 shows that for each type of death and sex the Negro mortality rates (total 4.4 %) were higher than those of the white counterpart (total 3.1 %) except in female stillbirths (1.4 % in both races). In Negroes the male mortality rates were consistently higher than those of the female particularly in infant and child deaths (1.3 % in males, 0.7 % in females). In whites no significant differences in mortality rates between the two sexes were noted. Autopsy rates ranged from 89% to 94% in stillbirths and neonatal deaths; in infant and child deaths it was 82 % in Negroes but only 60 % in whites.

General characteristics of malformations

The general incidences of Group A malformations are shown in Table 2-A. Also shown for each group are the ratios of cases with multiple to cases with single malformations (MM/SM ratios). Of the 1626 autopsied deaths, 259 or 15.9 % had Group A malformations. The total malformation rates in males (16.0 %) and females (15.8 %) were strikingly similar. Differences were noted when the cases were distributed by type of death, race, and multiplicity of malformations. For each type of death and sex the malformation rate was higher in whites than in Negroes (Table 2-B). Noteworthy was the high multiple malformation rate in white females particularly in stillbirths (10.4 %) compared to the other population groups. This was so not only in general (Table 2-B) but for most specific malformations where, in addition, multiplicity of malformations within the same system was more frequently seen in white females than in white males (Table 3-B). Concomitantly the MM/SM ratios were higher in white females (Table 2-B) especially in stillbirths (1.17). The lack of any consistent pattern of sex difference in Negroes largely stemmed from the generally low malformation rates in this race, with the exception of neonatal

Table 2-A Frequency of group A malformations according to type of death and sex

		Number of deaths	All malformations	Single malformations	Multiple malformations	Ratio multiple/single
Stillbirth	M	335	10.7 (36)	8.1 (27)	2.7 (9)	0.33
	F	302	13.6 (41)	7.0 (21)	6.6 (20)	0.95
Neonatal death	M	358	21.5 (77)	16.5 (59)	5.0 (18)	0.31
	F	284	16.2 (46)	10.2 (29)	6.0 (17)	0.59
Infant and child death	M	219	15.1 (33)	11.0 (24)	4.1 (9)	0.38
	F	128	20.3 (26)	14.1 (18)	6.3 (8)	0.44
Total	M	912	16.0 (146)	12.1 (110)	3.9 (36)	0.33
	F	714	15.8 (113)	9.5 (68)	6.3 (45)	0.66
Grand total		1626	15.9 (259)	10.9 (178)	5.0 (81)	0.46

Table 2-B Frequency of group A malformations according to race, type of death, and sex

			Number of deaths	All malformations	Single malformations	Multiple malformations	Ratio multiple/single
W h i t e	Stillbirth	M	125	14.4 (18)	10.4 (13)	4.0 (5)	0.38
		F	134	19.4 (26)	9.0 (12)	10.4 (14)	1.17
	Neonatal death	M	131	27.5 (36)	21.4 (28)	6.1 (8)	0.29
		F	102	21.6 (22)	11.8 (12)	9.8 (10)	0.83
	Infant and child death	M	58	24.1 (14)	17.2 (10)	6.9 (4)	0.40
		F	41	22.0 (9)	12.2 (5)	9.8 (4)	0.80
	Total	M	314	21.7 (68)	16.2 (51)	5.4 (17)	0.33
		F	277	20.6 (57)	10.5 (29)	10.1 (28)	0.97
N e g r o	Stillbirth	M	185	7.6 (14)	5.9 (11)	1.6 (3)	0.27
		F	140	9.3 (13)	5.7 (8)	3.6 (5)	0.63
	Neonatal death	M	210	18.6 (39)	13.3 (28)	5.2 (11)	0.39
		F	165	9.1 (15)	7.3 (12)	1.8 (3)	0.25
	Infant and child death	M	130	11.5 (15)	8.5 (11)	3.1 (4)	0.36
		F	77	18.2 (14)	13.0 (10)	5.2 (4)	0.40
	Total	M	525	13.0 (68)	9.5 (50)	3.4 (18)	0.36
		F	382	11.0 (42)	7.9 (30)	3.1 (12)	0.40

deaths where, in both races, single malformation rates were almost twice as high in males as in females (Table 2-B).

The malformation rates in white infant and child deaths should be interpreted with caution because of the low autopsy rate in this group (60 %). In such conditions as Sudden Unexpected Death (which constitutes roughly 1/3 of all infant and child deaths in the Collaborative Project) many cases had not been autopsied or no autopsy reports could be obtained from one area in which the Study population was predominantly white. It could be presumed that proportionately more of the malformed cases were autopsied since they often died in

Table 3-A Frequency of specific malformations by sex, type of death, and multiplicity of malformations

	Stillbirth		Neonatal death		Infant and child death		All malformations		Single malformations		Multiple malformations		Multiple malformations within the system	
Number of deaths	335	302	358	284	219	128	912	714	912	714	912	714	912	714
	M	F	M	F	M	F	M	F	M	F	M	F	M	F
Group A														
Central nervous system*	1.8 (6)	4.6 (14)	2.2 (8)	2.8 (8)	2.3 (5)	2.3 (3)	2.1 (19)	3.5 (25)	1.3 (12)	1.3 (9)	0.8 (7)	2.2 (16)	0.5 (5)	1.7 (12)
Anencephaly	0.6 (2)	3.3 (10)	1.4 (5)	1.4 (4)	0.0 (0)	0.0 (0)	0.8 (7)	2.0 (14)	0.7 (6)	1.0 (7)	0.1 (1)	1.0 (7)	0.0 (0)	0.8 (6)
Arnold-Chiari	0.3 (1)	0.3 (1)	0.3 (1)	1.1 (3)	0.9 (2)	0.8 (1)	0.4 (4)	0.7 (5)	0.2 (2)	0.1 (1)	0.2 (2)	0.6 (4)	– (–)	– (–)
Spina bifida, all types	0.0 (0)	2.3 (7)	0.0 (0)	0.7 (2)	0.5 (1)	0.0 (0)	0.1 (1)	1.3 (9)	0.1 (1)	0.3 (2)	0.0 (0)	1.0 (7)	0.0 (0)	1.0 (7)
Other CNS malformations	1.2 (4)	0.7 (2)	0.8 (3)	0.4 (1)	0.9 (2)	1.6 (2)	1.0 (9)	0.7 (5)	0.4 (4)	0.1 (1)	0.5 (5)	0.6 (4)	0.3 (3)	0.3 (2)
Cardiovascular system*	3.6 (12)	4.0 (12)	7.8 (28)	8.1 (23)	8.2 (18)	11.7 (15)	6.4 (58)	7.0 (50)	4.7 (43)	3.5 (25)	1.6 (15)	3.5 (25)	3.6 (33)	4.9 (35)
Ventricular septal defect	1.8 (6)	1.3 (4)	3.4 (12)	3.9 (11)	2.7 (6)	3.1 (4)	2.6 (24)	2.7 (19)	2.1 (19)	1.0 (7)	0.5 (5)	1.7 (12)	1.8 (16)	2.2 (16)
Atresia or stenosis, L valves	0.0 (0)	0.7 (2)	0.8 (3)	2.5 (7)	0.5 (1)	0.8 (1)	0.4 (4)	1.4 (10)	0.4 (4)	1.0 (7)	0.0 (0)	0.4 (3)	0.2 (2)	1.1 (8)
Atresia or stenosis, R valves	0.6 (2)	0.3 (1)	0.6 (2)	0.7 (2)	1.8 (4)	0.8 (1)	0.9 (8)	0.6 (4)	0.5 (5)	0.1 (1)	0.3 (3)	0.4 (3)	0.8 (7)	0.6 (4)
Other valve anomalies	0.3 (1)	0.7 (2)	0.0 (0)	1.8 (5)	3.2 (7)	0.8 (1)	0.9 (8)	1.1 (8)	0.8 (7)	0.4 (3)	0.1 (1)	0.7 (5)	0.4 (4)	1.0 (7)
Atrial septal defect	0.6 (2)	0.3 (1)	1.7 (6)	1.8 (5)	0.9 (2)	0.8 (1)	1.1 (10)	1.0 (7)	0.8 (7)	0.6 (4)	0.3 (3)	0.4 (3)	0.7 (6)	0.4 (3)
Tetralogy of Fallot	0.0 (0)	0.3 (1)	0.0 (0)	0.0 (0)	0.0 (0)	2.3 (3)	0.0 (0)	0.6 (4)	0.0 (0)	0.3 (2)	0.0 (0)	0.3 (2)	– (–)	– (–)
Atrio-ventricularis communis	0.6 (2)	1.0 (3)	0.8 (3)	0.4 (1)	0.5 (1)	2.3 (3)	0.7 (6)	1.0 (7)	0.5 (5)	0.4 (3)	0.1 (1)	0.6 (4)	– (–)	– (–)

Preductal coarctation	0.7 (5)	0.5 (5)	0.7 (5)	0.3 (3)	0.6 (4)	0.5 (5)	1.3 (9)	0.9 (8)	1.6 (2)	0.5 (1)	1.8 (5)	1.7 (6)	0.7 (2)	0.3 (1)
Truncus communis	0.3 (2)	0.5 (5)	0.1 (1)	0.1 (1)	0.1 (1)	0.4 (4)	0.3 (2)	0.5 (5)	0.0 (0)	0.0 (0)	0.4 (1)	1.1 (4)	0.3 (1)	0.3 (1)
Transposition, great vessels	0.1 (1)	1.1 (10)	0.1 (1)	0.2 (2)	0.0 (0)	0.9 (8)	0.1 (1)	1.1 (10)	0.0 (0)	1.8 (4)	0.4 (1)	1.4 (5)	0.0 (0)	0.3 (1)
Vascular ring	0.6 (4)	0.2 (2)	0.4 (3)	0.2 (2)	0.4 (3)	0.1 (1)	0.8 (6)	0.3 (3)	3.9 (5)	0.9 (2)	0.0 (0)	0.0 (0)	0.3 (1)	0.3 (1)
Anomalous pulmonary venous drainage	0.4 (3)	0.3 (3)	0.1 (1)	0.1 (1)	0.3 (2)	0.2 (2)	0.4 (3)	0.3 (3)	0.8 (1)	0.0 (0)	0.7 (2)	0.3 (1)	0.0 (0)	0.6 (2)
Patent ductus arteriosus	0.8 (6)	0.8 (7)	0.3 (2)	0.2 (2)	0.6 (4)	0.9 (8)	0.8 (6)	1.1 (10)	3.1 (4)	4.1 (9)	0.7 (2)	0.3 (1)	– (–)	– (–)
Other CVS malformations	0.8 (6)	1.0 (9)	0.6 (4)	0.8 (7)	0.6 (4)	0.3 (3)	1.1 (8)	1.1 (10)	3.1 (4)	2.7 (6)	0.7 (2)	0.8 (3)	0.7 (2)	0.3 (1)
Other blood vessels	– (–)	– (–)	1.7 (12)	0.8 (7)	1.1 (8)	1.3 (12)	2.8 (20)	2.1 (19)	2.3 (3)	0.5 (1)	2.1 (6)	1.4 (5)	3.6 (11)	3.9 (13)
Arterio-venous aneurysm	– (–)	– (–)	0.0 (0)	0.0 (0)	0.0 (0)	0.2 (2)	0.0 (0)	0.2 (2)	0.0 (0)	0.0 (0)	0.0 (0)	0.6 (2)	0.0 (0)	0.0 (0)
Single umbilical artery	– (–)	– (–)	1.7 (12)	0.8 (7)	1.1 (8)	1.1 (10)	2.8 (20)	1.9 (17)	2.3 (3)	0.5 (1)	2.1 (6)	0.8 (3)	3.6 (11)	3.9 (13)
Respiratory system*	0.0 (0)	0.0 (0)	0.1 (1)	0.3 (3)	0.1 (1)	0.0 (0)	0.3 (2)	0.3 (3)	0.0 (0)	0.5 (1)	0.4 (1)	0.6 (2)	0.3 (1)	0.0 (0)
Genitourinary system*	1.4 (10)	1.4 (13)	3.1 (22)	2.0 (18)	1.5 (11)	1.9 (17)	4.6 (33)	3.8 (35)	3.1 (4)	3.2 (7)	5.3 (15)	5.9 (21)	4.6 (14)	2.1 (7)
Polycystic kidney	0.8 (6)	0.9 (8)	1.4 (10)	0.7 (6)	0.6 (4)	0.5 (5)	2.0 (14)	1.2 (11)	0.8 (1)	0.5 (1)	3.2 (9)	2.5 (9)	1.3 (4)	0.3 (1)
Atresia, ureter or urethra	0.4 (3)	1.0 (9)	0.6 (4)	1.3 (12)	0.3 (2)	0.8 (7)	0.8 (6)	2.1 (19)	0.8 (1)	0.9 (2)	1.1 (3)	3.9 (14)	0.7 (2)	0.9 (3)
Agenesis, kidney	0.3 (2)	0.2 (2)	0.3 (2)	0.2 (2)	0.3 (2)	0.3 (3)	0.6 (4)	0.5 (5)	0.0 (0)	0.0 (0)	0.4 (1)	1.1 (4)	1.0 (3)	0.3 (1)
Horseshoe kidney	0.0 (0)	0.0 (0)	0.3 (2)	0.1 (1)	0.1 (1)	0.2 (2)	0.4 (3)	0.3 (3)	0.8 (1)	0.5 (1)	0.4 (1)	0.3 (1)	0.3 (1)	0.3 (1)
Double ureter	0.0 (0)	0.1 (1)	0.1 (1)	0.0 (0)	0.4 (3)	0.3 (3)	0.6 (4)	0.3 (3)	0.8 (1)	0.9 (2)	0.4 (1)	0.0 (0)	0.7 (2)	0.3 (1)
Agenesis, urinary bladder	0.0 (0)	0.1 (1)	0.0 (0)	0.1 (1)	0.0 (0)	0.0 (0)	0.0 (0)	0.1 (1)	0.0 (0)	0.0 (0)	0.0 (0)	0.3 (1)	0.0 (0)	0.0 (0)

	Stillbirth		Neonatal death		Infant and child death		All malformations		Single malformations		Multiple malformations		Multiple malformations within the system	
Number of deaths	M 335	F 302	M 358	F 284	M 219	F 128	M 912	F 714	M 912	F 714	M 912	F 714	M 912	F 714
Persistent cloaca	0.3 (1)	0.3 (1)	0.0 (0)	0.0 (0)	0.0 (0)	0.0 (0)	0.1 (1)	0.1 (1)	0.0 (0)	0.0 (0)	0.1 (1)	0.1 (1)	0.1 (1)	0.1 (1)
Agenesis, uterus or ovary	- (-)	0.7 (2)	- (-)	0.4 (1)	- (-)	0.0 (0)	- (-)	0.4 (3)	- (-)	0.0 (0)	- (-)	0.4 (3)	- (-)	0.4 (3)
Bicornuate uterus	- (-)	0.3 (1)	- (-)	1.1 (3)	- (-)	0.0 (0)	- (-)	0.6 (4)	- (-)	0.1 (1)	- (-)	0.4 (3)	- (-)	0.3 (2)
Pseudohermaphroditism	0.0 (0)	0.0 (0)	0.0 (0)	0.0 (0)	0.5 (1)	0.8 (1)	0.1 (1)	0.1 (1)	0.1 (1)	0.0 (0)	0.0 (0)	0.1 (1)	- (-)	- (-)
Other GUS malformations	0.3 (1)	0.7 (2)	0.0 (0)	1.4 (4)	0.5 (1)	0.0 (0)	0.2 (2)	0.8 (6)	0.0 (0)	0.0 (0)	0.2 (2)	0.8 (6)	0.1 (1)	0.7 (5)
Digestive system*	1.5 (5)	3.3 (10)	4.5 (16)	2.5 (7)	5.0 (11)	5.5 (7)	3.5 (32)	3.4 (24)	1.5 (14)	1.0 (7)	2.0 (18)	2.4 (17)	0.5 (5)	0.8 (6)
Cleft palate	0.6 (2)	0.3 (1)	0.3 (1)	0.4 (1)	0.0 (0)	0.8 (1)	0.3 (3)	0.4 (3)	0.0 (0)	0.1 (1)	0.3 (3)	0.3 (2)	0.0 (0)	0.0 (0)
Cleft palate with cleft lip	0.0 (0)	0.3 (1)	0.3 (1)	0.0 (0)	1.4 (3)	0.8 (1)	0.4 (4)	0.3 (2)	0.3 (3)	0.0 (0)	0.1 (1)	0.3 (2)	- (-)	- (-)
Cleft lip	0.0 (0)	0.7 (2)	0.0 (0)	0.0 (0)	0.0 (0)	0.0 (0)	0.0 (0)	0.3 (2)	0.0 (0)	0.1 (1)	0.0 (0)	0.1 (1)	0.0 (0)	0.0 (0)
Tracheo-esophageal fistula	0.0 (0)	0.3 (1)	0.3 (1)	0.4 (1)	0.0 (0)	0.8 (1)	0.1 (1)	0.4 (3)	0.0 (0)	0.1 (1)	0.1 (1)	0.4 (3)	0.0 (0)	0.3 (2)
Atresia, small bowel	0.0 (0)	0.3 (1)	0.6 (2)	0.0 (0)	0.9 (2)	0.0 (0)	0.4 (4)	0.1 (1)	0.2 (2)	0.0 (0)	0.2 (2)	0.1 (1)	0.0 (0)	0.1 (1)
Meckel's diverticulum	0.6 (2)	1.0 (3)	1.7 (6)	1.4 (4)	0.9 (2)	0.8 (1)	1.1 (10)	1.1 (8)	0.5 (5)	0.3 (2)	0.5 (5)	0.8 (6)	0.1 (1)	0.6 (4)
Hirschsprung's disease	0.0 (0)	0.0 (0)	0.0 (0)	0.4 (1)	2.3 (5)	0.8 (1)	0.5 (5)	0.3 (2)	0.3 (3)	0.1 (1)	0.2 (2)	0.1 (1)	0.0 (0)	0.0 (0)
Imperforate anus	0.0 (0)	0.7 (2)	0.6 (2)	0.4 (1)	0.0 (0)	0.0 (0)	0.2 (2)	0.4 (3)	0.0 (0)	0.0 (0)	0.2 (2)	0.4 (3)	0.1 (1)	0.1 (1)

	(1)	(2)	(3)	(4)	(5)	(6)	(7)	(8)	(9)	(10)	(11)	(12)	(13)	(14)
Agenesis, gallbladder	0.0 (0)	0.3 (1)	0.6 (2)	0.0 (0)	0.0 (0)	0.8 (1)	0.2 (2)	0.3 (2)	0.0 (0)	0.0 (0)	0.2 (2)	0.3 (2)	0.1 (1)	0.1 (1)
Atresia, bile duct	0.0 (0)	0.7 (2)	0.3 (1)	0.0 (0)	0.0 (0)	0.0 (0)	0.1 (1)	0.3 (2)	0.1 (1)	0.0 (0)	0.0 (0)	0.3 (2)	0.0 (0)	0.0 (0)
Other DS malformations	0.3 (1)	0.0 (0)	0.6 (2)	0.7 (2)	0.0 (0)	2.3 (3)	0.3 (3)	0.7 (5)	0.1 (1)	0.0 (0)	0.2 (2)	0.7 (5)	0.1 (1)	0.4 (3)
Musculo-skeletal system*	1.2 (4)	2.6 (8)	4.5 (16)	3.2 (9)	0.9 (2)	3.9 (5)	2.4 (22)	3.1 (22)	1.0 (9)	0.8 (6)	1.4 (13)	2.2 (16)	0.7 (6)	0.8 (6)
Polydactyly	0.0 (0)	1.0 (3)	0.8 (3)	1.4 (4)	0.0 (0)	1.6 (2)	0.3 (3)	1.3 (9)	0.2 (2)	0.6 (4)	0.1 (1)	0.7 (5)	0.0 (0)	0.1 (1)
Syndactyly	0.0 (0)	0.0 (0)	0.3 (1)	0.0 (0)	0.5 (1)	0.0 (0)	0.2 (2)	0.0 (0)	0.0 (0)	0.0 (0)	0.2 (2)	0.0 (0)	0.0 (0)	0.0 (0)
Rib or vertebral malformations	0.3 (1)	1.0 (3)	1.1 (4)	1.1 (3)	0.5 (1)	0.8 (1)	0.7 (6)	1.0 (7)	0.2 (2)	0.0 (0)	0.4 (4)	1.0 (7)	0.2 (2)	0.7 (5)
Agenesis, finger or major bones	0.6 (2)	0.0 (0)	1.1 (4)	0.0 (0)	0.0 (0)	0.0 (0)	0.7 (6)	0.0 (0)	0.2 (2)	0.0 (0)	0.4 (4)	0.0 (0)	0.2 (2)	0.0 (0)
Skull bone or suture defects	0.3 (1)	1.0 (3)	0.3 (1)	0.4 (1)	0.5 (1)	0.8 (1)	0.3 (3)	0.7 (5)	0.1 (1)	0.1 (1)	0.2 (2)	0.6 (4)	0.1 (1)	0.1 (1)
Chondrodystrophy	0.0 (0)	0.0 (0)	0.3 (1)	0.0 (0)	0.0 (0)	0.0 (0)	0.1 (1)	0.0 (0)	0.1 (1)	0.0 (0)	0.0 (0)	0.0 (0)	– (–)	– (–)
Agenesis, abdominal or major muscles	0.0 (0)	0.0 (0)	0.8 (3)	0.4 (1)	0.0 (0)	0.0 (0)	0.3 (3)	0.1 (1)	0.1 (1)	0.0 (0)	0.2 (2)	0.1 (1)	0.1 (1)	0.0 (0)
Other MSS malformations	0.0 (0)	0.3 (1)	0.3 (1)	0.0 (0)	0.0 (0)	0.8 (1)	0.1 (1)	0.3 (2)	0.1 (1)	0.0 (0)	0.0 (0)	0.3 (2)	0.0 (0)	0.3 (2)
Unspecified systems														
Diaphragmatic hernia	0.0 (0)	1.0 (3)	2.5 (9)	1.1 (3)	0.0 (0)	0.0 (0)	1.0 (9)	0.8 (6)	0.3 (3)	0.1 (1)	0.7 (6)	0.7 (5)	– (–)	– (–)
Omphalocele	0.6 (2)	2.0 (6)	1.1 (4)	0.7 (2)	0.5 (1)	0.0 (0)	0.8 (7)	1.1 (8)	0.3 (3)	0.0 (0)	0.4 (4)	1.1 (8)	– (–)	– (–)
Agenesis, spleen	0.6 (2)	0.0 (0)	0.0 (0)	0.7 (2)	0.0 (0)	0.0 (0)	0.2 (2)	0.3 (2)	0.0 (0)	0.0 (0)	0.2 (2)	0.3 (2)	– (–)	– (–)
Atresia, ext. auditory meatus	0.9 (3)	0.0 (0)	0.0 (0)	0.0 (0)	0.0 (0)	0.0 (0)	0.3 (3)	0.0 (0)	0.1 (1)	0.0 (0)	0.2 (2)	0.0 (0)	– (–)	– (–)
Other UNS malformations	0.3 (1)	1.0 (3)	0.3 (1)	0.4 (1)	0.0 (0)	0.0 (0)	0.2 (2)	0.6 (4)	0.0 (0)	0.0 (0)	0.2 (2)	0.6 (4)	– (–)	– (–)

	Stillbirth		Neonatal death		Infant and child death		All malformations		Single malformations		Multiple malformations		Multiple malformations within the system	
	M	F	M	F	M	F	M	F	M	F	M	F	M	F
Number of deaths	335	302	358	284	219	128	912	714	912	714	912	714	912	714
Group B														
Hydrocephalus, NOS	0.0 (0)	1.7 (5)	0.3 (1)	0.0 (0)	2.3 (5)	1.6 (2)	0.7 (6)	1.0 (7)	0.5 (5)	1.0 (7)	0.1 (1)	0.0 (0)	– (–)	– (–)
Microcephalus	0.3 (1)	0.0 (0)	0.3 (1)	0.0 (0)	0.5 (1)	0.8 (1)	0.3 (3)	0.1 (1)	0.2 (2)	0.0 (0)	0.1 (1)	0.1 (1)	– (–)	– (–)
Hypoplasia, L heart	0.0 (0)	0.7 (2)	0.6 (2)	2.5 (7)	0.5 (1)	0.0 (0)	0.3 (3)	1.3 (9)	0.3 (3)	0.7 (5)	0.0 (0)	0.6 (4)	– (–)	– (–)
Hypoplasia, R heart	0.0 (0)	0.0 (0)	0.0 (0)	0.7 (2)	0.9 (2)	0.8 (1)	0.2 (2)	0.4 (3)	0.1 (1)	0.0 (0)	0.1 (1)	0.4 (3)	– (–)	– (–)
Primary endocardial fibroelastosis	0.0 (0)	0.3 (1)	0.0 (0)	0.4 (1)	1.8 (4)	1.6 (2)	0.4 (4)	0.6 (4)	0.4 (4)	0.6 (4)	0.0 (0)	0.0 (0)	– (–)	– (–)
Anomalous venous drainage (not pulmonary)	0.0 (0)	0.0 (0)	0.6 (2)	0.0 (0)	0.9 (2)	0.0 (0)	0.4 (4)	0.0 (0)	0.2 (2)	0.0 (0)	0.2 (2)	0.0 (0)	– (–)	– (–)
Hypoplasia, lungs	0.6 (2)	5.0 (15)	4.2 (15)	2.8 (8)	0.0 (0)	0.0 (0)	1.9 (17)	3.2 (23)	1.0 (9)	1.3 (9)	0.9 (8)	2.0 (14)	– (–)	– (–)
Abnormal lobation, lung	1.5 (5)	1.3 (4)	2.0 (7)	2.8 (8)	0.5 (1)	1.6 (2)	1.4 (13)	2.0 (14)	1.0 (9)	1.4 (10)	0.4 (4)	0.6 (4)	– (–)	– (–)
Malrotation, bowel	1.5 (5)	2.0 (6)	2.8 (10)	1.4 (4)	0.5 (1)	3.1 (4)	1.8 (16)	2.0 (14)	0.9 (8)	0.7 (5)	0.9 (8)	1.3 (9)	– (–)	– (–)
Hypoplasia, kidney	0.6 (2)	0.7 (2)	0.3 (1)	0.0 (0)	0.5 (1)	0.0 (0)	0.4 (4)	0.3 (2)	0.3 (3)	0.0 (0)	0.1 (1)	0.3 (2)	– (–)	– (–)
Hypospadias	1.2 (4)	– (–)	0.3 (1)	– (–)	0.0 (0)	– (–)	0.5 (5)	– (–)	0.3 (3)	– (–)	0.2 (2)	– (–)	– (–)	– (–)
Talipes, all types	0.6 (2)	2.0 (6)	2.8 (10)	3.2 (9)	1.8 (4)	1.6 (2)	1.8 (16)	2.4 (17)	1.3 (12)	0.8 (6)	0.4 (4)	1.5 (11)	– (–)	– (–)
Kyphosis or scoliosis	0.0 (0)	0.7 (2)	1.1 (4)	0.7 (2)	0.0 (0)	0.8 (1)	0.4 (4)	0.7 (5)	0.1 (1)	0.0 (0)	0.3 (3)	0.7 (5)	– (–)	– (–)

Arthrogryposis	0.3 (1)	0.0 (0)	1.1 (4)	0.4 (1)	0.5 (1)	0.0 (0)	0.7 (6)	0.1 (1)	0.3 (3)	0.1 (1)	0.3 (3)	0.0 (0)	— (—)	— (—)	— (—)
Inguinal hernia	0.0 (0)	0.0 (0)	0.3 (1)	0.0 (0)	0.9 (2)	0.0 (0)	0.3 (3)	0.0 (0)	0.2 (2)	0.0 (0)	0.1 (1)	0.0 (0)	— (—)	— (—)	— (—)
Accessory spleen	3.3 (11)	3.3 (10)	4.2 (15)	6.7 (19)	2.7 (6)	5.5 (7)	3.5 (32)	5.0 (36)	2.9 (26)	3.4 (24)	0.7 (6)	1.7 (12)	— (—)	— (—)	— (—)
Mongolism	0.0 (0)	0.3 (1)	0.3 (1)	0.7 (2)	2.7 (6)	2.3 (3)	0.8 (7)	0.8 (6)	0.4 (4)	0.8 (6)	0.3 (3)	0.0 (0)	— (—)	— (—)	— (—)
Trisomy 13 through 18	0.0 (0)	0.3 (1)	0.0 (0)	0.0 (0)	0.0 (0)	1.6 (2)	0.0 (0)	0.4 (3)	0.0 (0)	0.0 (0)	0.0 (0)	0.4 (3)	— (—)	— (—)	— (—)
Coloboma	0.0 (0)	0.0 (0)	0.3 (1)	0.4 (1)	0.0 (0)	0.8 (1)	0.1 (1)	0.3 (2)	0.1 (1)	0.0 (0)	0.0 (0)	0.3 (2)	— (—)	— (—)	— (—)
Microphthalmia	0.0 (0)	0.0 (0)	0.0 (0)	0.4 (1)	0.0 (0)	0.8 (1)	0.0 (0)	0.3 (2)	0.0 (0)	0.0 (0)	0.0 (0)	0.3 (2)	— (—)	— (—)	— (—)
Abnormal position or shape, ear	1.2 (4)	0.7 (2)	1.4 (5)	1.1 (3)	0.5 (1)	0.8 (1)	1.1 (10)	0.8 (6)	0.8 (7)	0.3 (2)	0.3 (3)	0.6 (4)	— (—)	— (—)	— (—)
Webbed neck	0.0 (0)	0.3 (1)	0.3 (1)	1.4 (4)	0.5 (1)	0.0 (0)	0.2 (2)	0.7 (5)	0.0 (0)	0.3 (2)	0.2 (2)	0.4 (3)	— (—)	— (—)	— (—)

* Numbers indicate overall count of cases in which organ system was involved.

178

Table 3-B Frequency of specific malformations by sex, race and multiplicity of malformations

	White								Negro							
	All malformations		Single malformations		Multiple malformations		Multiple malformations within the system		All malformations		Single malformations		Multiple malformations		Multiple malformations within the system	
	M	F	M	F	M	F	M	F	M	F	M	F	M	F	M	F
Number of deaths	314	277	314	277	314	277	314	277	525	382	525	382	525	382	525	382
Group A																
Central nervous system*	2.9 (9)	6.5 (18)	1.6 (5)	1.4 (4)	1.3 (4)	5.1 (14)	0.6 (2)	2.9 (8)	1.1 (6)	1.3 (5)	1.0 (5)	0.8 (3)	0.2 (1)	0.4 (2)	0.6 (3)	0.5 (2)
Anencephaly	1.6 (5)	4.0 (11)	1.3 (4)	1.4 (4)	0.3 (1)	2.5 (7)	0.0 (0)	1.8 (5)	0.2 (1)	0.3 (1)	0.2 (1)	0.3 (1)	0.0 (0)	0.0 (0)	0.0 (0)	0.0 (0)
Arnold-Chiari	0.6 (2)	1.1 (3)	0.0 (0)	0.0 (0)	0.6 (2)	1.1 (3)	– (–)	– (–)	0.4 (2)	0.5 (2)	0.4 (2)	0.3 (1)	0.0 (0)	0.3 (1)	– (–)	– (–)
Spina bifida, all types	0.0 (0)	2.5 (7)	0.0 (0)	0.0 (0)	0.0 (0)	2.5 (7)	0.0 (0)	1.8 (5)	0.0 (0)	0.0 (0)	0.0 (0)	0.0 (0)	0.0 (0)	0.0 (0)	0.0 (0)	0.0 (0)
Other CNS malformations	1.0 (3)	1.1 (3)	0.3 (1)	0.0 (0)	0.6 (2)	1.1 (3)	0.3 (1)	0.7 (2)	1.0 (5)	0.8 (3)	0.6 (3)	0.5 (2)	0.4 (2)	0.3 (1)	0.6 (3)	0.3 (1)
Cardiovascular system*	8.3 (26)	9.7 (27)	6.4 (20)	4.0 (11)	1.9 (6)	5.8 (16)	5.4 (17)	7.6 (21)	5.3 (28)	4.2 (16)	3.6 (19)	2.9 (11)	1.7 (9)	1.3 (5)	2.3 (12)	2.6 (10)
Ventricular septal defect	3.8 (12)	4.0 (11)	3.2 (10)	1.4 (4)	0.6 (2)	2.5 (7)	2.9 (9)	4.0 (11)	2.1 (11)	1.0 (4)	1.5 (8)	0.5 (2)	0.6 (3)	0.5 (2)	1.1 (6)	0.8 (3)
Atresia or stenosis, L valves	0.6 (2)	1.8 (5)	0.6 (2)	1.4 (4)	0.0 (0)	0.4 (1)	0.3 (1)	1.8 (5)	0.4 (2)	1.0 (4)	0.4 (2)	0.5 (2)	0.0 (0)	0.5 (2)	0.2 (1)	0.5 (2)
Atresia or stenosis, R valves	1.0 (3)	0.7 (2)	0.6 (2)	0.4 (1)	0.3 (1)	0.4 (1)	1.0 (3)	0.7 (2)	1.0 (5)	0.3 (1)	0.6 (3)	0.0 (0)	0.4 (2)	0.3 (1)	0.8 (4)	0.3 (1)
Other valve anomalies	1.6 (5)	2.2 (6)	1.6 (5)	0.7 (2)	0.0 (0)	1.4 (4)	0.3 (1)	2.2 (6)	0.0 (0)	0.0 (0)	0.0 (0)	0.0 (0)	0.0 (0)	0.0 (0)	0.0 (0)	0.0 (0)
Atrial septal defect	1.9 (6)	1.4 (4)	1.3 (4)	0.7 (2)	0.6 (2)	0.7 (2)	1.9 (6)	0.7 (2)	0.8 (4)	0.5 (2)	0.6 (3)	0.5 (2)	0.2 (1)	0.0 (0)	0.0 (0)	0.0 (0)
Tetralogy of Fallot	0.0 (0)	0.4 (1)	0.0 (0)	0.0 (0)	0.0 (0)	0.4 (1)	– (–)	– (–)	0.0 (0)	0.5 (2)	0.0 (0)	0.3 (1)	0.0 (0)	0.3 (1)	– (–)	– (–)

Malformation	1	2	3	4	5	6	7	8	9	10	11	12	13	14	15	16
Atrio-ventricularis communis	1.3 (4)	1.8 (5)	1.0 (3)	0.7 (2)	0.3 (1)	1.1 (3)	– (–)	– (–)	0.2 (1)	0.3 (1)	0.2 (1)	0.3 (1)	0.0 (0)	0.0 (0)	– (–)	– (–)
Preductal coarctation	1.6 (5)	2.2 (6)	1.0 (3)	0.4 (1)	0.6 (2)	1.8 (5)	1.3 (4)	1.1 (3)	0.6 (3)	0.8 (3)	0.4 (2)	0.8 (3)	0.2 (1)	0.2 (1)	0.2 (1)	0.3 (1)
Truncus communis	0.6 (2)	0.7 (2)	0.6 (2)	0.4 (1)	0.0 (0)	0.4 (1)	0.6 (2)	0.7 (2)	0.4 (2)	0.0 (0)	0.2 (1)	0.0 (0)	0.2 (1)	0.0 (0)	0.4 (2)	0.0 (0)
Transposition, great vessels	2.2 (7)	0.4 (1)	1.9 (6)	0.0 (0)	0.3 (1)	0.4 (1)	2.5 (7)	0.4 (1)	0.6 (3)	0.0 (0)	0.4 (2)	0.0 (0)	0.2 (1)	0.0 (0)	0.6 (3)	0.0 (0)
Vascular ring	0.0 (0)	1.1 (3)	0.0 (0)	0.4 (1)	0.0 (0)	0.7 (2)	0.0 (0)	1.1 (3)	0.6 (3)	0.5 (2)	0.2 (1)	0.3 (1)	0.4 (2)	0.0 (0)	0.4 (2)	0.5 (2)
Anomalous pulmonary venous drainage	0.3 (1)	0.7 (2)	0.3 (1)	0.4 (1)	0.0 (0)	0.4 (1)	0.3 (1)	0.7 (2)	0.4 (2)	0.3 (1)	0.2 (1)	0.3 (1)	0.2 (1)	0.3 (1)	0.4 (2)	0.3 (1)
Patent ductus arteriosus	1.0 (3)	1.1 (3)	0.6 (2)	0.4 (1)	0.3 (1)	0.7 (2)	1.0 (3)	1.4 (4)	1.0 (5)	0.5 (2)	0.8 (4)	0.5 (2)	0.2 (1)	0.0 (0)	0.6 (3)	0.5 (2)
Other CVS malformations	0.3 (1)	1.8 (5)	0.0 (0)	0.7 (2)	0.3 (1)	1.1 (3)	0.3 (1)	1.8 (5)	1.3 (7)	0.5 (2)	0.2 (1)	0.3 (1)	1.2 (6)	0.3 (1)	1.1 (6)	0.3 (1)
Other blood vessels	3.5 (11)	4.0 (11)	2.2 (7)	1.8 (5)	1.3 (4)	2.2 (6)	– (–)	– (–)	1.5 (8)	2.1 (8)	1.0 (5)	0.5 (2)	0.6 (3)	1.6 (6)	– (–)	– (–)
Arterio-venous aneurysm	0.3 (1)	0.0 (0)	0.3 (1)	0.0 (0)	0.0 (0)	0.0 (0)	– (–)	– (–)	0.2 (1)	0.0 (0)	0.2 (1)	0.0 (0)	0.0 (0)	0.0 (0)	– (–)	– (–)
Single umbilical artery	3.2 (10)	4.0 (11)	1.9 (6)	1.8 (5)	1.3 (4)	2.2 (6)	– (–)	– (–)	1.3 (7)	2.1 (8)	0.8 (4)	0.5 (2)	0.6 (3)	1.6 (6)	– (–)	– (–)
Respiratory system*	0.3 (1)	0.4 (1)	0.0 (0)	0.0 (0)	0.3 (1)	0.4 (1)	0.0 (0)	0.0 (0)	0.2 (1)	0.3 (1)	0.0 (0)	0.3 (1)	0.2 (1)	0.0 (0)	0.0 (0)	0.0 (0)
Genitourinary system*	3.2 (10)	5.8 (16)	1.6 (5)	1.1 (3)	1.6 (5)	4.7 (13)	1.0 (3)	1.8 (5)	4.6 (24)	3.7 (14)	1.9 (10)	1.6 (6)	2.7 (14)	2.1 (8)	1.1 (6)	1.0 (4)
Polycystic kidney	0.6 (2)	2.2 (6)	0.6 (2)	0.4 (1)	0.0 (0)	1.8 (5)	0.3 (1)	1.4 (4)	1.7 (9)	1.8 (7)	0.6 (3)	0.8 (3)	1.2 (6)	1.0 (4)	1.3 (7)	0.5 (2)
Atresia, ureter or urethra	2.2 (7)	1.1 (3)	0.6 (2)	0.4 (1)	1.6 (5)	0.7 (2)	0.6 (2)	0.4 (1)	2.3 (12)	0.8 (3)	1.0 (5)	0.3 (1)	1.3 (7)	0.5 (2)	1.3 (7)	0.5 (2)
Agenesis, kidney	1.3 (4)	0.4 (1)	1.0 (3)	0.0 (0)	0.3 (1)	0.4 (1)	0.3 (1)	0.4 (1)	0.2 (1)	0.3 (1)	0.0 (0)	0.0 (0)	0.2 (1)	0.3 (1)	0.0 (0)	0.3 (1)
Horseshoe kidney	0.3 (1)	1.1 (3)	0.0 (0)	0.4 (1)	0.3 (1)	0.7 (2)	0.0 (0)	0.0 (0)	0.4 (2)	0.0 (0)	0.4 (2)	0.0 (0)	0.0 (0)	0.0 (0)	0.0 (0)	0.0 (0)
Double ureter	0.0 (0)	0.0 (0)	0.0 (0)	0.0 (0)	0.0 (0)	0.0 (0)	0.0 (0)	0.0 (0)	0.4 (2)	1.0 (4)	0.4 (2)	0.8 (3)	0.0 (0)	0.3 (1)	0.0 (0)	0.0 (0)

	White								Negro							
	All malformations		Single malformations		Multiple malformations		Multiple malformations within the system		All malformations		Single malformations		Multiple malformations		Multiple malformations within the system	
	M	F	M	F	M	F	M	F	M	F	M	F	M	F	M	F
Number of deaths	314	277	314	277	314	277	314	277	525	382	525	382	525	382	525	382
Agenesis, urinary bladder	0.3 (1)	0.0 (0)	0.0 (0)	0.0 (0)	0.3 (1)	0.0 (0)	0.3 (1)	0.0 (0)	0.0 (0)	0.0 (0)	0.0 (0)	0.0 (0)	0.0 (0)	0.0 (0)	0.0 (0)	0.0 (0)
Persistent cloaca	0.0 (0)	0.0 (0)	0.0 (0)	0.0 (0)	0.0 (0)	0.0 (0)	- (-)	- (-)	0.2 (1)	0.3 (1)	0.0 (0)	0.0 (0)	0.2 (1)	0.3 (1)	- (-)	- (-)
Agenesis, uterus or ovary	- (-)	0.4 (1)	- (-)	0.0 (0)	- (-)	0.4 (1)	- (-)	0.0 (0)	- (-)	0.5 (2)	- (-)	0.0 (0)	- (-)	0.5 (2)	- (-)	0.5 (2)
Bicornuate uterus	- (-)	1.4 (4)	- (-)	0.4 (1)	- (-)	1.1 (3)	- (-)	0.7 (2)	- (-)	0.0 (0)	- (-)	0.0 (0)	- (-)	0.0 (0)	- (-)	0.0 (0)
Pseudohermaphroditism	0.0 (0)	0.4 (1)	0.0 (0)	0.0 (0)	0.0 (0)	0.4 (1)	- (-)	- (-)	0.0 (0)	0.0 (0)	0.0 (0)	0.0 (0)	0.0 (0)	0.0 (0)	- (-)	- (-)
Other GUS malformations	0.6 (2)	1.1 (3)	0.0 (0)	0.0 (0)	0.6 (2)	1.1 (3)	0.3 (1)	0.4 (1)	0.2 (1)	0.3 (1)	0.0 (0)	0.0 (0)	0.2 (1)	0.3 (1)	0.2 (1)	0.3 (1)
Digestive system*	4.5 (14)	4.7 (13)	1.6 (5)	1.4 (4)	2.9 (9)	3.2 (9)	0.3 (1)	0.4 (1)	2.7 (14)	2.4 (9)	1.1 (6)	0.5 (2)	1.5 (8)	1.8 (7)	0.6 (3)	0.8 (3)
Cleft palate	1.0 (3)	0.7 (2)	0.0 (0)	0.0 (0)	1.0 (3)	0.7 (2)	0.0 (0)	0.0 (0)	0.0 (0)	0.3 (1)	0.0 (0)	0.3 (1)	0.0 (0)	0.0 (0)	0.0 (0)	0.0 (0)
Cleft palate with cleft lip	0.0 (0)	0.4 (1)	0.0 (0)	0.0 (0)	0.0 (0)	0.4 (1)	- (-)	- (-)	0.6 (3)	0.3 (1)	0.4 (2)	0.0 (0)	0.2 (1)	0.3 (1)	- (-)	- (-)
Cleft lip	0.0 (0)	0.4 (1)	0.0 (0)	0.4 (1)	0.0 (0)	0.0 (0)	0.0 (0)	0.0 (0)	0.0 (0)	0.3 (1)	0.0 (0)	0.0 (0)	0.0 (0)	0.3 (1)	0.0 (0)	0.0 (0)
Tracheo-esophageal fistula	0.0 (0)	0.0 (0)	0.0 (0)	0.0 (0)	0.0 (0)	0.0 (0)	0.0 (0)	0.0 (0)	0.2 (1)	0.3 (1)	0.0 (0)	0.0 (0)	0.2 (1)	0.3 (1)	0.0 (0)	0.3 (1)
Atresia, small bowel	1.0 (3)	0.0 (0)	0.3 (1)	0.0 (0)	0.6 (2)	0.0 (0)	0.0 (0)	0.0 (0)	0.2 (1)	0.0 (0)	0.2 (1)	0.0 (0)	0.0 (0)	0.0 (0)	0.0 (0)	0.0 (0)
Meckel's diverticulum	1.3 (4)	1.8 (5)	0.6 (2)	0.4 (1)	0.6 (2)	1.4 (4)	0.0 (0)	0.7 (2)	0.8 (4)	0.5 (2)	0.2 (1)	0.3 (1)	0.6 (3)	0.3 (1)	0.2 (1)	0.3 (1)
Hirschsprung's disease	1.0 (3)	0.4 (1)	0.6 (2)	0.4 (1)	0.3 (1)	0.0 (0)	0.0 (0)	0.0 (0)	0.4 (2)	0.3 (1)	0.2 (1)	0.0 (0)	0.2 (1)	0.3 (1)	0.0 (0)	0.0 (0)

	C1	C2	C3	C4	C5	C6	C7	C8	C9	C10	C11	C12	C13	C14	C15	C16
Imperforate anus	0.3 (1)	0.4 (1)	0.0 (0)	0.0 (0)	0.3 (1)	0.4 (1)	0.3 (1)	0.0 (0)	0.2 (1)	0.5 (2)	0.0 (0)	0.0 (0)	0.2 (1)	0.5 (2)	0.0 (0)	0.3 (1)
Agenesis, gallbladder	0.6 (2)	0.4 (1)	0.0 (0)	0.0 (0)	0.6 (2)	0.4 (1)	0.3 (1)	0.4 (1)	0.0 (0)	0.3 (1)	0.0 (0)	0.0 (0)	0.0 (0)	0.3 (1)	0.0 (0)	0.0 (0)
Atresia, bile duct	0.0 (0)	0.4 (1)	0.0 (0)	0.0 (0)	0.0 (0)	0.4 (1)	0.0 (0)	0.0 (0)	0.2 (1)	0.3 (1)	0.2 (1)	0.0 (0)	0.0 (0)	0.3 (1)	0.0 (0)	0.0 (0)
Other DS malformations	0.3 (1)	0.7 (2)	0.0 (0)	0.0 (0)	0.3 (1)	0.7 (2)	0.3 (1)	0.0 (0)	0.2 (1)	0.5 (2)	0.0 (0)	0.0 (0)	0.2 (1)	0.5 (2)	0.0 (0)	0.8 (3)
Musculo-skeletal system*	2.2 (7)	4.7 (13)	1.3 (4)	0.7 (2)	1.0 (3)	4.0 (11)	0.0 (0)	1.8 (5)	2.5 (13)	2.1 (8)	0.8 (4)	1.0 (4)	1.7 (9)	1.0 (4)	1.1 (6)	0.3 (1)
Polydactyly	0.0 (0)	1.8 (5)	0.0 (0)	0.7 (2)	0.0 (0)	1.1 (3)	0.0 (0)	0.4 (1)	0.6 (3)	0.8 (3)	0.4 (2)	0.5 (2)	0.2 (1)	0.3 (1)	0.0 (0)	0.0 (0)
Syndactyly	0.0 (0)	0.0 (0)	0.0 (0)	0.0 (0)	0.0 (0)	0.0 (0)	0.0 (0)	0.0 (0)	0.4 (2)	0.0 (0)	0.2 (1)	0.0 (0)	0.2 (1)	0.0 (0)	0.0 (0)	0.0 (0)
Rib or vertebral malformations	1.0 (3)	2.2 (6)	0.6 (2)	0.0 (0)	0.3 (1)	2.2 (6)	0.0 (0)	1.4 (4)	0.4 (2)	0.3 (1)	0.0 (0)	0.0 (0)	0.4 (2)	0.3 (1)	0.4 (2)	0.3 (1)
Agenesis, finger or major bones	1.0 (3)	0.0 (0)	0.6 (2)	0.0 (0)	0.3 (1)	0.0 (0)	0.0 (0)	0.0 (0)	0.6 (3)	0.0 (0)	0.0 (0)	0.0 (0)	0.6 (3)	0.0 (0)	0.4 (2)	0.0 (0)
Skull bone or suture defects	0.3 (1)	1.1 (3)	0.0 (0)	0.0 (0)	0.3 (1)	1.1 (3)	0.0 (0)	0.4 (1)	0.2 (1)	0.5 (2)	0.2 (1)	0.3 (1)	0.0 (0)	0.3 (1)	0.0 (0)	0.0 (0)
Chondrodystrophy	0.0 (0)	0.0 (0)	0.0 (0)	0.0 (0)	0.0 (0)	0.0 (0)	– (–)	– (–)	0.2 (1)	0.0 (0)	0.2 (1)	0.0 (0)	0.0 (0)	0.0 (0)	– (–)	– (–)
Agenesis, abdominal or major muscles	0.0 (0)	0.0 (0)	0.0 (0)	0.0 (0)	0.0 (0)	0.0 (0)	0.0 (0)	0.0 (0)	0.6 (3)	0.3 (1)	0.2 (1)	0.0 (0)	0.4 (2)	0.3 (1)	0.2 (1)	0.0 (0)
Other MSS malformations	0.0 (0)	0.7 (2)	0.0 (0)	0.0 (0)	0.0 (0)	0.7 (2)	0.0 (0)	0.7 (2)	0.8 (4)	0.3 (1)	0.4 (2)	0.0 (0)	0.4 (2)	0.3 (1)	0.2 (1)	0.0 (0)
Unspecified systems																
Diaphragmatic hernia	1.9 (6)	1.1 (3)	0.6 (2)	0.0 (0)	1.3 (4)	1.1 (3)	– (–)	– (–)	0.6 (3)	0.3 (1)	0.2 (1)	0.3 (1)	0.4 (2)	0.0 (0)	– (–)	– (–)
Omphalocele	0.6 (2)	2.5 (7)	0.3 (1)	0.0 (0)	0.3 (1)	2.5 (7)	– (–)	– (–)	1.0 (5)	0.3 (1)	0.4 (2)	0.0 (0)	0.6 (3)	0.3 (1)	– (–)	– (–)
Agenesis, spleen	0.3 (1)	0.7 (2)	0.0 (0)	0.0 (0)	0.3 (1)	0.7 (2)	– (–)	– (–)	0.2 (1)	0.0 (0)	0.0 (0)	0.0 (0)	0.2 (1)	0.0 (0)	– (–)	– (–)
Atresia, ext. auditory meatus	0.6 (2)	0.0 (0)	0.3 (1)	0.0 (0)	0.3 (1)	0.0 (0)	– (–)	– (–)	0.2 (1)	0.0 (0)	0.0 (0)	0.0 (0)	0.2 (1)	0.0 (0)	– (–)	– (–)

	White								Negro							
	All malformations		Single malformations		Multiple malformations		Multiple malformations within the system		All malformations		Single malformations		Multiple malformations		Multiple malformations within the system	
	M	F	M	F	M	F	M	F	M	F	M	F	M	F	M	F
	314	277	314	277	314	277	314	277	525	382	525	382	525	382	525	382
Other UNS malformations	0.0 (0)	0.7 (2)	0.0 (0)	0.0 (0)	0.0 (0)	0.7 (2)	– (–)	– (–)	0.4 (2)	0.3 (1)	0.0 (0)	0.0 (0)	0.4 (2)	0.3 (1)	– (–)	– (–)
Group B																
Hydrocephalus, NOS	0.0 (0)	1.1 (3)	0.0 (0)	1.1 (3)	0.0 (0)	0.0 (0)	– (–)	– (–)	0.6 (3)	0.8 (3)	0.6 (3)	0.8 (3)	0.0 (0)	0.0 (0)	– (–)	– (–)
Microcephalus	0.0 (0)	0.4 (1)	0.0 (0)	0.0 (0)	0.0 (0)	0.4 (1)	– (–)	– (–)	0.2 (1)	0.0 (0)	0.0 (0)	0.0 (0)	0.2 (1)	0.0 (0)	– (–)	– (–)
Hypoplasia, L heart	0.3 (1)	1.4 (4)	0.3 (1)	0.7 (2)	0.0 (0)	0.7 (2)	– (–)	– (–)	0.4 (2)	1.0 (4)	0.4 (2)	0.5 (2)	0.0 (0)	0.5 (2)	– (–)	– (–)
Hypoplasia, R heart	0.3 (1)	0.4 (1)	0.0 (0)	0.0 (0)	0.3 (1)	0.4 (1)	– (–)	– (–)	0.2 (1)	0.3 (1)	0.2 (1)	0.0 (0)	0.0 (0)	0.3 (1)	– (–)	– (–)
Primary endocardial fibro-elastosis	0.0 (0)	0.7 (2)	0.0 (0)	0.7 (2)	0.0 (0)	0.0 (0)	– (–)	– (–)	0.6 (3)	0.5 (2)	0.6 (3)	0.5 (2)	0.0 (0)	0.0 (0)	– (–)	– (–)
Anomalous venous drainage (not pulmonary)	1.0 (3)	0.0 (0)	0.6 (2)	0.0 (0)	0.3 (1)	0.0 (0)	– (–)	– (–)	0.0 (0)	0.0 (0)	0.0 (0)	0.0 (0)	0.0 (0)	0.0 (0)	– (–)	– (–)
Hypoplasia, lungs	3.2 (10)	5.4 (15)	1.6 (5)	1.1 (3)	1.6 (5)	4.3 (12)	– (–)	– (–)	1.3 (7)	1.3 (5)	0.8 (4)	0.8 (3)	0.6 (3)	0.5 (2)	– (–)	– (–)
Abnormal lobation, lung	2.5 (8)	1.8 (5)	1.9 (6)	0.7 (2)	0.6 (2)	1.1 (3)	– (–)	– (–)	1.0 (5)	2.1 (8)	0.6 (3)	2.1 (8)	0.4 (2)	0.0 (0)	– (–)	– (–)
Malrotation, bowel	2.2 (7)	3.2 (9)	1.3 (4)	0.7 (2)	1.0 (3)	2.5 (7)	– (–)	– (–)	1.5 (8)	0.8 (3)	0.8 (4)	0.8 (3)	0.8 (4)	0.0 (0)	– (–)	– (–)
Hypoplasia, kidney	0.3 (1)	0.0 (0)	0.0 (0)	0.0 (0)	0.3 (1)	0.0 (0)	– (–)	– (–)	0.6 (3)	0.5 (2)	0.6 (3)	0.0 (0)	0.0 (0)	0.5 (2)	– (–)	– (–)
Hypospadias	0.3 (1)	– (–)	0.3 (1)	– (–)	0.0 (0)	– (–)	– (–)	– (–)	0.8 (4)	– (–)	0.4 (2)	– (–)	0.4 (2)	– (–)	– (–)	– (–)
Talipes, all types	2.2 (7)	4.7 (13)	1.6 (5)	1.1 (3)	0.6 (2)	3.6 (10)	– (–)	– (–)	1.5 (8)	0.8 (3)	1.1 (6)	0.5 (2)	0.4 (2)	0.3 (1)	– (–)	– (–)

Kyphosis or scoliosis	1.0 (3)	1.4 (4)	0.3 (1)	0.0 (0)	0.6 (2)	1.4 (4)	– (–)	– (–)	0.2 (1)	0.3 (1)	0.0 (0)	0.0 (0)	0.2 (1)	0.3 (1)	– (–)	– (–)
Arthrogryposis	1.0 (3)	0.0 (0)	0.6 (2)	0.0 (0)	0.3 (1)	0.0 (0)	– (–)	– (–)	0.6 (3)	0.3 (1)	0.2 (1)	0.3 (1)	0.4 (2)	0.0 (0)	– (–)	– (–)
Inguinal hernia	0.3 (1)	0.0 (0)	0.0 (0)	0.0 (0)	0.3 (1)	0.0 (0)	– (–)	– (–)	0.4 (2)	0.0 (0)	0.4 (2)	0.0 (0)	0.0 (0)	0.0 (0)	– (–)	– (–)
Accessory spleen	5.1 (16)	5.8 (16)	3.8 (12)	3.2 (9)	1.3 (4)	2.5 (7)	– (–)	– (–)	3.0 (16)	5.0 (19)	2.7 (14)	3.9 (15)	0.4 (2)	1.0 (4)	– (–)	– (–)
Mongolism	0.6 (2)	1.1 (3)	0.3 (1)	1.1 (3)	0.3 (1)	0.0 (0)	– (–)	– (–)	1.0 (5)	0.8 (3)	0.6 (3)	0.8 (3)	0.4 (2)	0.0 (0)	– (–)	– (–)
Trisomy 13 through 18	0.0 (0)	0.7 (2)	0.0 (0)	0.0 (0)	0.0 (0)	0.7 (2)	– (–)	– (–)	0.0 (0)	0.3 (1)	0.0 (0)	0.0 (0)	0.0 (0)	0.3 (1)	– (–)	– (–)
Coloboma	0.0 (0)	0.4 (1)	0.0 (0)	0.0 (0)	0.0 (0)	0.4 (1)	– (–)	– (–)	0.2 (1)	0.3 (1)	0.2 (1)	0.0 (0)	0.0 (0)	0.3 (1)	– (–)	– (–)
Microphthalmia	0.0 (0)	0.4 (1)	0.0 (0)	0.0 (0)	0.0 (0)	0.4 (1)	– (–)	– (–)	0.0 (0)	0.3 (1)	0.0 (0)	0.0 (0)	0.0 (0)	0.3 (1)	– (–)	– (–)
Abnormal position or shape, ear	1.0 (3)	1.1 (3)	0.6 (2)	0.4 (1)	0.3 (1)	0.7 (2)	– (–)	– (–)	1.0 (5)	0.3 (1)	0.6 (3)	0.3 (1)	0.4 (2)	0.0 (0)	– (–)	– (–)
Webbed neck	0.3 (1)	1.1 (3)	0.0 (0)	0.0 (0)	0.3 (1)	1.1 (3)	– (–)	– (–)	0.0 (0)	0.3 (1)	0.0 (0)	0.0 (0)	0.0 (0)	0.0 (0)	– (–)	– (–)

* Numbers indicate overall count of cases in which organ system was involved.

the hospital. Because there is a possibility of bias in the direction of malformed cases, the malformation rates in white infant and child deaths may be artificially high.

CNS Malformations and stillbirths

As was emphasized above, multiple malformations were frequent in white females especially in stillbirths (Table 2-B).   Central nervous system (CNS) malformations were high in female stillbirths (Table 3-A) especially in whites (Table 3-B).   In contrast, involvement of the CNS was far less common in Negroes of either sex and in white males.   Of the 14 multiply malformed white female stillbirths 11 had CNS malformations of which 7 were anencephaly. Reports from the British Isles[1,4,18,20], this country[3], and most of the 24 different centers in the world which participated in the WHO project[18], all show a female preponderance of congenital malformations among stillbirths.   The role of CNS malformations is emphasized in the data from the British Isles[1,4,10,18], which report some of the highest incidences of CNS malformations.   WOOLF[20] in addition demonstrates a distinct female excess in multiple malformation among stillbirths (sex ratio 0.60).   Murphy[13], in a graphic presentation of the influence of maternal origin, shows a malformation rate of over 130/1000 deaths where the mother's origin was England, Scotland, or Wales, compared to the lowest rate of slightly over 20/l000 deaths in Negroes.   One would suspect that the high rate in the former group was mainly the effect of CNS malformations.

Single and cardiovascular malformations in males

The high incidence of single malformations in male neonatal deaths (Table 2-B) arouses curiosity as to which organ system was largely responsible for this picture as it is possible that if the malformation were surgically correctable, some of these male deaths could have been prevented or at least delayed by surgery.   It is noteworthy that nearly half of the cases with cardiovascular malformations died during the neonatal period, in this series (Table 3-A). When males were affected it was usually as a single malformation, i.e., limited to the cardiovascular system.   Since the cardiovascular system was the system most frequently involved by malformations (Table 4) the possibility of salvaging affected males is a challenging one.   It may be noted that transposition of the great vessels shows a distinct male preponderance (Tables 3-A and B).

Genito-urinary malformations in male Negroes

For the most part the incidence of each malformation was low in Negroes, but involvement of the genito-urinary system, in particular atresia of the ureter or urethra, was relatively common in male Negroes (Table 3-B).   The majority of these deaths occurred in the early neonatal period (Table 3-A) implying that involvement was severe or bilateral.   Unlike cardiovascular malformations, genito-urinary malformations were of the multiple variety in 50 % or more of the involved males.   The numbers are small and caution is again advised in the comparison of these numbers with normative data.   It is well known that many of the less severe genito-urinary malformations are not discovered till childhood or later in life.

Frequency of organ system involvement

In Table 4 the malformed case was entered only once in the involved system, regardless of the number of malformations within the system.   The cardiovascular system was most frequently involved in both sexes and races (38.1 % to 47.4 %). In white females, the CNS was of second order of importance, whereas in Negroes of either sex the genito-urinary system took second place. The CNS was relatively infrequently involved in white males and in Negroes, especially Negro males (11.9 %), compared to white females (31.6 %). According to the statistics of the WHO (1956)[8] the mortality rates due to malformations of the circulatory system headed the list of organ systems at every age, especially in males (over 40 %); in females it was sometimes preceded by deaths due to malformations of the CNS. DAVIS and POTTER's figures[2] covering 240 cases of perinatal deaths show that CNS malformations were most frequent as a cause of death (40 %) followed by cardiac malformations (16 %).

Birth weight and gestational age

According to gestational age there was a stepwise increase in nearly all malformation rates with increments of gestational age (Table 5). All malformation rates were highest in the 38th week or more gestational age group.

Table 4 Frequency of organ system involvement in malformed cases by race and sex

	White		Negro	
	Male	Female	Male	Female
Total No. of malformed cases	68	57	68	42
Central nervous system	13.2 (9)	31.6(18)	8.8 (6)	11.9 (5)
Cardiovascular system	38.2(26)	47.4(27)	41.2(28)	38.1(16)
Other blood vessels	16.2(11)	19.3(11)	11.8 (8)	19.0 (8)
Respiratory system	1.5 (1)	1.8 (1)	1.5 (1)	2.4 (1)
Genito-urinary system	14.7(10)	28.1(16)	35.3(24)	33.3(14)
Digestive system	20.6(14)	22.8(13)	20.6(14)	21.4 (9)
Musculo-skeletal system	10.3 (7)	22.8(13)	19.1(13)	19.0 (8)
Unspecified system	16.2(11)	24.6(14)	16.2(11)	7.1 (3)

Note: Numbers in parentheses are number of malformed cases.

Higher frequencies in the lower birth weight groups were noted in white males with multiple malformations and in white females suggesting the possibility of runting of some babies in these groups (Table 6). With the exception of multiply malformed white females, malformation rates were lowest in the lowest birth weight (1500 grams or less) and gestational age (31 weeks or less) groups for both races and sexes. This implies that malformations play a relatively small role in the premature compared to the mature baby that dies. In view of these findings the widely accepted association between malformations and prematurity may have to be reexamined. Such a reportedly higher incidence of malformations in prematures as a whole may in part be explained by the higher mortality in this group, with resulting greater chance for discovery by postmortem examination of internal defects otherwise missed in a surviving infant. In addition malformed infants could be mature by gestational age but premature by birth weight (runted)[5], as was suggested previously. Another implication of the increasing malformation incidence with increasing gestational age is that the

Table 5 Malformation rates by gestational

Gestational age (weeks)	All races								Number of deaths	
	Number of deaths		All malf.		Single malf.		Mult. malf.			
	M	F	M	F	M	F	M	F	M	F
31 or less	323	248	10.2 (33)	8.5 (21)	7.4 (24)	4.8 (12)	2.8 (9)	3.6 (9)	103	88
32–37	228	198	14.0 (32)	13.6 (27)	10.5 (24)	7.1 (14)	3.5 (8)	6.6 (13)	75	74
38 or more	361	268	22.4 (81)	24.3 (65)	17.2 (62)	15.7 (42)	5.3 (19)	8.6 (23)	136	115
Total	912	714	16.0 (146)	15.8 (113)	12.1 (110)	9.5 (68)	3.9 (36)	6.3 (45)	314	277

Table 6 Malformation rates by birth weight,

Birth weight (gms.)	All races								Number of deaths	
	Number of deaths		All malf.		Single malf.		Mult. malf.			
	M	F	M	F	M	F	M	F	M	F
1500 or less	337	290	8.3 (28)	8.9 (30)	6.2 (21)	5.2 (15)	2.1 (7)	5.2 (15)	115	115
1501–2500	193	176	17.6 (34)	22.2 (39)	11.9 (23)	14.8 (26)	5.7 (11)	7.4 (13)	65	68
2501 or more	382	248	22.0 (84)	17.7 (44)	17.3 (66)	10.9 (27)	4.7 (18)	6.9 (17)	134	94
Total	912	714	16.0 (146)	15.8 (113)	12.1 (110)	9.5 (68)	3.9 (36)	6.3 (45)	314	277

Table 7 Frequency of group A malformations

Maternal age	All races								All deaths	
	All deaths		All malf.		Single malf.		Multiple malf.			
	M	F	M	F	M	F	M	F	M	F
19 or less	204	151	10.8 (22)	16.6 (25)	8.8 (18)	9.3 (14)	2.0 (4)	7.3 (11)	41	41
20–24	308	231	16.9 (52)	17.8 (41)	12.7 (39)	10.4 (24)	4.2 (13)	7.4 (17)	108	94
25–29	168	154	15.5 (26)	15.6 (24)	9.5 (16)	10.4 (16)	6.0 (10)	5.2 (8)	70	65
30 or more	232	178	19.8 (46)	12.9 (23)	15.9 (37)	7.9 (14)	3.9 (9)	5.1 (9)	95	77
Total	912	714	16.0 (146)	15.8 (113)	12.1 (110)	9.5 (68)	3.9 (36)	6.3 (45)	314	277

age, race, sex, and multiplicity of malformations

| White | | | | | | Negro | | | | | |
| All malf. | | Single malf. | | Mult. malf. | | Number of deaths | | All malf. | | Single malf. | | Mult. malf. | |
M	F	M	F	M	F	M	F	M	F	M	F	M	F
12.6 (13)	10.2 (9)	9.7 (10)	5.7 (5)	2.9 (3)	4.5 (4)	213	149	8.9 (19)	7.4 (11)	6.1 (13)	4.7 (7)	2.8 (6)	2.7 (4)
20.0 (15)	18.9 (14)	17.3 (13)	8.1 (6)	2.7 (2)	10.8 (8)	125	108	12.8 (16)	8.4 (9)	8.8 (11)	6.5 (7)	4.0 (5)	1.9 (2)
28.7 (39)	29.6 (34)	20.6 (28)	15.7 (18)	8.1 (11)	13.9 (16)	187	125	18.2 (34)	17.6 (22)	13.9 (26)	12.8 (16)	4.3 (8)	4.8 (6)
21.3 (67)	20.6 (57)	16.2 (51)	10.5 (29)	5.1 (16)	10.1 (28)	525	382	13.1 (69)	11.0 (42)	9.5 (50)	7.9 (30)	3.6 (19)	3.1 (12)

race, sex, and multiplicity of malformations

| White | | | | | | Negro | | | | | |
| All malf. | | Single malf. | | Mult. malf. | | Number of deaths | | All malf. | | Single malf. | | Mult. malf. | |
M	F	M	F	M	F	M	F	M	F	M	F	M	F
12.2 (14)	14.8 (17)	10.4 (12)	5.2 (6)	1.7 (2)	9.6 (11)	206	161	6.8 (14)	6.8 (11)	4.4 (9)	4.3 (7)	2.4 (5)	2.5 (4)
23.1 (15)	26.5 (18)	13.8 (9)	17.7 (12)	9.2 (6)	8.8 (6)	108	84	14.8 (16)	13.1 (11)	10.2 (11)	9.5 (8)	4.6 (5)	3.6 (3)
28.4 (38)	23.4 (22)	22.4 (30)	11.7 (11)	6.0 (8)	11.7 (11)	211	137	18.5 (39)	14.6 (20)	14.2 (30)	10.9 (15)	4.3 (9)	3.6 (5)
21.3 (67)	20.6 (57)	16.2 (51)	10.5 (29)	5.1 (16)	10.1 (28)	525	382	13.1 (69)	11.0 (42)	9.5 (50)	7.9 (30)	3.6 (19)	3.1 (12)

according to maternal age, race, sex and multiplicity

| White | | | | | | Negro | | | | | |
| All malf. | | Single malf. | | Multiple malf. | | All deaths | | All malf. | | Single malf. | | Multiple malf. | |
M	F	M	F	M	F	M	F	M	F	M	F	M	F
12.2 (5)	29.3 (12)	9.8 (4)	7.3 (3)	2.4 (1)	22.0 (9)	141	100	9.2 (13)	10.0 (10)	7.8 (11)	9.0 (9)	1.4 (2)	1.0 (1)
25.0 (27)	21.3 (20)	20.4 (22)	9.6 (9)	4.6 (5)	11.7 (11)	178	129	13.5 (24)	10.9 (14)	9.0 (16)	7.0 (9)	4.5 (8)	3.9 (5)
18.6 (13)	16.9 (11)	10.0 (7)	13.8 (9)	8.6 (6)	3.1 (2)	81	74	13.6 (11)	13.5 (10)	8.6 (7)	9.5 (7)	4.9 (4)	4.1 (3)
24.2 (23)	18.2 (14)	18.9 (18)	10.4 (8)	5.3 (5)	7.8 (6)	125	79	16.0 (20)	10.1 (8)	12.8 (16)	6.3 (5)	3.2 (4)	3.8 (3)
21.7 (68)	20.6 (57)	16.2 (51)	10.5 (29)	5.4 (17)	10.1 (28)	525	382	13.0 (68)	11.0 (42)	9.5 (50)	7.9 (30)	3.4 (18)	3.1 (12)

presence of malformations does not necessarily result in early intrauterine death or premature expulsion from the uterus; in fact such fetuses could survive in utero to full gestation and even beyond.

Malformations and maternal age

The incidence of Group A malformations was not impressively higher in the 30 or more maternal age group compared to the younger ages (Table 7). Neither were the malformation rates higher in the 19 or less age group, with the exception of white females in whom the high malformation rate was largely due to multiple malformations (22.0%). However, it should be noted that mongolism by itself, shown in this series (Tables 8 and 9) and those of others

Table 8 Frequency of selected specific malformations according to maternal age

Selected malformations	Maternal age				
	19 or less	20–24	25–29	30 or more	Total
All deaths	355	539	322	410	1626
Anencephaly	1.4 (5)	2.0 (11)	1.2 (4)	0.2 (1)	1.3 (21)
Spina bifida*	1.4 (5)	1.5 (8)	0.6 (2)	1.0 (4)	1.2 (19)
Multiple heart malf.	2.3 (8)	4.4 (24)	5.3 (17)	4.1 (17)	4.1 (66)
Isolated heart malf.	2.0 (7)	1.3 (7)	4.3 (14)	3.4 (14)	2.6 (42)
Single umbilical artery	1.7 (6)	2.4 (13)	3.1 (10)	2.0 (8)	2.3 (37)
Polycystic kidney	0.8 (3)	2.4 (13)	0.6 (2)	1.7 (7)	1.5 (25)
Atresia, ureter or urethra	0.8 (3)	3.0 (16)	0.9 (3)	0.7 (3)	1.5 (25)
Agenesis of kidney	0.8 (3)	0.7 (4)	0.3 (1)	0.2 (1)	0.6 (9)
Cleft palate**	0.6 (2)	0.7 (4)	0.6 (2)	1.0 (4)	0.7 (12)
Polydactyly/syndactyly	0.8 (3)	0.7 (4)	0.9 (3)	1.0 (4)	0.9 (14)
Diaphragmatic hernia	1.1 (4)	1.1 (6)	0.6 (2)	0.7 (3)	0.9 (15)
Omphalocele	0.6 (2)	0.7 (4)	0.9 (3)	1.5 (6)	0.9 (15)
Hypoplasia, lungs	3.7 (13)	2.6 (14)	1.2 (4)	2.2 (9)	2.5 (40)
Accessory spleen	3.4 (12)	4.3 (23)	5.6 (18)	3.7 (15)	4.2 (68)
Mongolism	0.3 (1)	0.4 (2)	0.6 (2)	2.0 (8)	0.8 (13)

  * Includes Arnold-Chiari
 ** Includes cleft palate with cleft lip

to be distinctly related to old age in the majority of cases, had been classified under Group B and therefore not included in Table 7. Douglas[4], Davis and Potter[2], as well as Hendricks[6] report higher incidences at extremes of maternal age. Since malformation incidences in those studies were based on total births, the higher rates may partly be the effect of the relatively small number of births in the extreme age groups. Murphy[13] indicates that the proportion of defective children increases after age 30. McIntosh[9] and Sotelo-Avila and Shanklin[17] claim no effect of maternal age.

Table 9 shows that in whites the mean maternal age of all malformed cases (26.1 years) was a year greater than that of white single livebirths (25.1 years) but not different from that of white autopsied deaths (26.0 years). In Negroes the mean maternal age of all malformed cases (25.2 years) was 2 years greater

Table 9 Mean maternal age in selected specific malformations according to race, sex, and multiplicity of malformations

	White	Negro	Male	Female	Single malformations	Multiple malformations	Total
Single live births*	25.1 (1129)	23.3 (1237)	24.6 (1316)	24.9 (1269)	– (–)	– (–)	24.4 (2585)
All deaths	26.0 (591)	24.3 (907)	24.9 (912)	25.2 (714)	– (–)	– (–)	25.1 (1626)
All group A malformations	26.1 (125)	25.2 (110)	25.7 (146)	25.1 (113)	25.6 (178)	25.3 (81)	25.5 (259)
Anencephaly	22.6 (16)	22.5 (2)	25.3 (7)	20.9 (14)	23.2 (13)	21.0 (8)	22.4 (21)
Spina bifida**	24.2 (12)	29.3 (4)	28.0 (5)	23.7 (14)	24.8 (6)	24.9 (13)	24.8 (19)
Multiple heart malformations	26.9 (38)	28.1 (23)	26.0 (32)	27.1 (34)	27.3 (37)	25.7 (29)	26.6 (66)
Isolated heart malformations	26.0 (15)	26.1 (22)	27.0 (27)	25.3 (15)	26.8 (30)	25.4 (12)	26.4 (42)
Single umbilical artery	24.6 (21)	24.5 (15)	25.3 (17)	24.3 (20)	24.5 (18)	24.9 (19)	24.7 (37)
Polycystic kidney	25.0 (8)	25.9 (16)	24.5 (11)	26.4 (14)	21.6 (9)	27.9 (16)	25.6 (25)
Atresia, ureter or urethra	24.7 (10)	23.2 (15)	23.3 (19)	24.8 (6)	21.7 (9)	24.8 (16)	23.6 (25)
Agenesis of kidney	22.2 (5)	24.5 (2)	26.0 (5)	21.8 (4)	20.4 (5)	26.0 (4)	22.9 (9)
Cleft palate***	29.2 (6)	30.0 (5)	28.1 (7)	29.0 (5)	31.8 (5)	26.9 (7)	28.5 (12)
Polydactyly or syndactyly	26.0 (5)	26.1 (8)	28.2 (5)	24.8 (9)	25.3 (6)	26.7 (8)	26.0 (14)
Diaphragmatic hernia	25.4 (9)	23.5 (4)	25.9 (9)	20.5 (6)	27.3 (4)	22.5 (11)	23.7 (15)
Omphalocele	25.6 (9)	32.2 (6)	28.1 (7)	28.3 (8)	29.0 (3)	28.0 (12)	28.2 (15)
Hypoplasia, lungs	25.3 (25)	22.8 (12)	25.5 (17)	23.4 (23)	25.1 (18)	23.7 (22)	24.3 (40)
Accessory spleen	25.6 (32)	24.4 (35)	25.1 (32)	25.0 (36)	25.3 (50)	24.3 (18)	25.0 (68)
Mongolism	33.0 (5)	34.7 (8)	32.9 (7)	34.3 (6)	33.9 (10)	32.3 (3)	33.5 (13)

  * 4 year old survivors randomly sampled from the general population
 ** Includes Arnold–Chiari
*** Includes cleft palate with cleft lip

than that of Negro single livebirths (23.3 years) and a year greater than that of autopsied Negro deaths (24.3 years). It is noteworthy that the Negro women in the Collaborative Study were generally younger than the whites. However, of the 15 specific malformations analyzed all but three (atresia of ureter or urethra, diaphragmatic hernia, hypoplastic lungs) showed maternal ages in Negroes which were equal to or higher than those of corresponding whites. Also, with the exception of these 3 malformations the Negro mean maternal age for each specific malformation was at least one year greater than the age for single livebirths. Therefore it appears that most specific malformations were associated frequently with somewhat later years (24 years of age and beyond) corresponding to the ages past the peak of reproductivity in Negroes. This may have had an influence on the generally lower incidence of malformations in Negroes of our population.

The mean maternal ages of cases with single malformations were equal to or higher than the mean maternal ages of those with multiple malformations, with the exception of kidney malformations (Table 9). In fact there was a relatively high risk of multiple malformations in white females born to young mothers (Table 7), particularly those 19 years of age or less (22.0 %). Dou-GLAS[4] emphasized the association between fetal defects (as a cause of death) and young mothers. The high multiple malformation rate among white females born to young mothers was closely associated with the high incidence of CNS malformations, notably anencephaly, in this group. It is curious that whereas the mean maternal age for anencephaly in our population was 22.4 years (20.9 years when the anencephalic was female) that reported by NAGGAN[14] was 27.9 years, in a retrospective study of anencephalics in the Boston area. The reason for this marked difference is not clear. It must be remembered, however, that our study was based on a consecutive series of randomly selected gravida, and known "high-risk" women, such as known diabetics, who would then be somewhat older, were excluded from this series. Mean maternal ages (Table 9) roughly matched the ages at which the peak of malformation rates for each specific malformation (Table 8) occurred, indicating that mean maternal ages are fairly accurate indicators of the optimum ages for these malformations. The mean maternal age was low in female anencephalics (20.9 years) and females with diaphragmatic hernia (20.5 years). Mean maternal ages were high in mongolism (33.5 years), Negroes with omphalocele (32.2 years) and Negroes with cleft palate (30.0 years). With these exceptions, the mean maternal ages of specific malformations were between 21–29 years.

Association of malformations and critical period of development

Table 10 is a cross tabulation showing the distribution of malformations found in combination with selected specific malformations. The associated malformations were arranged in the order of expected critical time of development[7,12,19]. With the exception of malformations associated with mongolism the associated malformations were more of less diffusely scattered throughout the entire spectrum of critical periods of development, rather than being limited to the same time period as that in which the specific malformation was expected to have occurred. This scattered distribution demonstrates once more the etiologic complexity of human malformations. Had there been clustering of associated malformations at the same critical time period when the selected malformation was expected to have occurred, a causal relationship could be more easily established as is frequently possible in experimental teratology. But as expected, this was not the case, indicating that the pathogenesis of human malformations rests on the interaction of a multiplicity of factors. Certain associations were noted which were probably on the basis of simultaneous occurrences such as anencephaly with spina bifida. Other associations could have been secondary interference phenomena. For example, bilaterally hypoplastic lungs were frequently associated with anencephaly, spina bifida, diaphragmatic

Table 10 Selected malformations and the frequency of associated malformations

Selected malformations	No. of cases	Critical* time-weeks	Single umbilical artery (37)	Anencephaly (21)	Omphalocele (15)	Spina bifida, all types (10)	Other CNS malformations (14)	Arnold-Chiari (9)	Agenesis, kidney (9)	Horseshoe kidney (6)	Tracheo-esophageal fistula (4)	Diaphragmatic hernia (15)	Rib or vertebral malformations (13)	Cleft lip (8)	Atresia, small bowel (5)	Agenesis, ovary (1)	Agenesis, urinary bladder (1)	Atresia, ureter or urethra (25)	Polycystic kidney (25)	Cleft palate (12)	Imperforate anus (5)	Meckel's diverticulum (18)	Agenesis, gallbladder (3)	Isolated heart malformations (42)	Multiple heart malformations (66)	Agenesis, spleen (4)	Atresia, ext. auditory meatus (3)	Atresia, bile duct (2)	Polydactyly-syndactyly (14)	Bicornuate uterus (4)	Accessory spleen (68)	Hypoplasia, lungs (40)	Talipes, all types (33)	Hydrocephalus, NOS (13)	Abnormal position or shape, ear (14)	Mongolism (13)	Kyphosis or scoliosis (9)	Webbed neck (7)
			Group A																												Group B							
Single umbilical artery	37	3-4	–	4	4	2	1	1	1	0	2	3	1	0	1	1	1	3	6	1	2	2	2	2	6	1	1	1	2	0	4	4	4	0	2	0	1	1
Anencephaly	21	3-4	4	–	3	6	0	0	0	0	0	0	1	0	0	1	0	1	3	1	0	0	0	1	1	0	0	0	0	0	3	8	3	0	0	0	2	0
Omphalocele	15	3-4	4	3	–	5	1	0	1	0	0	1	2	0	0	0	1	1	3	0	3	1	1	3	2	1	0	1	1	1	3	5	6	0	0	0	5	0
Spina bifida, all types	10	3-4	2	6	5	–	0	5	0	0	0	1	1	0	0	0	0	2	2	0	1	1	0	1	1	0	0	0	0	0	2	6	3	1	0	0	3	0
Other CNS malformations	14	3--	1	0	1	0	–	5	1	1	0	0	3	2	0	0	0	2	1	2	0	1	0	2	2	0	0	0	1	0	1	2	4	0	0	0	1	0
Arnold-Chiari	9	4--	1	0	0	5	5	–	0	0	0	1	2	0	0	0	0	3	1	0	0	2	0	1	0	0	0	0	0	0	1	3	8	1	1	0	2	1
Agenesis, kidney	9	4-5	1	0	1	0	1	0	–	0	0	0	3	0	0	1	0	2	0	1	0	1	0	2	0	0	0	0	0	0	1	5	1	1	0	0	2	0
Diaphragmatic hernia	15	4-5	3	0	1	1	0	1	0	0	0	–	3	1	0	0	1	1	0	1	1	1	1	3	2	0	0	0	0	0	3	10	3	1	1	1	1	0
Polycystic kidney	25	6--	6	3	3	2	1	1	0	0	0	0	1	1	0	0	0	8	–	0	1	2	1	3	5	0	0	0	3	0	3	7	5	0	1	1	1	1
Cleft palate	12	6-9	1	1	0	0	2	0	1	0	1	1	3	1	0	0	0	1	0	–	0	3	0	3	3	0	1	0	3	1	2	2	3	1	3	1	0	2
Isolated heart malformations	42	6-8	2	1	3	1	0	2	1	0	3	3	3	0	0	0	0	3	3	3	0	0	1	–	0	1	1	0	1	2	4	4	3	0	3	1	1	2
Multiple heart malformations	66	6-8	6	1	2	2	2	1	0	2	3	2	3	2	2	0	0	3	5	3	0	5	1	0	–	4	1	0	4	4	13	11	1	1	3	7	1	2
Polydactyly-syndactyly	14	7-8	2	0	1	0	1	0	0	0	1	0	2	1	2	0	0	2	3	3	0	3	0	1	4	0	0	0	–	1	2	1	2	0	1	1	0	0
Accessory spleen	68		4	3	3	2	1	1	1	1	2	3	1	1	0	0	0	5	3	2	0	3	0	4	13	–	0	0	2	0	–	4	5	2	3	2	3	1
Hypoplasia, lungs	40		7	8	5	6	2	3	5	1	1	10	5	0	0	0	1	7	7	3	2	2	1	4	11	1	0	0	1	1	4	–	11	2	3	1	3	4
Talipes, all types	33		4	3	6	3	4	8	1	1	0	3	2	1	0	1	0	7	5	3	3	1	0	3	1	1	0	0	2	1	5	11	–	0	3	1	4	1
Hydrocephalus, NOS	13		0	0	0	1	0	1	1	1	0	1	2	1	1	0	1	0	0	1	0	0	0	0	1	1	0	0	0	0	0	2	0	–	0	0	0	1
Mongolism	13		0	0	0	0	0	0	0	0	0	1	0	1	0	0	0	1	1	2	0	2	0	1	7	0	0	0	0	0	2	1	1	0	0	–	0	0

* adapted from MILLER[12] and STREETER[19]

hernia, talipes, and kidney malformations.   Talipes was often seen in association with CNS malformations especially the Arnold-Chiari syndrome, as well as with omphalocele, atresia of ureter or urethra, and hypoplastic lungs. Accessory spleen was commonly seen with multiple heart malformations.   Some of these associations have been reported previously[16].

SUMMARY

A review of 1,626 autopsied stillbirths, neonatal and infant and child deaths out of a total of 43,127 single births in the Collaborative Study was undertaken, in which 259 or 15.9 % had unequivocal (Group A) congenital malformations. Malformation rates for each type of death and sex were consistently higher in whites than in Negroes.   In either race there was no significant difference in overall malformation rates between males and females.   However, multiple malformations were frequent in white females, especially in stillbirths, and were in direct relationship with the high rate of CNS malformations in this group. In both whites and Negroes the malformation rates were higher in females among stillbirths and infant and child deaths.   However, malformation rates were remarkably higher in male neonatal deaths, mostly due to a preponderance of single malformations especially of the cardiovascular system.   All but one of the multiply malformed cases and 61.9 % of those with single malformations had at least one lethal malformation indicating that differences in malformation rates were largely influenced by lethal malformations.   Malformation rates increased stepwise with increments of gestational age, the highest rates being consistently those in the 38 weeks or more gestational age group.   Higher incidences in the lower birth weight intervals were noted in white males with multiple malformations and in all malformed white females, suggesting the possibility of runting in these groups.   That malformation rates were highest in the highest gestational age interval suggests that malformations are of greater significance in the mature than in the premature baby that dies, and also that the presence of malformations in viable fetuses does not necessarily result in early intrauterine death or premature expulsion from the uterus.

In single live births the mean maternal age in Negroes was lower than in whites.   But for most selected malformations the mean maternal age in Negroes was equal to or higher than in whites.   This suggests that the optimum ages for many malformations are past the peak of reproductivity in the Negro and may have an influence on the generally lower incidence of malformations in Negroes. Mothers of multiply malformed cases were not older than those with single malformations.   The incidence of malformations was not significantly higher in the extremes of maternal age except in white females, where the high rate in those 19 years old or less was mainly due to multiple malformations (22.0 %).

Anencephaly was particularly common among white females, and their mothers were usually young.   Atresia of the ureter or urethra was more common in males particularly in Negroes.   In males of both races involvement of the cardiovascular system was frequently limited to this system, in contrast to females.   Transposition of great vessels was more frequent in males.

The cardiovascular system was the system most often involved by malformations in both sexes and races.   Second in rank was the central nervous system in white females and the genito-urinary system in Negroes of both sexes.

The lack of clustering of associated malformations at the specific critical time period when the selected malformation was expected to have occurred demonstrates the etiologic complexity of this problem in humans.

ACKNOWLEDGEMENTS

The Collaborative Study of Cerebral Palsy, Mental Retardation and Other Neurological and Sensory Disorders of Infancy and Childhood is supported by the National Institute of Neurological Diseases and Stroke. The following institutions participate: Boston Lying-in Hospital; Brown University; Charity Hospital, New Orleans; Children's Hospital of Buffalo; Children's Hospital of Philadelphia; Children's Medical Center, Boston; Columbia University; The Johns Hopkins University; Medical College of Virginia; New York Medical College; Pennsylvania Hospital; University of Minnesota; University of Oregon; University of Tennessee; and the Perinatal Research Branch, National Institute of Neurological Diseases and Stroke.

REFERENCES

1. BUTLER, N.R. and BONHAM, D.G.: Perinatal Mortality. p. 224. E & S Livingstone, Ltd., London, 1963.
2. DAVIS, M.E. and POTTER, E.L.: Congenital malformations and obstetrics. Pediat. 19: 719–724, 1957.
3. CIOCCO, A.: The masculinity of stillbirths and abortions in relation to the duration of uterogestation and to the stated causes of foetal mortality. Hum. Biol. 10: 235 –250, 1938.
4. DOUGLAS, C.A.: Infant and Perinatal Mortality in Scotland. Vital and Health Statistics, Series 3, No. 5. p. 7, U.S. Department of Health, Education and Welfare, Washington, D.C., 1966.
5. GRUENWALD, P.: Chronic fetal distress and placental insufficiency. Biol. Neonat. 5: 215–265, 1963.
6. HENDRICKS, C.H.: Congenital malformations analysis of the 1953 Ohio records. Obst. Gynec. 6: 592–598, 1955.
7. INGALLS, T.H.: Epidemiology of Congenital Malformations. In: Mechanisms of Congenital Malformation p. 16, Association for the Aid of Crippled Children, New York, 1954.
8. LAMY, M. and FREZAL, J.: The Frequency of Congenital Malformations. In: Congenital Malformations, edited by M. FISHBEIN. p. 34–43. J.B. Lippincott Co., Philadelphia, 1961.
9. MCINTOSH, R., MERRITT, K.K., RICHARDO, M.R., SAMUELS, M.H. and BELLOWS, M.T.: The incidence of congenital malformations—a study of 5,964 pregnancies. Pediat. 14: 505–522, 1954.
10. MCKEOWN, T. and RECORD, R.G.: Malformations in a Population Observed for Five Years After Birth. In: Ciba Foundation Symposium on Congenital Malformation, edited by G.E.W. WOLSTENHOLME and C.M. O'CONNOR. p. 2–21. Little, Brown and Co., Boston, 1960.
11. MELLIN, G.W.: The Frequency of Birth Defects. In: Birth Defects, edited by M. FISHBEIN p. 1–17. J.B. Lippincott Co., Philadelphia, 1963.
12. MILLEN, J. W.: Timing of human congenital malformations—With a timetable of

human development. Develop. Med. Child. Neurol. 5: 343–350, 1963.

13. MURPHY, D.P.: Congenital Malformations—A' study of parental characteristics with special reference to the reproductive process. p. 15 and 24, J.B. Lippincott Co., Philadelphia, 1947.

14. NAGGAN, L. and MACMAHON, B.: Ethnic differences in the prevalence of anencephaly and spina bifida. New Eng. J. Med. 277: 1119–1123, 1967.

15. NEEL, J.V.: A study of major congenital defects in Japanese infants. Am. J. Human Genet. 10: p. 398–445, 1958.

16. NORMAN, A.P.: Congenital Abnormalities in Infancy. p. 2, 34, 82, F.A. Davis Co., Philadelphia, 1963.

17. SOTELO-AVILA, C. and SHANKLIN, D.R.: Congenital malformations in an autopsy population. Arch. Path. 84: 272–279, 1967.

18. STEVENSON, A.C., JOHNSTON, H.A., STEWART, M.I.P. and GOLDING, D.R.: Congenital Malformations. A report of a study of series of consecutive births in 24 centers. World Health Organization, Geneva, 1966.

19. STREETER, G.L.: Developmental horizons in human embryos. Contr. Embryol. Carnegie Inst. 30: 211–245, 1942; 31: 27–63, 1945; 32: 133–203, 1948.

20. WOOLF, B.: Vital statistics of stillbirths and neonatal deaths. Brit. Med. Bull. 4: 170–173, 1946.

FINDINGS AND LESSONS FOR THE FUTURE FROM A COMPARATIVE STUDY OF CONGENITAL MALFORMATIONS AT 24 CENTRES IN 16 COUNTRIES

Alan C. Stevenson

*Medical Research Council, Population Genetics Research Unit,
Oxford, England.*

We should all like to know the true frequencies of specified congenital malformations in different countries and in people of different ethnic origins, and to have good information on secular trends and seasonal variations. Such epidemiological information would give us clues as to etiology which could be pursued by *ad hoc* studies and would enable us to think more sensibly about preventive measures. There would still be many complications, as we all know, even if we had good data along these lines. For example, frequencies of mature, live or still born infants who are malformed are those of survivors and the relative frequencies of earlier losses may vary in different communities.

Unfortunately, it is only in relatively few countries in the world that medical, social and statistical services are adequate to permit of proper screening of large series of consecutive births in a population. Our comparative information is therefore fragmentary and such few conclusions which we can draw are based on the findings of a few good studies from centres in highly developed countries and many smaller studies based on hospital births and not reported in sufficient detail.

Unfortunately, the data which were collected in my Unit on behalf of the World Health Organization contribute relatively little to our understanding of comparative frequencies. This was inevitable because the only possibility of getting data from most of the twenty-four centres in the sixteen collaborating countries was from hospital births. That such biased sources had severe limitations was recognised when the study was first considered as a possibility, but it was decided to go ahead for several reasons. First, the World Health Organization had, when the study started, relatively little experience in such centrally organized investigations and it was felt that in certain studies which required collection of information in the same way in different countries, only the Organization which has such prestige could get the necessary collaboration from the Ministries of Health and senior doctors in hospitals. Second, there were many countries where little or nothing had been published about malformations and some information, however inadequate, would be of interest. Third, it was considered that in all the collaborating centres, the fact that a study was being undertaken would be to some extent educative, would enhance interest in the problems and would probably lead to further more detailed studies. This indeed

Table 1 Outline of data—WHO malformations study

24 Centres	
Outcomes of 421,781 pregnancies	resulting in 426,932 post-27th week births
Major malformations frequency	12.7 per 1,000 total births
Minor malformations frequency	4.6 per 1,000 total births
Mean consanguinity frequency	37.5 per 1,000 pregnancies
Sex proportions M/M+F	Malformed 0.520
	Not malformed 0.515
Twinning frequency	12.5 per 1,000 pregnancies
Estimated Monozygous frequency	4.41 per 1,000 pregnancies
Dizygous frequency	8.00 per 1,000 pregnancies

$$DZ/MZ = 1.82$$

happened. All the staff in the centres appeared to be interested, many have continued the special recording started during the WHO Study and several have embarked on more extensive programmes bringing into collaborative projects, embryologists and cytologists as well as pathologists and paediatric surgeons.

The work involved was considerable, as will be seen from Table 1 which gives an overall picture of the data collected. It was not possible to include hospitals where the numbers of births each year were small, otherwise to collect sufficient data would have taken many years. The size of maternity hospitals varies considerably in different parts of the world. For example, in Great Britain few hospitals have over 2,000 births per year and in most of Eastern Europe the average mother and child unit has only about 100 beds for all purposes. In contrast, in Latin America there are many large maternity hospitals having over 20,000 births per year and the same situation holds in Spain and in South East Asia.

The bases of our final choices of centres are elaborated in the WHO Report[4] and I need not consider them here. The data collected were minimal because many of the hospitals were very short of medical and clerical staff. A notable omission was the absence of any information on the condition of the mother during pregnancy. At first sight this seems odd, but after much discussion and thought it was decided that even recording of toxaemia or hydramnios in pregnancy would not be worth while in the circumstances in which the recordings were made. This was because diagnostic criteria are so difficult to define and because in many hospitals only a minority of patients had received proper ante-natal care. The recording form used is shown in Table 2.

It is hazardous to say the least, to draw conclusions about relative frequencies of malformations from hospital data. No hospitals admit patients fully representative of all mothers and no two hospitals have precisely the same biasses in admission policy. Nevertheless, if the differences in frequencies of certain malformations are really large and there is little likelihood of failure to recognise a malformation and little likelihood of differing diagnostic standards then these differences are probably real. By these criteria the only types of defect where real differences of frequency were detected in the Study, were in neural tube defects, harelip and oblique or cleft palate, and polydactyly. We already knew

Table 2

WORLD HEALTH ORGANIZATION
COMPARATIVE STUDY OF CONGENITAL MALFORMATIONS

Hospital No. 8 2 2 3   21 **717420**

Hospital *Kandang Kerbau Hospital Singapore.*   Mother's Name *Sim Shoot Ch...*

A Mother's age in years   20

B Ethnic Group of mother ① 2 3 4 5 6 7

C Number of previous pregnancies   0.

D Consanguinity ① 2 3 4 5 6 7 8 9 0

E Single Birth 1.   Twins ②.   Triplets 3

F Male ①   Female 2

G Liveborn ①   Stillborn 2

H Malformations: Yes ①   No 2

I If liveborn: Left hospital alive 1.   Died in hospital ②

J If stillborn: Autopsy: Yes ①.   No 2

K Cause of Death

   OESOPHAGEAL ATRESIA

19	20	21
7	0	0

MALFORMATIONS Describe here and on back of card

   1. MONGOL.
   2. VENTRICULAR Septal DEFECT
   3. OESOPHAGEAL ATRESIA

No. 3

2nd CHILD OF TWINS OR TRIPLETS

Hospital No. 8223 :   Serial No. 717, 420
(please copy from White Card)

F Male ①   Female 2

G Liveborn 1,   Stillborn ②

H Malformations: Yes ①   No 2

I If liveborn: Left hospital alive 1,   Died in hospital 2

J If stillborn or died: Autopsy: Yes 1.   No ②

K Cause of death

19	20	21

MALFORMATIONS DESCRIPTION

   ONLY Two LEGS & PELVIS
   (ABSENT UPPER HALF OF
   BODY   )

	8	8	0
	22	23	24
	8	8	0
	25	26	27
	28	29	30
	31	32	33
	34	35	36
	37	38	39

No. 4

---

that there were frequency differences in respect of these defects so that findings were not unexpected.

The data from the Study have been set out in very great detail in the Report and in a 550-page booklet of tabulations[5] and lists of malformations separately from each centre, so that readers have, for practical purposes, as much information as was available to the writers of the Report. The problem of classification of defects is an extremely difficult one. Over a long time many adaptations of the International Statistical List of Injuries, Diseases and Causes of Death and many elaborate new classifications were tried. It had been hoped that some simple way of classifying each defect in the same child could be found. However, the complexities were too great and eventually the simple empirical classification set out in Table 3 was used. The headings can easily be cross-referenced to those of the old or new International List.

I shall now discuss some of the findings of the Report which seem to be of particular interest and I shall be somewhat speculative when talking about these findings in order to stimulate discussion.

Table 3 Grouping of malformations in WHO study

Serial code No.	Major malformation	Serial code No.	Major malformation
A	Mongolism	3	Cleft palate
B 1 α	Anencephalus	H	Talipes
2	Anencephalus and S. bifida	I	Hip (dislocation or dysplasia)
3	Hydrocephalus	J 1	Polydactyly (ulnar)
4	Hydrocephalus and S. bifida	2	Polydactyly (radial)
5	Occipital meningo (myelo) coele	3	All other polydactyly
6	"S. bifida"	4	Syndactyly
7	Other neural tube	5	Other digital anomalies
C	Other CNS	6	Reduction deformities (limbs)
D	Heart and great vessels	7	Other limb deformities
E 1	Trach. -oesophag. fist., etc.	K 1	Other local skeletal
2	Anal atresia	2	Chondrodystrophy
3	Other gastro-intestinal	3	Osteogenesis imperfecta
4	Exomphalos	4	Pierre Robin syndrome
F	Diaphragm	5	Other general skeletal
G 1	Hare lip	L	Urogenital
2	Hare lip and cleft palate	M	Miscellaneous (single)

N   Multiple

NEURAL TUBE DEFECTS

We considered as a group all infants who had neural tube defects irrespective of whether there were other associated malformations. With the exception of lesser degrees of hydrocephalus without spina bifida and brain malformations without external signs such as absent corpus callosum, it seems likely that affected children would always be recognised. As is clear from Table 3 we classify these defects in six groups, anencephalus alone, anencephalus with spina bifida, hydrocephalus alone, and hydrocephalus with spina bifida, spina bifida alone and other neural tube defects. The last was a heterogeneous group, mostly encephalocoeles. It can hardly be doubted from the data that there were real differences in the frequency of all these neural tube defects, except the last, the "other" group, where in any event the numbers were too small for adequate comparisons. Regarding anencephalus with and without spina bifida there was a fortyfold variation between the highest and lowest frequencies (standardized for maternal age), with the highest frequency of all in Belfast closely followed by that in Alexandria. What was more interesting was that the frequencies of each of the defects was positively correlated with each of the others as is shown in Table 4. Two-thirds of these correlations were technically significant and of those which were not, the numbers of one or of both defects were small.

These findings suggest strongly (a) that there are common etiological factors to all of these developmental failures, (b) that these etiological factors are more common or more powerful in some countries than in others and possibly in some

Table 4

Groups correlated	Coefficient of correlation r	Significance p
B 1 and B 2 Anencephalus only and Anencephalus and spina bifida	+0. 611	<0. 005
B 1 and B 3 Anencephalus only and Hydrocephalus only	+0. 514	<0. 02
B 1 and B 4 Anencephalus only and Hydrocephalus and spina bifida	+0. 607	<0. 005
B 1 and B 5 Anencephalus only and Occipital meningocoele	+0. 269	>0. 1
B 1 and B 6 Anencephalus only and Spina bifida	+0. 749	<0. 001
B 1 and B 7 Anencephalus only and Other neural tube	+0. 614	<0. 005
B 2 and B 3 Anencephalus and spina bifida and Hydrocephalus only	+0. 691	<0. 001
B 2 and B 4 Anencephalus and spina bifida and Hydrocephalus and spina bifida	+0. 576	<0. 005
B 2 and B 5 Anencephalus and spina bifida and Occipital meningocoele	+0. 677	<0. 001
B 2 and B 6 Anencephalus and spina bifida and Spina bifida	+0. 475	<0. 02
B 2 and B 7 Anencephalus and spina bifida and Other neural tube	+0. 351	>0. 1
B 3 and B 4 Hydrocephalus only and Hydrocephalus and spina bifida	+0. 450	<0. 05
B 3 and B 5 Hydrocephalus only and Occipital meningocoele	+0. 622	<0. 005
B 3 and B 6 Hydrocephalus only and Spina bifida	+0. 459	<0. 05
B 3 and B 7 Hydrocephalus only and Other neural tube	+0. 429	<0. 05
B 4 and B 5 Hydrocephalus and spina bifida and Occipital meningocoele	+0. 120	>0. 1
B 4 and B 6 Hydrocephalus and spina bifida and Spina bifida	+0. 793	<0. 001
B 4 and B 7 Hydrocephalus and spina bifida and Other neural tube	+0. 276	>0. 1
B 5 and B 6 Occipital meningocoele and Spina bifida	+0. 080	>0. 1
B 5 and B 7 Occipital meningocoele and Other neural tube	+0. 262	>0. 1
B 6 and B 7 Spina bifida and Other neural tube	+0. 420	<0. 05

races than in others. Previous clinical, family and socioeconomic class studies in several countries have suggested that the etiological factors were predominantly environmental, probably very heterogeneous and more time-specific than agent-specific. They have also suggested a maternal influence which in turn would incriminate the intrauterine environment early in pregnancy. Evidence for genetic factors, notoriously difficult to evaluate in such circumstances in man has been scanty. Although consanguinity had been noted by POLMAN[3] evidence for an association was not impressive in his data and absent in the data of others. That genetic factors were relatively unimportant was also suggested by the very small number of cases where monozygous twins were both affected, and the large number of published cases where monozygous twins were discordant for neural tube anomalies. In this study of 24 pairs of twins with one affected by neural tube defect only one (a female-female pair) was concordant for a neural tube defect (spina bifida and hydrocephalus and spina bifida, most likely both having an Arnold-Chiari malformation).

It was a surprise therefore to find, in the WHO Study data, a significantly high association of parental consanguinity with anencephalus and with all the other neural tube defects. In brief, the situation found on closer examination was that most of the contribution to this phenomenon came from Alexandria and from Bombay. In the former centre the frequency of neural tube defects in the offspring of first cousin marriages was 14.2 per 1,000, in those offspring whose parents were related in lesser degree 8.6 per 1,000, and in those of unrelated parents 5.7 per 1,000.

If we consider together all the other centres excluding Alexandria the frequency in the offspring of consanguineous marriages was still significantly greater (P<0.001) and even after excluding Bombay from the data there was still an excess of neural tube defects in the offspring of related parents, although it was no longer technically significant. It is difficult to avoid the conclusion from these findings that there is some genetic contribution to the etiology from both parents, but it would be a bolder man than I who would advance a specific hypothesis.

The overall importance of neural tube defects as a cause of mortality was again evidenced in this study. Of all malformed children who were stillborn or died in hospital, about 50% had neural tube defects, and this high proportion was remarkably constant in the different countries, although the highest proportion of deaths due to neural tube defects was understandably in the two centres with the highest neural tube defects frequencies.

MULTIPLE BIRTHS

It is convenient to comment on the twinning data before going on to consider some of the other types of malformation, because there was a remarkable relationship between the frequency of neural tube defects and the twinning frequencies. When estimates of monozygous and dizygous twin frequencies had been made, it was noted that the dizygous frequency in Alexandria and in Belfast was high. As neural tube frequencies were also high in these centres this suggested the possibility of a correlation between the two sets of frequencies. Appropriate calculations showed a positive correlation with anencephalus with and without spina bifida and dizygous twinning frequencies of +0.578 (P<0.01) and of all neural tube defects with dizygous twinning frequencies of +0.651 (P< 0.001). I can offer no explantation for this remarkable and interesting finding.

The twin data were of some inherent interest as there was no significant heterogeneity in monozygous twin frequencies in the twentyfour centres but considerable differences between the dizygous twin frequencies (P<0.001). Thus the significant heterogeneity in twinning rates in the different centres appears to be entirely determined by the dizygous twin frequencies.

The finding of relatively low dizygous twinning rates in people of Chinese origin was confirmed in this study. Rates in people of Malay origins were also consistently low whereas those in people of Indian and African origin were high. The higher perinatal mortality in monozygous as opposed to dizygous twins in each sex found in other studies[1] was confirmed in this one (Table 5). Another

Table 5 Mortality frequencies in twins by zygosity WHO study

	Males		Females	
	in DZ pairs	in MZ pairs	in DZ pairs	in MZ pairs
Estimated mortality per 1,000 twin births	147.5	195.1	138.6	170.9

Compare with rates in single births:

Males	43.6
Females	38.3

previous finding was also confirmed, namely, that malformation rates were not significantly higher in infants who were one of a twin pair than in single born children. Although there was a suggestion of a slightly higher frequency in monozygous twins, this is probably simply a reflection of the common genotype of both monozygous twin pairs rather than a higher risk that the zyogte would develop abnormally. The details of the types of malformations in twins by sex, concordant or discordant for malformation, are set out in the Report. Both twins in 12 pairs had a malformation but only in six could the malformations be considered as the same, and these were all in like-sexed pairs. There were, however, 114 pairs where only one child was malformed.

HARELIP, HARELIP AND CLEFT PALATE, AND POSTERIOR CLEFT PALATE

As would be expected there was a significant correlation between harelip alone and harelip and cleft palate occurring as the only detected defects, and there was a big excess of males in these cases, the sex proportion being 0.64. There was also a very high mortality in these cases even if no other defects were detected. This was significantly higher than in all the births ($P < 0.001$). It seems likely that some, but improbably all, of this excess mortality was determined by undetected internal malformations in cases where no autopsy was performed. Two pairs of M/M twins both had these defects and there was an overall small but non-significant increase in the frequency of parental consanguinity in these cases. The male excess of cases was even more marked (sex proportion 0.78) where the defects were only one of multiple malformations in the same child.

The frequencies of posterior cleft palate were not positively correlated with

Table 6 Correlations of frequencies of harelip (G 1) harelip and cleft palate (G 2) and cleft palate (G 3) in WHO study

	r	
G 1 and G 2	+0.432	$p < 0.05$
G 1 and G 3	−0.384	$p > 0.05$
G 2 and G 3	−0.400	$p > 0.05$
G 1 + G 2 and G 3	−0.460	$p < 0.05$

those of harelip and cleft palate. Indeed the correlation was negative and was significant at a 5 % level. Again there was a non-significant association of posterior cleft palate with parental consanguinity (Table 6).

SINGLE GENE TRAITS

As is well known only a small proportion of developmental anomalies which are usually detected at birth, are due to manifestations of single gene mutations. When we considered the WHO data we concluded that probably between one and two hundred of these 5,430 single born malformed children were suffering from defects determined by single genes, i. e., less than 4 %. However, these must be rough estimates. It was easy to sort out the few clear-cut dominant and recessive gene traits (providing the diagnosis was accurate) but impossible to assess with confidence the single gene contribution to many skeletal defects, and conditions where there are disorders which may or may not be so determined, and where even careful study may or may not serve to distinguish between gene traits and phenocopies.

MULTIPLE ABNORMALITIES IN THE SAME CHILD

Children having neural tube defects or Down's syndrome were classed to these diagnoses even if the defects were multiple. Of the remaining 3,864 malformed children 3,535 had either only one recognised defect, or the several defects observed were the end results of the same developmental deviation, as in so many children with congenital heart disease and urogenital tract deformities. Undoubtedly in these children other defects must have occurred but were not recognised or recognisable at birth but would only be manifest later or at autopsy. 329 children were classified as having multiple defects and it is impossible in this short account to analyse these cases. However, Table 7 shows the types of malformations which occurred most frequently as one of these defects. These will come as no surprise to those familiar with human congenital malformations.

There is a great need of different types of analyses of the grouping of these multiple anomalies. Such studies might illuminate the question of timing of origins of different defects in the same child. It is significant, however, that although this is a well-recognised problem the difficulties of devising a satisfactory grouping of specific anomalies for such a statistical procedure appear to have prevented anyone from publishing such an analyses.

CONSANGUINITY

In all, in this study, there were 14,000 consanguineous marriages in the 39,472 marriages where any relationship of parents were recorded, a frequency of about 3.7 %. The frequencies vary enormously from about 0.1 % to 33 % and grouping of the data together is clearly difficult to justify. Nevertheless there are one or two points of interest. As already noted, the malformations most strongly associated were neural tube defects. There was a suggestion of

Table 7 Numbers of certain defects occurring in the 329 cases
in the N group

Cases where one of the malformations was:	Number of cases				
	M	F	? Sex	T	%[a]
Malformations of heart and great vessels	41	32	0	73	22.2
Tracheo-oesophageal fistula/oesophageal atresia	8	7	0	15	4.5
Atresia ani (excluding cases of sirenomelia)	26	10	3	39	9.9
Other stenosis of gut	6	4	0	10	3.0
Exomphalos (including agenesis of abdominal wall)	17	13	3	33	10.0
Diaphragm defect	4	6	0	10	3.0
Harelip	7	2	1	10	3.0
Harelip and cleft palate	36	10	0	46	14.0
Cleft palate	18	19	0	37	11.2
Talipes	32	19	1	52	15.8
Polydactyly (ulnar) or (NFS) of hands	16	9	0	25	7.6
Polydactyly of hands and feet	5	0	0	5	1.5
Polydactyly (radial) (bifid thumb)	4	2	0	6	1.8
Syndactyly	5	5	0	10	3.0
Other digital anomalies	8	7	0	15	4.5
Reduction deformities	3	5	0	8	2.4
Other limb anomalies	18	10	1	29	8.8
All urogenital anomalies	69	24	9	102	31.0
Anophthalmia or microphthalmia	9	11	0	20	6.1
Abnormal ears	19	21	0	40	12.1
Atresia of external auditory meatuses	5	6	0	11	3.3

a: Percentage of total cases in N group where specified anomaly occurred.

Table 8 Malformations, perinatal mortality and parental
consanguinity in WHO study

	First cousins and closer	Less than first cousins	Not related
Mortality (malformed excluded)	692/10,492 (65.9 per 1,000)	163/3,271 (49.8 per 1,000)	12,779/355,710 (35.9 per 1,000)
Malformation frequency	180/10,672 (16.9 per 1,000)	57/3,328 (17.1 per 1,000)	4,352/360,061 (12.1 per 1,000)

an association with harelip and cleft palate and with isolated cleft palate. There
was no suggestion, as found in the Japanese data by NEEL and SCHULL[2] of an
association with rare combinations of malformations in the same child.

Indeed when the neural tube defects and known recessive gene traits were
ignored, there was no significant increase in the frequency of malformations in
the offspring of consanguineous over those of unrelated parents. These findings,

confirmatory of those of other authors, suggest strongly that there is a very small recessive gene component in etiology of most of these types of gross developmental mistakes.

As in all consanguinity studies there was good evidence of increased still-birth frequencies and early newborn mortalities in the offspring of consanguineous marriages (Table 8).

WHAT MAY BE DEDUCED FROM THE STUDY

Most of the findings in the Study are only confirmations of what was to be expected. It, however, underlined one or two lessons which recurringly need emphasis and I should like to discuss one or two of them briefly.

This international study and other rather superficial national studies all suggest the need for more careful *ad hoc* epidemiological studies of individual malformations. However, most individual malformations are very uncommon and very few have individual birth frequencies in any country as high as 1/1,000. It follows that epidemiological studies designed to test for associations which might give clues as to etiology are extremely laborious. When it is remembered that there is suggestive evidence in respect of nearly all of these individual malformations that clinical heterogeneity is paralleled by etiological heterogeneity the question must be asked in many instances, "Just how rewarding are such studies likely to be?" The question cannot be answered in any general way, only in respect of individual anomalies.

In many countries in the world, in one form or another there is some registration of malformations which are recognised in stillborn and newborn infants. The data may be available locally or nationally. Further, there are many experiments being made whereby records referring to the relatives of a child and subsequently recorded information regarding the same child can be linked. There is no question but that much good use can be made of such pre-recorded data. Nevertheless, there is always much doubt about the accuracy and specificity of diagnoses in such records. We continually have a paradox. Use of such abundant data enables much more elaborate statistical analyses to be made and it would be physically impossible for any one investigator or even a group exercising carefully worked out diagnostic criteria to see all the cases. Yet whenever a sample of such cases are seen in an *ad hoc* study the vagueness and inaccuracies of the diagnoses become evident.

That many drugs and substances to which pregnant women are exposed are teratogenic is quite evident. To what extent do such controllable factors in fact, contribute to malformation frequencies is another question. Sometimes when reading the scientific press one has the impression that one certain way to be sure of contributing entirely original work to the literature is to take some organic chemical dictionary, open it at a page, close the eyes and select a substance with a pin. Then take a taxonomic list and repeat the procedure. Bring the chemical and embryonic organism together and at some dosage the chemical is teratogenic. That experimental pharmacology like radiation is a valuable research tool needs no emphasis. Further, no knowledge can ever be regarded as without value ultimately to our understanding of living things and to human welfare but work of this kind seems illconceived.

It would appear that (a) there are combinations of naturally occurring factors which determine most malformations in man and different combinations can determine the same or very similar malformations; (b) no doubt some malformations are caused by specific teratogenic agents contributed to the environment by man but these cases are seldom individually identifiable. The teratogens may be very numerous although individually they very seldom are the cause of malformations. Meanwhile, our only advice to women in very early pregnancy is to avoid taking any drug, however harmless.

We badly need better information on repeat frequencies in successive pregnancies of the same or different malformations and there are many other kinds of useful information which can be collected. What is very clear, however, is that for a very long time the great majority of malformations are not going to be explicable in defined environmental and genetic terms.

REFERENCES

1. BARR, A. and STEVENSON, A.C.: Stillbirths and infant mortality in twins. Ann. hum. Genet. 25: 131–140, 1961.
2. NEEL, J.V. and SCHULL, W.J.: The Effect of Exposure to the Atomic Bombs on Pregnancy Termination in Hiroshima and Nagasaki. Washington, D.C., National Academy of Sciences (National Research Council Publication No. 461) 1956.
3. POLMAN, A.: Anencephaly, spina bifida and hydrocephaly. Genetica 25: 29–78, 1950.
4. STEVENSON, A.C., JOHNSTON, H.A., STEWART, M.I.P. and GOLDING, D.R.: Congenital malformations: A report of a study of series of consecutive births in 24 centres. Bull. Wld. Hlth. Org. Suppl. Vol. 34, 1966.
5. STEVENSON, A. C., JOHNSTON, H. A., STEWART, M. I. P. and GOLDING, D. R.: Comparative Study of Congenital Malformations. Basic Tabulations in Respect of Consecutive Post 28–week Births Recorded in Co-operating Centres. Medical Research Council, Population Genetics Research Unit, Oxford, 1966.

THE USE OF A REGISTRY FOR THE STUDY
OF CONGENITAL DEFECT

James R. Miller

Professor, Division of Medical Genetics, Department of Paediatrics,
University of British Columbia, Vancouver, Canada.
(Visiting Research Associate, Department of Anatomy, Faculty of Medicine,
Kyoto University, Kyoto, Japan.)

It is clear from the variety of topics discussed in this Workshop that congenital defect may be studied in many ways. Each one makes some valuable contribution to our understanding of a very serious health problem. The degree of seriousness will vary from country to country and will depend upon other social and health problems in existence. Many of the participants at this Workshop come from countries where the problem of congenital defect is of minor consequence when compared with other pressing social and health problems. However, as the extensive studies of Dr. Stevenson and his colleagues have shown[7,8], no country is free of congenital defect and it seems certain that, as other health problems are gradually resolved, the problem of the malformed individual will assume increasing importance.

From a practical point of view, governmental health agencies may ask two questions about congenital defect: 1) How big a problem is this in terms of the numbers of individuals involved and the resources required to rehabilitate or to maintain them in hospitals or institutions, and 2) If the causes are known, can preventive measures be instituted; if not, what can be done to explore causation?

These questions are not easily answered. As you have learned, the causation of congenital malformation is complex and in only a relatively small percentage of cases can a precise answer be given to questions of etiology. Even questions of how many congenitally malformed individuals occur in a given time and space are not readily answered, although many attempts have been made by means of surveys of varying extent, both in time and space (i. e., geographical extent). Even in a study of the scope and importance of Dr. Stevenson's, the returns are somewhat disappointing and the questions posed out-number the problems answered.

In the province of British Columbia in Canada, an attempt has been made to approach some of these problems by the use of Registry for Handicapped Children and Adults. As you may judge from its title, this registry encompasses more than congenital conditions, but they make up the majority of cases. Many registries have been or are in existence in many countries. These registries have been concerned with individuals who are of interest to health scientists, e. g., twins, individuals with genetically determined disease, malignancies, malformations, etc. I shall not attempt to compare or contrast these various registries with the British Columbia Registry, but simply describe the manner in which the latter operates and the type of service and information it can provide.

ORIGIN AND OPERATION

The Registry was established in 1952 and is administered by the Division of Vital Statistics of the Department of Health Services and Hospital Insurance of the Province. It is financed in part by a National Health Grant (Canada). An attempt is made to obtain as complete a record as possible of all individuals in the province with a handicapping condition. At present, there are close to 35,000 cases on the register. The working definition of a handicapped person is: one who possesses a physical, mental, and/or emotional problem which is likely to be permanently disabling, to interfere with his education, or to prevent full and open employment. This includes children with congenital malformations or familial conditions which may or may not be permanently disabling.

Registration is voluntary. However, all defects reported to the Division of Vital Statistics on the "Physician's Notice of Live or Still Birth Form"—a report which must be completed within 48 hours after every birth—are routinely referred to the Registry. Most of the other registrations come primarily from the excellent provincial public health staff, special treatment centres, and private physicians.

The registration card becomes the basic record for each case. The data recorded on this form are placed on punch cards for statistical processing. This permits correlation or linkage of Registry data with other vital statistics (birth, marriage, death, etc.) which are placed routinely on punch cards also. I shall return to the significance of this point later.

USES OF THE REGISTRY

The basic data gathered in the Registry have two main uses. First, they serve as a continuing source for the estimation of incidence and prevalence statistics. Second, they comprise an index of specific diseases or disabilities which can be used for a number of purposes—both service and research.

1. Data relating to incidence rates of congenital malformation

The incidence rate of a congenital defect is usually expressed as the number of affected children born in a defined time and space for every 1,000 live births occurring in the same period and space. Such data are useful in many ways and I shall illustrate only three here, namely, as a means of a) determining fluctuations and trends in the occurrence of defects, b) studying variation in sex-specific incidence rates, and c) studying racial or ethnic variation in incidence rates.

a) Table 1 shows the rates of registration (estimated incidence rates) for four common congenital malformations for the period 1952-64. The same data are presented graphically in Figure 1. Because registration is voluntary and also because case finding extends over many years after birth, these rates may be considered as minimal estimates of true incidence rates for the population of British Columbia from 1952-64 inclusive. In some instances, these rates are probably quite good approximations of the true rates. This is probably the case in those defects which are detectable at birth and adequately reported on the Physician's Notice, e.g., club foot, spina bifida and meningocele, and cleft lip and palate. However, for such defects as the congenital heart anomalies,

Table 1 Estimated incidence rates for four common congenital malformations

Malformation	Birth year—Rates per 1,000 live births*													
	1952	1953	1954	1955	1956	1957	1958	1959	1960	1961	1962	1963	1964	1952–1964
Club foot	2.45	2.71	2.49	2.58	2.48	2.06	2.50	2.15	1.92	1.50	1.34	2.05	2.26	2.17
Cleft lip and/or palate	1.48	1.73	1.97	2.17	1.68	1.88	1.72	1.58	1.65	1.50	1.42	1.65	1.62	1.69
Spina bifida and meningocoele	1.04	0.95	1.18	1.03	0.97	0.72	0.76	1.08	0.67	0.60	0.66	0.61	0.89	0.85
Congenital heart defects	3.89	4.19	3.76	4.25	4.22	3.97	3.71	2.70	2.14	2.33	2.28	2.13	1.89	3.15

* There were on the average, about 36,400 live births per year.

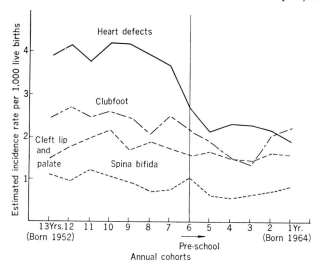

Fig. 1 Estimated incidence rates for four common congenital malformations

these rates are gross underestimates of the true rates, particularly in the pre-school age group. It is noticed in Figure 1 that there is a sharp drop between the seven and six year old groups and that the rate in the pre-school group is approximately one half that in the school age group. This trend does not reflect a decline in the rate of these defects in British Columbia but rather the fact that many defects are undetected or unregistered in the pre-school group. Since the provincial health program provides school health services, we can assume that these cases will be registered as they enter school.

The fluctuations in the rates of the defects shown in Table 1 and Figure 1 are intriguing. Do they represent random fluctuations about a theoretical true incidence rate, or is there an underlying biological significance of which we are ignorant? The ability to examine fluctuations and trends is one significant advantage of the registry system over the usual short term survey procedures for obtaining statistics of this type.

It should be pointed out that, while annual rates have been used in this example, examination of other time (e. g., seasonal) and space (e. g., specific

Table 2 Number of cases registered with selected malformations, born 1952-1964 and estimated sex-specific incidence rates per 1,000 live births.

Malformation	Number of cases		Rate per 1,000 live births	
	Male	Female	Male	Female
Club foot	609	419	2.51	1.81
Congenital dislocation of hip	49	217	0.20	0.94
Spina bifida and meningocoele	187	214	0.77	0.93
Cleft lip with palate	233	138	0.96	0.60
Cleft lip (isolated)	123	54	0.51	0.23
Cleft palate (isolated)	125	128	0.52	0.55

localities within the Province) intervals might be of value.   Since the precise date and place of birth is available on the registry card, the calculations of these rates are readily possible.

b) Table 2 shows data on the sex-specific incidence rates of several common congenital defects. It is seen that there are defects which occur more frequently in females (e. g., congenital dislocation of the hip), others which occur more frequently in males (e. g., club foot) and others which occur with equal frequency in both sexes (e. g., isolated cleft palate).   These sex differences presumably reflect differences in the nature and/or rate of morphological events occurring during embryogenesis.

The data on the cleft lip and palate complex are of interest because they indicate the existence of two quite distinct entities: isolated cleft palate, in which the frequency is approximately the same in each sex, and cleft lip with or without cleft palate, which occurs approximately 1.75 times as often in males as in females. Data presented below suggest further divisions of this complex may be possible.

c) The studies of Dr. STEVENSON and others have indicated differences in the rates with which various defects occur in different parts of the world.   These differences might reflect the existence of environmental and/or genetic differences between various populations.   It is of interest, therefore, to obtain information on types and frequencies of defects in various racial or ethnic groups living

Table 3 Number of cases registered with cleft-lip and palate complex, born 1952-1964 and estimated race specific incidence rates per 1,000 live births.

Type of CLP	Number of cases		Rate per 1,000 live births	
	Indian	Non-Indian	Indian	Non-Indian
Cleft lip only	5	172	0.25	0.38
Cleft palate only	9	244	0.44	0.54
Cleft lip and palate	50	321	2.48	0.71
All type	64	737	3.17	1.63

(LOWRY and RENWICK, in press)

within a defined geographical region under approximately the same environmental conditions.

In Table 3, data are presented relating to the incidence of cleft lip and palate in the North American Indian population and non-Indian population (mostly Caucasian) of British Columbia. It is seen that the rate for this complex is about twice as great in the Indian as in the non-Indian population. As indicated in Table 2, the cleft lip and palate complex comprises two major components— isolated cleft palate and cleft lip with or without cleft palate. When the statistics are broken down, it is seen that the difference between the two populations is not in the frequency of isolated cleft palate or isolated cleft lip but in the frequency of cleft lip with cleft palate (LOWRY and RENWICK, in press).

It should be pointed out that the Indians in British Columbia do not have an over-all increase in the frequency of congenital malformations compared to the non-Indian population. In certain defects (e. g., central nervous system defect such as spina bifida), the Indian population has a much lower incidence.

2. The use of the registry as an index

The possession of an up to date register of individuals with specific defects has many advantages and I shall discuss only two which are representative, namely, its value a) in follow-up studies to assess rehabilitative and educational needs and progress, and b) for research studies into various aspects of etiological significance.

a) As I indicated at the outset, one of the more practical questions which may be posed by governmental health agencies relates to the number of malformed individuals in the region under their jurisdiction and the special needs of these individuals with respect to medical, educational, and rehabilitative resources. The British Columbia Registry has provided statistics relating to these questions for various health agencies within the Province and has been indirectly instrumental in having special services provided when gaps were found to exist.

At the level of the individual patient, questions may be asked about whether satisfactory progress is being made and whether all of the existing available services are being utilized. The Registry, through the cooperation of local public health staffs, obtains regular follow-up reports on all registry cases. If problems relating to medical treatment, or educational and rehabilitative services are detected, these are brought to the attention of the appropriate service agency. In this way, the Registry provides a vital on-going service (without direct involvement with the patient) to the individuals on the register.

b) The register may also be used for studies into etiology. These are retrospective studies for the most part, but can also be prospective if used in conjunction with other vital and health records. The registry index can be used for many retrospective studies regardless of whether a particular individual on the register is living or dead at the time of study. The full potential of such an index in terms of the amount of information extractable and the ease of operation will depend upon how the index is linked with other vital and health records. The value of linked records is receiving a great deal of attention at the present time[1]. The fact that the British Columbia Registry is part of the vital statistics services of the Province makes possible linkage of Registry data with vital statistics such as births, marriages and deaths and with other health records.

As an illustraion, I should like to present some results of a recent study of certain epidemiological aspects of Down's syndrome (mongolism) in British Columbia. Within the past few years, evidence has been presented to indicate that there is a clustering of such cases in time and space and it has been suggested that a viral agent might be operating to produce the chromosomal error observed in Down's syndrome. Specifically, it has been suggested that the infectious hepatitis virus might be responsible[9]. Several studies carried out to investigate this have indicated on good association but in most of these no specific tests for clustering have been used. However, in a recent study in Michigan by STARK and MANTEL[6] specific statistical tests were employed. Using data from the British Columbia Registry, supplemented with other vital statistics and health data, it was possible to apply appropriate statistical analysis to this problem. No significant variation in yearly or seasonal incidence of Down's syndrome was found. Using a special statistical method for detecting clusters it was possible to observe highly significant clustering of hepatitis cases but no clustering of cases of Down's syndrome could be detected. In addition the incidence of Down's syndrome could not be correlated with the incidence of infectious hepatitis nine months previously (Table 4)[2].

Table 4 Incidence of infectious hepatitis compared with the incidence of Down's syndrome nine months later

Year	Infectious hepatitis	Down's syndrome			
	Number of cases reported per 100,000 population	Year of birth (Oct.-Sept.)	Number cases	Number live births	Incidence per 1,000
1952	17.7	1952–53	45	31,107	1.45
1953	63.2	1953–54	42	32,966	1.27
1954	94.2	1954–55	52	33,655	1.54
1955	62.6	1955–56	32	35,860	0.89
1956	24.5	1956–57	42	37,901	1.11
1957	26.4	1957–58	54	39,604	1.36
1958	36.3	1958–59	49	39,811	1.23
1959	57.9	1959–60	53	40,525	1.31
1960	57.7	1960–61	50	38,542	1.30
Total			419	329,971	1.27

As I mentioned at the outset, I have cited only certain examples of the use of Registry data. For more detailed examples the reader is referred to the reports of RENWICK and his colleagues[3,4,5].

DISCUSSION

I would not like to give the impression that a registry is some magical solution for the study of population aspects of congenital defect. In fact, some people are skeptical that registries are of any value at all. This attitude is based on the fact that many registries have been started and have soon become filing cabinets filled with cases of questionable reliability in terms of precise diagnosis and which are never followed up or analyzed in any way. However, if the limitations and problems of a registry are recognized and if it is realized that constant hard work is necessary to maintain registration of new cases, check accuracy of diagnosis, keep old cases up to date, etc., it is my opinion that the information derived from such a system is of great value and can be obtained in no other way.

It is often asked if a registry need be based in or associated with some governmental agency. My own belief is that it must if proper use is to be made of the data collected. It is vital that the registry staff is conversant with many aspects of the health sciences, that adequate statistical services are available, and that there is a guarantee of long term financial support. Registries established by voluntary health agencies, by local medical associations, or within university complexes may possess adequate health personnel but will often lack adequate statistical consultation and undoubtedly not have a firm guarantee of long-term financial support. In addition, they will lack the means to relate the information on their registry to other vital and health records maintained by government agencies. In order that the maximum use can be made of its data, the registry should be based in a situation such that adequate personnel and financial support is guaranteed and designed so that responsible investigators not directly involved with its operation may make use of the accumulated data.

SUMMARY

As may be realized from the material presented in the Workshop, the biological problems presented by congenital malformations are exceedingly complex. In order to study many of the population aspects of these problems, as well as to assess the impact of congenital defect on the health, educational, and rehabilitative services of a community, it seems essential that methods be devised for the routine documentation of individuals with these defects. To be used effectively, this information must be linked with routine vital and health statistics. I have given examples to support this thesis using data derived from the British Columbia Registry for Handicapped Children and Adults.

ACKNOWLEDGEMENTS

I should like to thank the following persons who helped and advised in making this presentation.

Miss NANCY SCOTT and Dr. D. PATERSON of the Registry for Handicapped Children and Adults; Dr. R. B. LOWRY, Dr. P. A. BAIRD, and Miss S. MANNING of the Division of Medical Genetics, Department of Paediatrics, University of British Columbia. Dr. R.W. MILLER kindly drew my attention to the report of STARK and MANTEL.

REFERENCES

1. ACHESON, E.D.: Medical Record Linkage. Oxford: University Press, 1967.
2. BAIRD, P.A. and MILLER, J.R.; Some epidemiological aspects of mongolism in British Columbia. Brit. J. Prev. Soc. Med. 22: 81–85, 1968.

3. RENWICK, D.H.G.: Estimating prevalence of certain chronic childhood conditions by use of a central registry. Public Health Reports 82: 261–269, 1967.

4. RENWICK, D.H.G.: The combined use of a central registry and vital records for incidence studies of congenital defects. Brit. J. Prev. Soc. Med. 22: 61–67, 1968.

5. RENWICK, D.H.G., MILLER, J.R. and PATERSON, D.: Estimates of the incidence and prevalence of mongolism and of congenital heart disease in British Columbia. Canad. Med. Ass. J. 91: 365–371, 1964.

6. STARK, C.R. and MANTEL, N.; Lack of seasonal- or temporal-spatial clustering of Down's syndrome birth in Michigan. Amer. J. Epid. 86: 199–213, 1967.

7. STEVENSON, A.C., JOHNSTON, H.A., STEWART, M.I.P. and GOLDING, D.R.: Congenital Malformations: A report of a study of series of consecutive births in 24 centres. World Health Organization; Geneva (Suppl. to vol. 34 of the Bulletin of WHO), 1966.

8. STEVENSON, A.C.: Findings and lessons for the future from a comparative study of congenital malformations at 24 centres in 16 countries. In: Methods for Teratological Studies in Experimental Animals and Man. Edited by NISHIMURA, H. and MILLER, J.R., Igaku Shoin, Tokyo, 1969.

9. STOLLER, A. and COLLMANN, R.D.: Incidence of infective hepatitis followed by Down's syndrome nine months later. Lancet. 2: 1221–1223, 1965.

DISCUSSION

FRASER (Canada)

Is it possible that a virus could act to predispose to non-disjunction by some indirect means, such as antibody production, or by decreasing chiasma association in a dictyotene oocyte? Such an effect would tend to blur the temporal association between virus epidemic and malformation frequency.

MILLER

Of course such a possibility is a real one and if it existed the initiating event could presumably occur at any time during the mother's life. Since infections are not routinely recorded, and attempts at correlating a particular epidemic with malformations such as Down's syndrome years later would be most difficult.

I think it may be relevant here to point out that many of the Indians in British Columbia live under conditions in which infectious hepatitis is endemic and thus far we have not been able to detect any increase in the incidence of Down's syndrome or any other chromosomally determined defect in these people.

SEVER (U.S.A.)

The data for a relation between hepatitis and Down's syndrome from Australia was analyzed in a way which showed a 9 month delay between increased hepatitis and increased Down's syndrome. Can your data be analyzed in this way instead of the 1 year intervals?

MILLER

Yes, and perhaps we were negligent in not breaking down our analysis in monthly intervals. However, we did do one additional analysis which is reported in our original paper. There were four quarterly intervals during the period studied when there were dramatic peaks in the prevalence of hepatitis. We examined the incidence of Down's syndrome in the quarterly periods 9 months after each of these peaks and still could not demonstrate a significant change.

MILLER, R.W. (U.S.A.)

It is good that we both described lack of an association between Down's syndrome and hepatitis because publicity has been widespread that there is an association between the 2 diseases. There are now 5 studies in which no relationship was found, indicating that circumstances in Australia were special or that the finding there is not valid.

With reference to your previous comment*that anyone can be an epidemiologist. Vaccination against smallpox developed from an observation made by a milkmaid; as already mentioned Warkany (a pediatrician) through an epidemiologic effort brought about the eradication of acrodynia; a secretary is said to have been the first to recognize microcephaly among the children exposed in utero to the atomic bomb in Hiroshima; the same anomaly following therapeutic irradiation of the pelvis during pregnancy was discovered by MURPHY, an obstetrician; GREGG was an ophthalmologist; and there are many other examples.

(*The coment here refers to an incidental statement by J. R. MILLER that while statistical advice was available the study on the possible relation of hepatitis and Down's syndrome was carried out by two people who were not trained in epidemiology.)

NISHIMURA (Japan)

I think sometimes human congenital malformations have some bearing on the problem of the rights of privacy. I am wondering whether you have experienced some implications in this respect, through your contacts with the Registry you describe.

MILLER

This is a very important point. Every effort is made by Registry personnel to protect the confidentiality of the records and to guarantee that no interference between a physician and his patient occurs. The Registry has no direct contact with the individuals on the register and all communication for follow-up or research studies is made through the registering agency most frequently the local public health officer.

ENVIRONMENTAL FACTORS IN THE ETIOLOGY OF CONGENITAL MALFORMATIONS IN MAN: SOME GAPS AND PROBLEMS

JOSEF WARKANY

Professor of Research Pediatrics, Children's Hospital Research Foundation, University of Cincinnati, Cincinnati, Ohio, U.S.A.

You have been listening to many lectures which taught you many facts and you may feel discouraged and overawed by the knowledge of the faculty. I plan to point out to you how little we know and that we need your help in improving teratologic knowledge. In contrast to the speakers who shared with you their knowledge, I plan to share with you my ignorance hoping to stimulate you to work that is still to be done.

The field of viruses and congenital malformations, that has been so well discussed by Dr. SEVER seems to me a very fruitful one. Nobody knows how many malformations are caused by viruses but there may be many more than we suspect. I believe and hope that in the future virus research will yield a rich harvest and contribute particularly to the elucidation of mental retardation, an area which greatly overlaps that of teratology. Although Dr. SEVER has pointed out the number of teratologic models available to the virus expert, I should like to emphasize how underdeveloped experimental virus teratology is as compared to chemical and nutritional teratology, branches which may have much fewer applications to man than microbiological teratology. There is an immense field for courageous investigators who like to gamble. Let us remember that not only viruses but also other microorganisms such as toxoplasmosis can be involved in such congenital defects as hydrocephalus and microcephalus.

The field of radiation has been covered thoroughly by Dr. BRENT. Radiation has been widely used in experimental teratology. It is a rather accurate and useful instrument particularly when applied during the organogenetic period. The future may lie in the application of this fine instrument to the production of mutations and of cytogenetic anomalies. A less spectacular application may be one to neurology. Like others, we have been impressed with the behavior of micrencephalic rats whose brains were damaged by radiation at the end of their embryonic period. Dr. BRENT told you about this and showed you one example. These rats can live a rather normal life and reproduce in spite of their lack of important brain structures. This is in contrast to mentally deficient children we see who often have almost normal brain morphology. Again it will take a courageous person to try to explain to us how such gross deficiencies are compatible with normal life and reactivity of these animals.

In the area of nutrition and teratology, covered by Dr. ASLING, we find a wealth of experimental evidence that deficiencies can be teratogenic, but we are hard pressed to find parallel human situations. To quote one example: Vitamin A deficiency is teratogenic in pigs and rats. The effects are almost identical in these different species as shown by the work of HALE, PALLUDAN and our group. It would be likely that man is equally affected, yet proof of this is lacking. Vitamin A deficiency was endemic in Indonesia and parts of India as we know by the high incidence of keratomalacia that existed there and may still exist in some parts. Yet there are not many reports of congenital malformations specifically associated with this deficiency. Where such deficiencies prevail physicians have to deal with problems other than congenital malformations and fetal wastage. It would be fortunate if some members of this workshop from Indonesia or other areas where vitamin A deficiency is prevalent could make investigations along these lines.

That nutritional deficiency of the mother can damage the human fetus is proven by endemic cretinism. Where lack of iodine leads to endemic goiter endemic cretins may be born to goitrous mothers. I first became acquainted with this remarkable condition as a young boy hiking through the Alps of Austria. There we found dwarfs with goiters, mental deficiencies and physical deficiencies which, I was told were due to iodine deficiency. This actually got me into the field of nutritional teratology. Endemic cretinism is and was not a rarity like phenylketonuria or similar metabolic errors but a national disaster which affected the history of entire peoples. Hundreds of thousands of people were physically and mentally impaired because of maternal iodine deficiency. I should like to point out that mothers with endemic goiters sometimes had several cretin children so that pedigrees of such families look like those of families whith genetic disorders.

Chemical compounds and drugs causing congenital malformations have not often been identified with the exception of thalidomide. The role of androgens causing female pseudohermaphroditism has been mentioned. Aminopterin, an antifolic acid metabolite is an established, though rare, teratogen in man. We saw a child in Cincinnati, whose mother had taken aminopterin for abortive purpose. She was very frank about it and we got excellent information. Although she was 42 weeks pregnant, the child weighed only 1300 grams, in other words, it had marked intrauterine growth retardation. The skull was soft, the bones of the cranium were not ossified. The ears were low set and the jaw underdeveloped. There was a posterior palate cleft and there were clubbed feet. I like to discuss the case to raise the question of proof of teratogenicity of drugs in single cases. The fact that a mother used a drug and then had a child with congenital malformation does not prove, of course, that the drug caused the malformation. In our case we thought that aminopterin was guilty for the following reasons.

1. Folic acid antagonists have been proven to be teratogenic in experimental animals.
2. Human embryos with congenital maformations such as anencephaly, exencephaly, hydrocephaly, have been observed by THIERSCH in Seattle after mothers had been given aminopterin for therapeutic abortion.
3. The malformations of the child that I have just discussed above were quite unusual. They did not correspond to any known or common

syndrome.

4. The malformations observed were compatible with the mother's statement of the time at which the drug was taken, namely the period of the end of organogenesis.
5. The child's brothers and sisters were normal. There were no congenital malformations in the entire pedigree available.

We suggested that the syndrome was possibly due to aminopterin, but certainty was not obtained from one case. However, when other children were observed whose mothers had tried abortion with aminopterin, and the children had a soft skull, absence of cranial bones, cleft palate etc., the case for the implication of aminopterin seemed established.

It is recommended that the guilt of drugs taken by mothers during pregnancy should not be assumed unless it can be sustained by critical evaluation which may permit conclusions from very few cases.

The known environmental teratogens are few, and only few congenital malformations can be explained by external events. There may be many more non-genetic factors responsible for congenital malformations but these seem to be of an intricate and elusive nature. This is demonstrated by many cases of monozygotic twins who differ in regard to congenital malformations. They suggest that local intrauterine factors can determine congenital malformations. Such factors may be common and varied though unknown to us at the present time. They are demonstrated only if we get a control in the form of an identical twin.

These local factors can be teratogenic but interestingly they can as also be preventive as suggested by identical twins discordant for an inherited trait. There are pedigrees in which cleft lip and palate occur in certain families. Then a pair of identical twins is born and only one is affected. There must be something that prevents this inherited tendency to cleft palate from manifesting itself. Nature can prevent such an inherited tendency to cleft palate but we cannot. There seems to be a huge field of teratology that has hardly been considered yet. These local factors may very well be a field of investigation for obstetricians.

Dr. TAKANO has discussed maternal disease as a cause of congenital malformations. No doubt there is something in this subject, but again the answers are elusive. As he told you there are cases on record of hyperthyroid mothers who gave birth to micro- or hydrocephalic children and there are hyperthyroid mothers who give birth to normal children. The same situation exists in diabetes mellitus. You may have heard about the "caudal regression syndrome" (absence of sacrum and short femur) discovered only a few years ago, in children born to diabetic mothers. The fact that this syndrome was discovered only recently makes one think that something has happened recently, possibly that a new treatment may be responsible for these defects. The question was raised at this workshop by Dr. McBRIDE whether well treated cases of diabetes mellitus result in anomalies of children. Can good treatment of the mother prevent anomalies in her children? I do not know. But I do remember that some years ago Dr. HERBERT MILLER, Professor of Pediatrics in Kansas City, assembled good evidence that certain anomalies in children of diabetic mothers appeared before the mother's diabetes became manifest, i.e., in the prediabetic stage. I do not know if this is still accepted; but I remember a child born with cleft lip and palate and hypospadias. The child's mother had had a miscarriage; then she gave birth to a child with hydrocephalus and polydactyly, then she had two miscarriages, subsequently diabetes was diagnosed and insulin treatment began. Then she had another miscarriage and then she had the baby with facial clefts and hypospadias. The mother had diabetes, her mother had diabetes and the great-grandmother had diabetes also.

Is all this coincidence, or are there different kinds of diabetes? I think there are. It is possible that some types of diabetes tend to defective offspring whereas the common type does not. If the special cases were diluted in statistics by the common ones, the teratogenic effects of some forms could be concealed.

One could say here a few words about epidemiological research in teratology. I subscribe enthusiastically to the statements of BOB and JIM MILLER that epidemiologic approaches can be fruitful in the search for etiologic factors causing congenital malformations. But as they pointed out such investigations can also be quite sterile—for many reasons. If categories of heterogeneous origin are lumped together, and covered up by one common label, the results will be disappointing. I mentioned the possibility that diabetes mellitus may not be a single entity. Statistical research is usually sterile if it deals with a malformation which is a symptom but not an etiologic entity. Take, for instance, cleft lip and palate. Before 1942 the contortions of some geneticists who tried to press these clefts into a Mendelian mold were pitiful. When FOGH-ANDERSEN in 1942 distinguished between the cleft lip-palate complex and isolated cleft palate, things improved. But since then the facial clefts have been further subdivided according to causation. We know of a few environmental causes: aminopterin or myleran administration and the factors manifested by discordant monozygotic twins. We know of clefts attributable to chromosomal changes. It is well known that trisomy 13–15 is frequently associated with facial cleft but other trisomies are also capable of cleft formation. It seems that in trisomy 13–15, 75% of the patients have harelip or cleft palate or both. In trisomy 18, 15%; in trisomy 21, only 1.5%. It is rare that a child with Down's syndrome has a cleft, but it is still 10 times more frequent than in the general population. Deletion of the short arm of chromosome 4 and various translocation syndromes have been associated with facial clefts. In addition there are now at least 10 syndromes known which contain cleft palate, and each one of these has its own etiology. Now mix all these clefts together in a "cleft stew" and ask for the stew's etiology—well, you cannot expect meaningful results. The secret of Dr. ROBERT MILLER's success in epidemiologic research is that he is a pediatrician with knowledge of, or feeling for, etiologic entities which lend themselves to statistical analysis. Yet, as both Drs. MILLER pointed out even simple descriptive epidemiology has its value. Twenty-five years ago when the medical profession showed very little interest in teratology, the Vital Statistics of the United States and other countries pointed out the increasing rates of congenital malformations as a cause of death, a fact which induced the National Institutes of Health to form a study section on Human Embryology and Development which made possible much of the work in teratology about which you heard in this Workshop.

And now let me add a few remarks about experimental teratology, as it relates to questions of human malformations. When we became interested 30 years ago in experimental mammalian teratology, it was in the hope that creation of animal models would be instrumental in the prevention of congenital malformations. We had seen that the rachitic rat led to the solution of the rickets problem and the scorbutic guinea pig to that of scurvy. It was, and still is my hope that experimental teratology will contribute to the prevention of congenital malformations. To find the etiologic factors and to remove them is our final goal. On the way to that goal we can indulge in the study of mechanisms and pathogenesis which are of great interest to the curious scientist. Dr. FRASER has presented the work of teratologists who consistently contribute to the elucidation of cleft palate morphogenesis; Dr. MURAKAMI and I showed you how we enjoy following in experimental animals the abnormal morphogenesis of the central nervous system. But the public that supports us does not care a bit about mechanisms that lead to congenital malformations. The public wants prevention. Of course understanding of mechanism sometimes helps in the recognition of causes; pathogenesis can not be sharply separated from etiology, but the study of mechanism should not have priority over the study of etiology, the study of causation. History shows that when the etiology of a disease is once elucidated, and the disease eradicated the interest in mechanisms is quickly lost. There are few who work today on the mechanisms involved in rickets, scurvy, endemic cretinism or poliomyelitis, to name a few whose history I know. This waning interest is regrettable to the scientist but parents have now other worries. Fear of having a deformed or mentally retarded child is now more prevalent. To bring possible infectious agents to the laboratory to this purpose, to test drugs in animals are important practical tasks. But now we do not know what animal to use, what methods to apply for standard tests. The rat is a much used animal, and it was chosen officially for this purpose; but thalidomide is not teratogenic in rats, whereas aspirin is. Yet you can buy the "rat-teratogenic" aspirin without prescription in big quantities in the drug store, but you cannot obtain thalidomide for any price. There is of course no logic in this, and there is no simple answer. One had to learn that vitamin C can not be tested in rats, and vitamin D can not be tested in guinea pigs. One will have to find similarly different models for different classes of drugs and for different anatomical anomalies. There is great hope that primate teratology may be best suited for drug testing. Dr. WILSON's experiments are most promising, but even monkeys may not simulate man completely. One hears often that tests with monkeys will be too expensive for practical purposes. I can not agree with this opinion. One hundred dollars spent for a meaningful primate test is cheaper than one dollar spent for a meaningless rat test. Whatever the answer will be, it will not be obtained easily. Governments, industries and the public will have to pay to make drugs safe. I recommend that you, as teratologists, refuse to give cheap answers that are scientifically wrong. There are many other questions we can not answer readily; questions of genetic counselling, and questions of law. Our ignorance is vast.

After this confession, we have to ask: "Was this Workshop a success ?".

No doubt, for those who wanted general and ready answers it was not; but those who are eager to work in this field should find satisfaction that there is so much to be done. If you have learned that important and fundamental work can be done in any place and without much money, you have learned a great deal. It would be most fortunate if cooperative work would develop as a result of this Workshop. As you return to your countries you may find that you have unique genetic or nutritional situations which may lend themselves to excellent teratological research.

Not only the participants but also the observers, and the faculty have learned a great deal. We have learned to admire the splendid organizational ability of our Japanese colleagues who under Dr. NISHIMURA's leadership arranged this Workshop. The Japanese hospitality can not be topped by any nation. We have learned to admire the devotion of his staff to the execution of the Workshop. I am deeply impressed by the enthusiasm of the young people we have seen here who are eager to serve and to contribute to the success of this undertaking. There have always been excellent relations among teratologists of our generation, nationally and internationally, and many members of your faculty have worked together for many years in the past. If this spirit of cooperation and mutual understanding has been promoted here, this International Workshop in Teratology can be considered a success. I think I speak for all of you if I thank our hosts for the opportunity to meet here and to work together.

PART II. DEMONSTRATIONS

COMPARISON BETWEEN MAN AND SOME OTHER MAMMALS OF NORMAL AND ABNORMAL DEVELOPMENTAL PROCESSES

Hideo Nishimura, *Professor*, and Hideki Yamamura, *Graduate Student*

Department of Anatomy, Faculty of Medicine,
Kyoto University, Kyoto, Japan.

Investigators engaged in teratological experiments must be familiar with the normal development and also spontaneously occurring maldevelopment of the animals which they use. In this demonstration, some of the fundamental results obtained mainly from our own experiments on the development of two species, ICR-JCL mice and Dutch rabbits will be given.

The ICR-JCL strain from the Central Institute for Experimental Animals in Tokyo has an excellent capability of growth and reproduction. Its average litter size is 12–13. Dutch rabbits are characterized by small body size. They weigh on the average about 2 kg, that is, about a half the weight of the New Zealand White. They have the reputation of being good mothers according to a personal communication from Dr. Sawin in The Jackson Laboratory, U.S.A.

In addition, these observations will be compared with those made on a large number of undamaged human embryonic specimens in our laboratory. These specimens were obtained from mothers whose pregnancy was interrupted by curettage mostly because of social reasons. Knowledge obtained from these comparative studies is expected to be useful in experiments in which the potential embryotoxicity of various agents is tested in animals.

DEVELOPMENT IN GENERAL

Table 1 gives data on some developmental phenomena of the three species. This Table shows that there is an evident difference in developmental rate among the three species. Also, some other differences are found: the period between conception and puberty is 9 % of the life span in mice, 13 % in rabbits and 18 % in man; both mouse and rabbit are born in less mature state, that is, blind, closed-eared, naked, and therefore require a warm nest; some bodily movement at birth in these two species is also less developed than in human newborns. However, it is of great importance that most of the developmental events take place in almost the same manner among the three species.

NORMAL PRENATAL DEVELOPMENT

The developmental period covers not only the prenatal stage but also the postnatal period. For instance, differentiation of nervous system (such as myeli-

Table 1 Comparison of some developmental phenomena among three species

Species	Interval between fertilization and implantation (hours)	Length of gestation (days)	Developmental states at birth	Age, initiation of weaning (weeks)	Interval, birth to puberty (months)
Mouse (ICR-JCL)	72	18–20	Eye and ear closed by epithelial coalescence, naked, motor ability underdeveloped	3	1
Rabbit (Dutch)	70	31–34	Eye and ear closed by epithelial coalescence, naked, motor ability underdeveloped	6	4
Man	140	266–294	Eye and ear opened, hairy, myelogenesis of central nervous system more progressed, grasping reflex positive	20	144

nation, lamination of cells in the cerebral cortex), teeth, skeleton, lymphoid tissues and gonads take place during the postnatal period. However, the most striking developmental changes occur in the early period of pregnancy. This stage, especially the time of organogenesis corresponds to the so called critical period and this is characterized by a high sensitivity to teratogenic agents. Because of the emphasis of this Workshop, my review will be restricted to this period.

While developmental processes may be studied in a variety of ways this presentation which emphasizes comparative aspects will deal mainly with gross morphological features which may be studied by external examination.

A. Mode of external development

To stage human embryos, we adopted Streeter's horizon system[1,11-14]. Figure 1 shows the relation between developmental horizon and age. A striking fact in man is that a wide range of variation in developmental horizon is observed at any given clinical age[8]. So, we sometimes use the "standardized age" derived from my regression curve in Figure 1 instead of individual clinical age.

The figures in Plates I, II and III show photographs of representative developmental stages in the three species under study. Since there are relatively few examples of good photographs of human embryos available in the literature, emphasis has been placed on human specimens (Plates I and II) obtained from our own large collection.

The development of most external features takes place in almost the same manner in most mammals, if the viewpoint of age is neglected. However, there are some cases in which a certain organ of one species shows different developmental pathways from that observed in other species. Examples of these phenomena are as follows:

a. Scalp vascular plexus: in *man,* a distinct vascular plexus of the scalp appears at first on the half way between eye-ear level and vertex on the both sides (Fig. 14) and it moves towards the vertex as development proceeds (Figs. 15–17); in *rabbit* and *mouse* no distinct movement of the scalp vascular plexus is seen.

b. Auricle: in *mouse* and *rabbit,* the free margin of the auricle turns

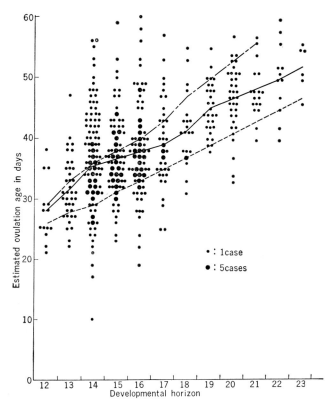

Fig. 1 Relationship beween developmental horizon and estimated ovulation age of human embryos (The heavy line indicates the regression curve drawn from our plotted 675 cases from mothers with regular menstrual cycle; the dash line and chain line present the regression curve obtained by STREETER[11-14] and WITSCHI[16] respectively.)

forward (Fig. 20) and later its surface is attached to the head, covering the external auditory pore completely (Figs. 21 and 24). This condition exists until after birth in *mouse,* but in *rabbit* it continues only for about 3 days during prenatal life. In *man,* the auricle develops without turning and attachment of its free margin to the head.

    c.   Upper lip: in *man,* the inner borders of two medial nasal processes meet each other and fuse to form the median part of the upper lip; in *rabbit* and *mouse,* the fusion is incomplete and the median cleft persists throughout life.

    d.   Whiskers: *in rabbit* and *mouse,* the follicles of whiskers appear on the snout (Figs. 20, 21, 24 and 25) and later at a certain prenatal stage the whiskers erupt from these follicles; in *man* no whiskers develop.

    e.   Limbs: in *man* and *mouse,* the forelimbs develop earlier than the hind-limbs (Figs. 7–16); in *rabbit,* both fore- and hindlimbs show almost the same developmental stage (Figs. 23–25).

Table 2 Some external developmental features with

Value assigned to each feature	Central nervous system	Eyes	Ears	Palate	Developmental Branchial arches
	neural groove: unrecognizable	unrecognizable	unrecognizable	palatine shelves: unrecognizable	unrecognizable
1	open through-out the whole length	optic evagination			
2	closed in the midtrunk region				I
3			auditory vesicle: open		I, II
4	ant. neuropore closed				I, II, III
5					
6	⌐ post. neuropore closed		closed		I, II, III, IV
7		lens vesicle: open			
8		closed			III and/or IV disappeared
9		eye-lids: ⌐ indicated	external auditory pore surround-ed by hillocks	⌐ recognizable	⌐ all arches disappeared
10			⌐ auricle recogniz-able		
11		spindle shaped opening		horizontal position or ap-proaching to that condition	
12					
13				fused partially	
14		slit-like opening		fused completely	
15		closed com-pletely			
16					

the arbitrarily assigned values as criteria in rating embryos

features

Forelimb	Hindlimb	Physiological umbilical hernia	Somite	Integument	External genitalia
unrecognizable	unrecognizable	unrecognizable	unrecognizable	nipples: unrecognizable	genital tubercle: unrecognizable
			recognizable, but not on the whole length of the back		
small ridge					
low longish swelling	small ridge		recognizable on the whole length of the back		
semicircular or fin shaped ridge	low longish swelling				
horseshoe shaped ridge	semicircular or fin shaped ridge	∟ recognizable			∟ recognizable
paddle shaped ridge	horseshoe shaped ridge		disappeared in the cervical region	∟ recognizable	
digital ray with or without indentation on ∟ dorsal surface	paddle shaped ridge ∟		∟		
all interdigital notches present	digital ray with or without indentation on dorsal surface		disappeared in the cervical and thoracal region	follicles of whiskers or eyebrow recognizable	
all interdigital notches become deeper and acute angled	all interdigital notches present		disappeared from the back		
	all interdigital notches become deeper and acute angled				
fingers separated completely or fused proximally again, but still divergent					
	toes separated completely or fused proximally again, but still divergent				
fingers II to IV situated parallel to each other		disappeared			
	toes II to IV situated parallel to each other				

f. Digits: in *mouse* and *rabbit* as the development of digits proceeds, their separation from each other becomes complete and then later they become attached to each other by dermal adhesion of the proximal part (Figs. 21 and 25); in *man*, such dermal adhesion does not take place.

g. Tail: in *man*, the tail regresses gradually and by the beginning of fetal stage (older than horizon 23) it almost disappears (Figs. 14–17); in *rabbit* and *mouse* no regression of the tail takes place.

h. Turning of the embryo: in *mouse* a process of turning of the whole trunk takes place at early embryonic stage and it results in a reversal of the curvature of the body from S-form (Fig. 18) to C-form (Fig. 19); in *man* and *rabbit*, such a turning does not take place.

Besides these differences in mode of external development, there are some differences in the number of organ primordia such as somites, nipples and toes among the three species

B. Morphological age determined by numerical rating system

This numerical rating system for embryos, I am proposing, may be called "morphological age" and serves as a method of comparing prenatal development at the stage of organogenesis in several mammalian species. Its usefulness is comparable to body weight or body length as an indicator of bodily growth. This is an extension of an idea proposed by WALKER and CRAIN[15] who developed a method of calculating morphological ratings on mouse embryos by employing many of the external developmental features described by GRÜNEBERG[3].

When we observe an embryo with retarded development, we must use some objective criteria to determine whether this is normal or abnormal variation. The morphological rating system which is a numerical evaluation of the developmental state as a whole fulfills such requirement. Furthermore the corresponding developmental stage of different species can be obtained by using this system. In addition, it enables us to compare individual variation of the developmental state at a corresponding embryonic stage among species or strains.

The form to be used for rating embryos is shown as Table 2. The items of criteria in the form are mainly external developmental features which are distinct phenomena and change rapidly as age proceeds. The value attached to each item is assigned arbitrarily depending on the progress of development. Various items with the same value occur at a similar age. A rating will be made as follows: a given embryo will be observed under the stereomicroscope and the recognized features with some value will be marked (examples with ✓ are shown in the form). The average value of the marked items will be calculated (in case of the example: $6+9+10+9+9+10+10+7+10+8+7=95$, $95/11=8.6$). If the same organ primordia on both sides show different developmental stages, the average value of the two ratings will be adopted. The value obtained is the morphological age.

Figure 2 shows the relationship between morphological age and chronological age of embryos in the three species. On the basis of these ratings it may be postulated that twelve-day mouse embryo corresponds to fourteen-day rabbit embryo and to seven-week human embryo. It is remarkable that human embryos show a great variation of morphological age for a given chronological age. A large part of this can, of course, be attributed to the inadequate knowledge

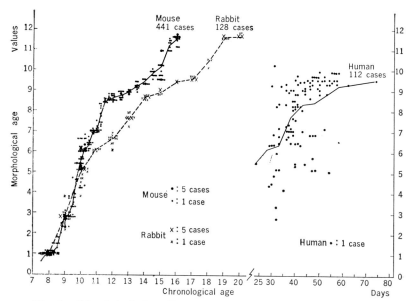

Fig. 2 "Morphological age" in relation to chronological age of embryos

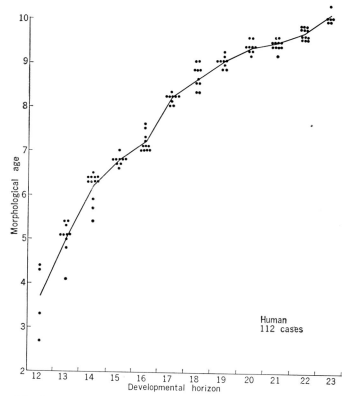

Fig. 3 "Morphological age" in relation to developmental horizon of human embryos

regarding chronological age in human specimens.

Figure 3 shows the relationship between morphological age and developmental horizon of human embryos. It is clear that there is a close correlation between the two variables. I think our numerical rating system may be more precise than the STREETER's horizon system at least for the period of horizon 12–23, because it is more objective and it permits individual variation to be measured. Unlike our criteria, some of the criteria used by STREETER are indistinct and not objective. For example, on the developmental features of the extremities included within horizon 18, STREETER described that the extremities are *somewhat longer:* the digital rays of the hand *definitely notched;* the elbow region is *usually discernible,* and on the foot plate the toe rays can be seen *in some specimens.* Also, on the development of the ear, he gave such indistinct criteria as: the ear vesicles are *almost closed* but not detached (horizon 12) and the auricular hillocks on the surface of the hyoid bar are *becoming distinct* (horizon 16). According to our experience, an embryonic specimen sometimes shows external features characteristic of two horizons and this makes it difficult to assign the specimen to a single horizon. In our system, such variation is expressed exactly.

C. Mode of organogenesis

The remarkable fact is that for the most part the mode of organogenesis in the three species is the same. Only a few organs show species difference. The development of the uterus and vagina is an example. In *man*, the caudal part of the MÜLLERIAN ducts of both sides fuses to each other to form the unicornuate uterus; in *mouse* and *rabbit,* its fusion occurs in the restricted region of uterogenic part, which leads to the formation of bicornuate uterus. The vagina originates in *mouse* from both the MÜLLERIAN epithelium and the wall of urogenital sinus; in *rabbit,* from both the MÜLLERIAN and WOLFFIAN epithelium; and in *man*, from WOLFFIAN epithelium, while the MÜLLERIAN duct makes no appreciable contribution.

D. Age of various stages of morpho- and histogenesis

It is occasionally required in teratological studies to possess knowledge regarding the time at which organogenesis takes place, which organ primordia of a given species (or strain) appear at about the same age, and whether or not a given species (or strain) shows the same sequence of organogenesis as man. In order to meet such demands, a diagram on the comparative chronology of various external and internal developmental phenomena of the three species was prepared (Fig. 4). We determined the earliest age at which the primordia of certain organs appear or the clearly recognizable external changes take place by observation of 529 mouse, 128 rabbit and 187 human embryonic specimens. The most remarkable finding is that there is a similarity in the sequence of the age of various morpho- and histogenesis in the three species.

SPONTANEOUS MALDEVELOPMENT

It should be noted that control animals have a variable incidence of spontaneous maldevelopment even in a well controlled environment. Our experience in this regard is shown as an example in Table 3. The incidence of malformations ranges from 0.4 to 5.8 % and that of intrauterine death from 6.6 to 11.4 %.

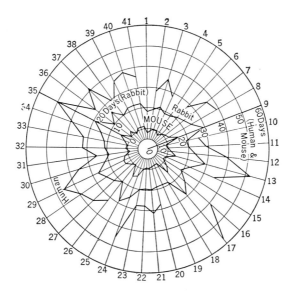

Fig. 4 Comparison of age of various features of morpho- and histogenesis
among the three species

1. Head fold
2. Closure of anterior neuropore
3. Cerebral hemisphere
4. Closure of posterior neuropore
5. Optic evagination
6. Optic cup
7. Closure of lens vesicle
8. Eye-lids
9. Closure of eye-lids
10. Optic invagination
11. Closure of auditory vesicle
12. External auditory pore surrounded by hillocks
13. Corti's organ
14. Olfactory pit
15. Stomodeum
16. Dental lamina
17. Complete fusion of palate
18. Branchial arch I
19. Branchial arch II
20. Branchial arch III
21. Branchial arch IV
22. Liver diverticulum
23. Dorsal pancreas
24. Perforation of anal membrane
25. Disappearance of physiological umbilical hernia
26. Lung
27. Aortic pulmonary septum
28. Atrioventricular valves
29. Completion of interventricular septum with closed foramen
30. Spleen
31. Mesonephric duct (Pronephric duct ?)
32. Metanephros
33. Ureteric bud
34. Müllerian duct
35. Fusion of caudal part of Müllerian duct
36. Germinal epithelium
37. Gonad with sex differentiation
38. Thyroid gland
39. Parathyroid gland
40. Hypophysis
41. Adrenal gland

We were aware that some fluctuation of developmental errors is inevitable.

It is important that investigators realize that these spontaneous events occur and they should keep sufficient record of these phenomena on test animals to be employed. Such data will be needed for interpreting the results of animal experiments in which the embryotoxicity of various agents are being tested. Guides to this problem are to be found in the publications of GRÜNEBERG[4,5] and DAGG[2] for mice, SAWIN[10] and ROBINSON[9] for rabbits and NACHTSHEIM[6] for rodents in general.

The frequency and type of malformed and dead embryos among our human specimens is shown in Table 4.

Externally malformed embryos were found with increased frequency with

Table 3 Monthly incidence of spontaneous malformations of ICR-JCL mice observed at term (Diet: pellet for mice and rats manufactured by FUNAHASHI Farm, Japan; room temperature: $23° \pm 0.5°C$)

Month	No. of litters	Fetuses			
		Total implants	Dead (%)	Malformed (%)[+]	Type[*] and no. of each anomaly
9. –10. '65	10	141	13 (9.2)	1 (0.8)	1 Cp
11. –12. '65	15	200	22 (11.0)	5 (2.8)	1 Cf, 2 Cp, 1 Ex, 1 Odh, 1 Oe
1. – 2. '66	9	137	11 (8.0)	4 (3.2)	2 Cf, 2 Ct
3. – 4. '66	19	243	19 (7.8)	13 (5.8)	5 Cf, 6 Cp, 2 Ct
5. – 6. '66	23	315	36 (11.4)	2 (0.7)	1 Cf, 1 Cp
7. – 8. '66	41	565	56 (9.9)	2 (0.4)	2 Cp
9. –10. '66	20	241	16 (6.6)	1 (0.4)	1 Cp
Total	137	1842	173 (9.4)	28 (1.7)	

+: % of the fetuses live *in utero*
*: Cf: club foot, Cp: cleft palate, Ct: curled tail, Ex: exencephaly, Odh: oligodactyly (hand), Oe: open eye-lids

Table 4 Incidence of malformed and dead human embryos retained *in utero* from mothers with healthy course of pregnancy

No. of cases	Malformed (%)[+]	Type[*] and number of each malformation	Dead (%)
1184	14 (1.28)	2 Cp, 1 Cp+Sh, 3 Cy, 2 Ex, 2 My, 1 Od, 3 Pd	94 (7.9)

+: % of the embryos live *in utero*
*: Cp: cleft palate, Cy: cyclopia, Ex: exencephaly, My: myeloschisis, Od: oligodactyly, Pd: polydactyly, Sh: split hand

advancing developmental stage[8]. Some other investigations by our group reveals that the incidence of most of these malformations is far higher than that observed in newborn infants[7].

It is of interest that counterparts of most types of spontaneous malformations shown in ICR mice and Dutch rabbits were found in human embryos.

It has been known that a fairly large percentage of intrauterine death occurs in the early stage of pregnancy in any species. Embryonic death is identified by signs of the maceration or of complete resorption of an embryo indicated by an implantation site in rodents. The frequency of intrauterine death was found to be 6.7% among 675 ICR-JCL mouse embryos at day 12 obtained from 56 dams, 7.5% among 1326 ICR-JCL mouse embryos at day 14 from 100 dams, and 5% among 160 embryos of Dutch rabbits at day 17 from 21

233

Plate I. External development of human embryos. The standardized age is given inside the bracket.

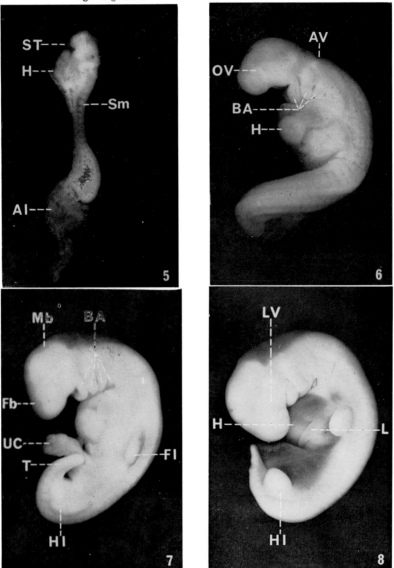

Fig. 5 Horizon 11 (25.0 days), crown-rump length (C.R.L.): 3.55 mm.
Al: allantois H: heart Sm: somite St: stomodeum

  6 Horizon 12 (27.8 days), C.R.L.: 3.82 mm.
AV: auditory vesicle (open) BA: branchial arches H: heart
OV: optic vesicle

  7 Horizon 13 (31.6 days), C.R.L.: 5.15 mm.
BA: branchial arches Fb: forebrain Fl: forelimb bud Hl: hind-limb bud Mb: midbrain T: tail UC: umbilical cord

  8 Horizon 14 (35.2 days), C.R.L.: 6.93 mm.
H: heart Hl: hindlimb bud L: liver LV: lens vesicle (open)

234

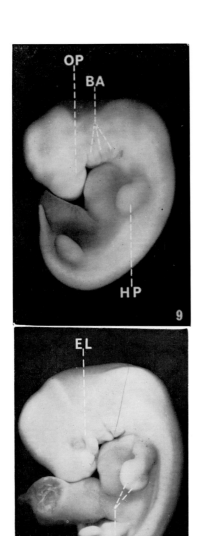
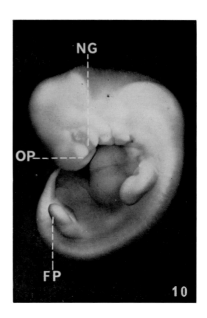

Fig. 9 Horizon 15 (36. 5 days), C.R.L.: 8. 80 mm.
BA: branchial arches HP: hand plate OP: olfactory pit
10 Horizon 16 (37. 9 days), C.R.L.: 9. 80 mm.
FP: foot plate NG: naso-maxillary groove OP: olfactory pit
11 Horizon 17 (38. 9 days), C.R.L.: 10. 2 mm.
DR: digital rays EL: eye-lid

Plate II. External development of human embryos. The standardized age is given inside the bracket.

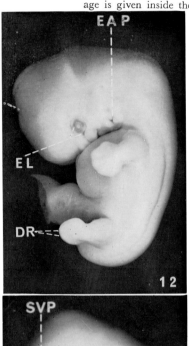

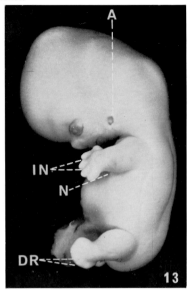

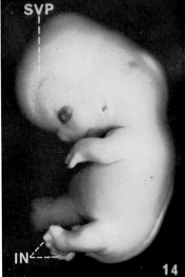

Fig. 12 Horizon 18 (41.0 days), C.R.L.: 13.9 mm.
DR: digital rays EAP: external auditory pore EL: eye-lids
13 Horizon 19 (45.1 days), C.R.L.: 17.8 mm.
A: auricle DR: digital rays IN: interdigital notches N: nipple
14 Horizon 20 (46.7 days), C.R.L.: 18.9 mm.
IN: interdigital notches SVP: scalp vascular plexus

236

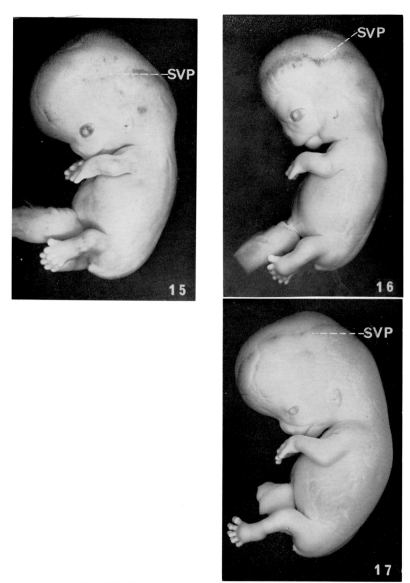

Fig. 15 Horizon 21 (48.5 days), C.R.L.: 21.2 mm.
　　　　SVP: scalp vascular plexus
　　16　Horizon 22 (50.2 days), C.R.L.: 21.4 mm.
　　　　SVP: scalp vascular plexus
　　17　Horizon 23 (52.2 days), C.R.L.: 25.2 mm.
　　　　SVP: scalp vascular plexus

Plate III. Some characteristic external developmental features of rabbit or mouse embryos.

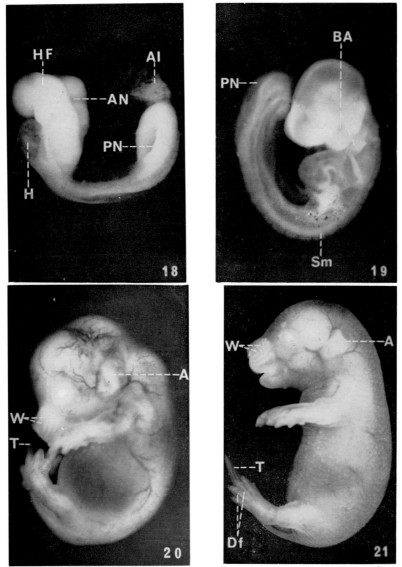

Fig. 18 Mouse; 8 days 12 hours p.c., C.R.L. (from head fold to tail fold): 1.31 mm.
Al: allantois AN: anterior neuropore H: heart HF: head fold
PN: posterior neuropore
   19 Mouse; 9 days p.c., C.R.L.: 2.02 mm.
BA: branchial arches PN: posterior neuropore Sm: somite
   20 Mouse; 13 days 12 hours p.c., C.R.L.: 10.8 mm.
A: auricle T: tail W: whiskers
   21 Mouse; 16 days p.c., C.R.L.: 19.0 mm.
A: auricle Df: digits (fused proximally again) T: tail W: whiskers

238

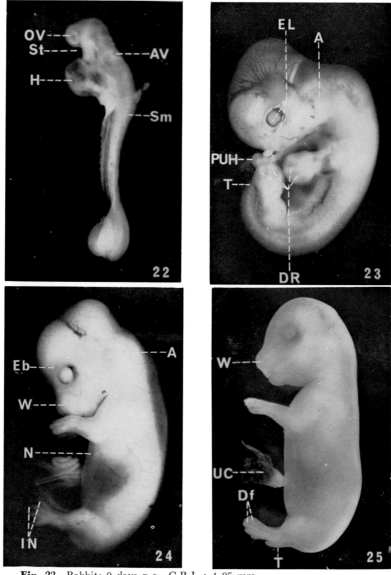

Fig. 22 Rabbit; 9 days p.c., C.R.L.: 4.25 mm.
AV: auditory vesicle H: heart OV: optic vesicle Sm: somite
St: stomodeum
  23 Rabbit; 14 days p.c., C.R.L.: 12.4 mm.
A: auricle DR: digital rays EL: eye-lids PUH: physiological
umbilical hernia T: tail
  24 Rabbit; 18 days p.c., C.R.L.: 21.7 mm.
A: auricle Eb: eyebrow IN: interdigital notches N: nipple
W: whiskers
  25 Rabbit; 20 days p.c., C.R.L.: 38.2 mm.
Df: digits (fused proximally again) T: tail UC: umbilical cord
W: whiskers

does. In man, the frequency of dead embryos retained *in utero* was found to be 7.9 % (Table 4). It should be mentioned that besides the macerated human embryos, the empty sacs which are presumed to be the result of complete embryonic absorption are occasionally found.

ACKNOWLEDGEMENT

I am indebted to Mr. T. Fujii, Research Laboratories, Nippon Merck-Banyu Co. Ltd., Mr. H. Otori, Aburahi Laboratories, Shionogi & Co. Ltd. and Mr. F. Ariyuki, Department of Clinical Pharmacology, Products Control Laboratory, Tanabe Seiyaku Co. Ltd. as well as my colleagues in the Department of Anatomy of Kyoto University for their aid in carrying out the investigations. Further, I wish to express my gratitude to the National Institutes of Health, Public Health Service, U.S.A. (HD 01401), the Association for the Aid of Crippled Children, New York and Ministry of Education, Japan for their support of my work.

REFERENCES

1. Böving, B.G.: Anatomy of Reproduction. In: Obstetrics, edited by J.P. Greenhill. pp. 3–101. W.B. Saunders, Philadelphia; Igaku Shoin, Tokyo (Asian edition), 1965.

2. Dagg, C.P.: Teratogenesis. In: Biology of the Laboratory Mouse, edited by E.L. Green. pp. 309–328. The Blackiston Division, McGraw-Hill, New York, 1966.

3. Grüneberg, H.: The development of some external features in mouse embryos. J. Hered. 33: 89–92, 1943.

4. ——————: The genetics of the mouse. Martinus Nijhoff, the Hague, 1952.

5. ——————: The Pathology of Development: a study of inherited skeletal disorders in animals. Blackwell Scientific Publication, Oxford, 1963.

6. Nachtsheim, N.: Erbpathologie der Nagetiere. In: Pathologie der Laboratoriumstiere, Band II, edited by P. Cohrs, R. Jaffé and H. Meessen. pp. 310-452. Spirnger-Verlag, Berlin, 1958.

7. Nishimuar, H., Takano, K., Tanimura, T., Yasuda, M. and Uchida, T.: High incidence of several malformations in the early human embryos as compared with infants. Biol. Neonat. 10: 93–107, 1966.

8. Nishimura, H., Takano, K., Tanimura, T. and Yasuda, M.: Normal and abnormal development of human embryos—the first report of analysis of 1213 intact embryos. Teratology 1: 281–290, 1968.

9. Robinson, R.: Genetic studies of the rabbit. Bibliographia Genet. 17: 229–558, 1958.

10. Sawin, P.B.: Recent genetics of the domestic rabbit. Advances Genet. 7: 183–226, 1955.

11. Streeter, G.L.: Developmental horizons in human embryos, description of age groups XI and XII. Carnegie Contrib. to Embryol. 30: 211–245, 1942.

12. ——————: Developmental horizons in human embryos, description of age groups XIII and XIV. Carnegie Contrib. to Embryol. 31: 27–63, 1945.

13. ——————: Developmental horizons in human embryos, description of age groups XV, XVI, XVII and XVIII. Carnegie Contrib. to Embryol. 32: 133–203, 1948.

14. ——————: Developmental horizons in human embryos, description of age groups XIX, XX, XXI, XXII and XXIII. Carnegie Contrib. to Embryol. 34: 165-

196, 1951.

15. WALKER, B.E. and CRAIN, B.: Effects of hypervitaminosis A on palate development in two strains of mice. Amer. J. Anat. 107: 49–58, 1960.

16. WITSCHI, E.: Development of Vertebrates. W.B. Saunders, Philadelphia, 1965.

DIAGNOSTIC PROCEDURES IN THE
NURTURE OF RATS

C. Willet Asling

Professor, Department of Anatomy, University of California, San Francisco, U.S.A.

(The following is a modification of the material presented at the Workshop. That text was extracted from a manuscript entitled "Breeding and Nurture of the Rat for Embryological Studies", by Jack G. Chamberlain and C. Willet Asling, which will appear in "Embryology and Teratology" to be published by the University of Chicago Press. Readers interested in the amplified treatment of the topic are referred to that paper, or to the standard works listed at the end of this article.)

Accurate knowledge of the reproductive cycle is required for critical studies on normal and abnormal mammalian development. This presentation will be concerned with the rat. The estrus cycle is regulated by a feedback mechanism, in which the nervous system, the pituitary gland, and the ovary participate. In the ovary, oögenesis and hormone formation bring about changes in the reproductive passages which form the basis for diagnostic procedures used in breeding.

The events in the uterus, ovary, and vagina which reflect the estrus cycle are established at approximately 6 to 7 weeks of age in the rat. Subsequently, in the non-pregnant state cycles are repeated at 4 to 5 day intervals until senescence. The period of estrus occupies approximately 12 to 20 hours of the cycle, and ovulation occurs spontaneously near the end of this period. During estrus, the ovary produces hormones which result in structural alterations in the uterus and vagina. Cells of varying types are constantly being shed into the vaginal lumen throughout this cycle. Their appearance forms the most suitable guide for the purpose of consistent and reliable determinations of the short period of fertility. This is best determined by examinations of the vaginal smear.

The stages of the cycle are designated as diestrus, proestrus, estrus, and metestrus (divisible into early and late).

Inasmuch as the second of these, *estrus,* is the time of greatest receptivity of the male, the problem becomes that of selecting *proestrus* females from a group of sexually mature animals. In any such group, the largest number will probably be in *diestrus,* for that state occupies more than half of the time of the average cycle.

Diestrus vaginal smears consist of a mixture of polymorphonuclear leukocytes and nucleated epithelial cells, entangled in a somewhat viscid mucus. As the rat passes into the proestrus phase, the leukocytes disappear and the smear contains large numbers of sizable nucleated epithelial cells, of uniform size, single or in sheets. This appearance (Fig. 1) indicates that breeding may be attempted. With the advent of estrus, the cells become cornified—large scale-like elements with the nucleus obscured by keratin. At first they may be sparse or moderate in number. When seen in very large numbers, constituting a cheesy mass, they indicate early metestrus. Later, leukocytes are mixed in with these cornified cells (late metestrus), and toward the end of this stage the epithelial cells are again smaller, rounded, and nucleated rather than having the cornified

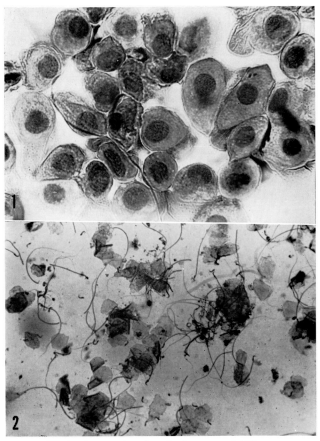

Photomicrographs of vaginal smears, 1,000×.

Fig. 1 Proestrus smear, showing cellular appearance at the time when breeding should be attempted. Note that the cell population is composed exclusively of groups of cells containing a rounded, easily visible nucleus.

   2 Estrus smear, taken the morning after the previous smear and following the overnight presence of a fertile male. Spermatozoa are mixed with the cornified cells from the vaginal epithelium.

appearance. In the absence of fertilization this appearance then again reverts to the diestrus type.

The spatulas used to obtain the vaginal sample for smears are made by modifying standard dental spatulas. The sides of the blade are ground to a slight taper, the edges blunted on the grinding stone, and any burrs removed with fine steel wool; the blade is bent slightly.   Two beakers or enamelled metal cups with a layer of absorbent cotten placed in the bottom of each are used. One contains a fast-acting disinfectant and the other, distilled water, fresh daily. Smears are made on glass slides.   With experience, cells become recognizable by morphology alone, and unstained wet smears suffice for routine diagnosis. Smears to be kept may be dried, fixed in Schaudinn's solution, and stained by the Papanicolaou solution, Mann's methyl-blue eosin, or Wright's stain.   A microscope with 10x objective and 10x ocular is adequate.

To start the diagnosis, place 6 to 12 spatulas in disinfectant solution.   Drain spatulas and transfer to distilled rinse-water.   Prepare a slide with droplets of water or physiological saline solution.   Hold the rat, ventral side up, in the left hand.   The position is like that used when administering an intraperitoneal injection, but the fifth finger holds the left hind leg and the remaining fingers support the back.   The spatula, held in the right hand and with the hollow of the blade directed downward, is dipped gently into the vagina about one centimeter and withdrawn with the tip passing along the dorsal vaginal wall.

The tip of the spatula is touched to the moistened slide, pressing the smear into a small circle.   The smear is examined under the microscope with slightly reduced illumination, at 100x.

Females 12 weeks old or older are usually preferred for breeding, although many show sexual maturity at 6 to 7 weeks.   When a female has been found in the proestrus state she is placed in the cage of a breeder male of proven vigor. (Males which fail to impregnate suitable females on three successive trials are rejected from the breeder stock.)   In routine breeding, the females are usually selected in late afternoon and placed with the male over-night.   At approximately 8:00 to 10:00 A.M. on the next day the females are removed and examined for presumptive evidence of copulation.   This may consist either of (a) a "copulation plug"—a small coagulated mass of semen in the vagina or on the bottom of the cage, or (b) a vaginal smear sample containing spermatozoa mixed with cells of an estrus or early metestrus smear (Fig. 2).

During the course of pregnancy, further vaginal smears may be found useful.   Normally these will show a predominance of leukocytes.   By about Day 12–14 (counting Day 0 as starting at 8:00 A.M. on the day of finding spermatozoa in the vaginal smear following the over-night presence of the male) the "placental sign" may be found, consisting of a slight blood-streaking on the spatula.   When it is found early (e.g., Day 10), and especially in animals on an experimental teratogenic regimen, it usually indicates that some embryos have resorbed.

The reader interested in more details of the foregoing procedures, and especially in maintenance of a stock or experimental colony of rats, is referred to the works listed below.   As described elsewhere in these proceedings, nutrition is of critical importance, and special attention should be given to assuring optimal diets.

REFERENCES

1. FARRIS, E.J.: The Care and Breeding of Laboratory Animals. John Wiley and

Sons, New York, 1960.
2. National Research Council, Institute of Laboratory Animal Resources.: Standards for the Breeding, Care and Management of Laboratory Rats. National Academy of Sciences, Washington, D.C., 3rd printing, 1967.
3. WARDEN, A.N. and LANE-PETTER, W. (eds.): The U.F.A.W. Handbook on the Care and Management of Laboratory Animals. Universities Federation for Animal Welfare, London, 2nd ed., 1957.

METHODOLOGY OF HUMAN CYTOGENETICS

AKIRA TONOMURA

Professor, Department of Human Cytogenetics,
Tokyo Medical and Dental University,
Tokyo, Japan.

The utilization of cell culture techniques has provided a number of advantages for cytological studies in man. Two important technological devices, the use of colchicine and the use of hypotonic solution, also made possible detailed observation of the chromosomes. At present there are three general methods for examining human somatic chromosomes using the short-term or long-term culture of biopsy specimens. 1) *The peripheral blood culture method:* this techniques is most widely used in many laboratories because the blood sample can be easily obtained not only from a patient but also from large numbers of "normal" persons. 2) *The short-term culture of bone-marrow cells:* for the study of leukemia this method is particularly noteworthy. 3) *The skin culture method:* the third is the use of relatively long-term cultures of fibroblasts derived from the skin or other solid tissue materials. Although the blood culture technique is now used extensively, these three methods should be regarded as complementary rather than alternative. The details of technical methods are presented in the Appendix. Further information is available in some monographs[1-4].

For the study of meiotic chromosomes in germ cells, a direct squash or air-drying method was developed by the use of hypotonic solution. However, the material is difficult to obtain, and this method can only be applied to selected patients.

Study of the sex chromatin in resting nuclei is also of fundamental importance in considering the karyotype of any patient, particularly those with abnormalities of sexual development. There are now two methods currently in use: the oral (or buccal) smear method and the neutrophil method.

Chromosome cytology is essentially a practical subject, which can only be thoroughly mastered by a study of actual preparations under the microscope. After the biopsy specimens have been collected, cultured, and treated with colchicine and hypotonic solution, all that remains is to stain, count and identify the chromosomes. Chromosome analysis is completed by photographing several representative metaphase figures, enlarging the photographs to a magnification of about 3000× and cutting out the individual chromosomes.

For identification of each pair of chromosomes a standard system of nomenclature was proposed by the Human Chromosomes Study Group in 1960. According to this system, the autosomes are serially numbered, 1–22, as nearly as possible in descending order of length, and then, using as criteria the arm-ratio (length of long arm/length of short arm) or the centromere-index (length of short arm/length of the chromosome) they are classified into seven groups, distinction between which can readily be made.

A number of investigators have applied the autoradiographic method to human chromosomes and suggested that certain chromosomes or chromosome arms exhibit replication patterns that might be highly useful for chromosome characterization and identification.

Although there are many other specialized techniques for the study of human chromosomes, the basic procedures employed in this field have been presented.   In this demonstration, the peripheral blood culture technique and the sex chromatin technique will be selected for detailed presentation.

REFERENCES

1. EGGEN, R.R.: Chromosome Diagnostics in Clinical Medicine. C.C. Thomas, Springfield, 1965.
2. MAKINO, S.: Human Chromosomes: Application to Clinical Medicine. Kinokuni-ya, Tokyo, 1963. (in Japanese)
3. MOORE, K.L. (ed.): The Sex Chromatin. W.B. Saunders Co., Philadelphia and London, 1966.
4. YUNIS, J.J. (ed.): Human Chromosome Methodology. Academic Press, New York and London, 1965.

APPENDIX

A. Peripheral blood culture technique
I. Preparation of leucocyte culture
   1) Draw 5–10 ml of venous blood using a sterile, heparinized syringe.
   2) Remove the blood into a centrifuge tube, and allow it to stand at room temperature for about 1 hour.
       Note: Leucocytes may be separated from the red cells by gravity sedimentation.   If phytohemagglutinin (Difco form M, 0.2 ml/10 ml of blood) is added to the blood sample, the agglutination of red cells may be more completely and more rapidly sedimented.   Since we add phytohemagglutinin to the culture medium when we make it, we rarely use it for sedimenting red cells.
   3) Add the supernatant cell-plasma suspension to culture medium in a rate of 1 part plasma to 2 parts of medium.
       Note: Most easily available commercial medium is TC 199 which can be obtained from Difco Laboratories, Detroit, Michigan 48201, U.S.A. or from Chiba Serum Institute, 2-6-1, Konodai, Ichikawa Chiba, Japan.
   4) Incubate cultures at 37°C for 3 days.
II. Pretreatment of cultured cells for chromosome study
   5) On the third day of culture (60–70 hours), add colchicine to the culture medium in final concentrations of not over 0.1 μg/ml of culture medium. Reincubate for another 4 to 6 hours.
   6) Transfer the cultures to centrifuge tubes, and centrifuge at 800 rpm for 5 minutes.   Carefully discard the supernatant.
   7) Resuspend the cells in 5 ml of HANK's balanced salt solution using gentle

agitation with a pipette. Centrifuge at 800 rpm for 5 minutes and remove the supernatant salt solution to the 0.5 ml mark on the tube. Suspend the cells throughly in this volume.

8) Add 1.5 to 2.0 ml of prewarmed distilled water or 0.95% sodium citrate solution. Incubate for 10 minutes at 37°C.

9) Resuspend the cells and centrifuge at 600 rpm for 5 minutes. Carefully aspirate the hypotonic solution without disrupting the button.

III. Preparation of slide

10) Add 3 to 4 ml of acetic alcohol fixative (glacial acetic acid 1: absolute methyl alcohol 3) carefully on the top of cell button, and leave at least 30 minutes.

11) Resuspend the cells in the fixative using a finely drawn pipette and gentle agitation. Centrifuge at 500 rpm for 5 minutes. Remove fixative. Add new fixative and resuspend the cells throughly.

   Note: Repeat this procedure twice or more, if cell clumping still occur at this point.

12) Recentrifuge and add 0.5 ml of new fixative.

13) Place a drop of the cell suspension on the wet slide and immediately pass through a flame. The slide should be hold horizontally until the flame extinguishes itself and the drop of fixative is dry.

14) Stain slides with Giemsa solution for 20-30 minutes.

15) Wash stained slides in distilled water, dry in air and mount in permanent.

B. Preparation of bone-marrow cells

1) Aspirate about 0.05–0.2 ml of sternal marrow.

2) Transfer to culture medium (TC 199) to which heparin and autologous plasma or fetal calf serum (10–20%) have been added.

3) Incubate at 37°C for 18–24 hours.

4) Add colchicine in a final concentration of not more than 0.1 μg/ml of culture medium, and incubate for 1–2 hours at 37°C.

From this point, the cultures are treated in the same procedures as are cultures from peripheral blood.

C. Skin (or solid tissue) culture method

Tissue may be selected according to its availability.

I. Primary culture

1) Mince tissue in about 10 ml of HANK's solution (without Mg and Ca).

2) Add 1 ml of 2.5% trypsin solution for every 10 ml of HANK's sol. being used in (1).

3) Stir in magnetic stirrer for 10 minutes.

4) Pipette off solution containing isolated cells: place in centrifuge tube with serum added to stop tryptic reaction.

5) Add new trypsin to tissue and repeat procedures above.

6) Centrifuge twice at about 1000 rpm.

7) Resuspend in complete media (1 ml per flask).

8) Inoculate culture flask with 1 ml of suspension.

9) Add remaining volume of medium to maxima of:

      a.   TD–15   2 ml

      b.   TD–40   8 ml

Note: When only a small material was avilable for culture, tissue specimens were cut into small pieces using forceps and scissors, and
planted directly on the glass surface of culture flask without trypsin
treatment.

II. Pretreatment of cultured cells for chromosome study
  10) Add 0.06 ml of 0.01 % colchicine solution.
     Note: Description for TD–15 flask; change volumes for other types of
     flasks.
  11) Reincubate for 2–3 hours.
  12) Remove old media, and add 1 ml of 0.2 % trypsin solution.
     Note: Dilute trypsin into Hank's solution (without Mg and Ca)
  13) Place in incubator at 37°C. Shake gently. Check every few minutes.
  14) After 5–10 minutes, or when tissue lifts off glass, transfer to centrifuge
     tube, and new Hank's solution to TD–15 and reclaim dispersed cells.
     Transfer to centrifuge tube and spin at 1000 rpm for 3–4 minutes.
  15) Resuspend in Hank's solution and rinse twice, followed by centrifuga-
     tions of 3–4 minutes.
  16) Discard supernatant, and resuspend cells in 0.95 % sodium citrate solution
     (prewarmed).
  17) Incubate at 37°C and leave 10–20 minutes.
  18) Centrifuge at 700 rpm for 5 minutes.
  19) Remove hypotonic solution.

III. Preparation of slide
  Proceed as in Section A–III.

D. Sex chromatin techniques
  a. Buccal smears method
     1) Obtain epithelial cells from the buccal aspect of the cheek using a
        metal spatula or wooden tongue depressor.
     2) Spread the smear on a clean glass slide.
     3) Immerse immediately in Papanicolaou's fixative (equal parts of 95 %
        ethyl alcohol and ether) and leave smears in fixative for 2 to 24 hours.
     4) Pass slides through 70 % alcohol, 50 % alcohol and distilled water,
        five minutes in each, with two changes of distilled water.
     5) Stain with 1 % solution of cresyl echt violet for 5 minutes.
     6) Differentiate in 95 % alcohol (two changes) for about 5 minutes.
     7) Clear in xylene (two changes)
     8) Mount
  b. Neutrophil method
     No specific techniques are necessary for the demonstration of the char-
     acteristic nuclear appendages "drumstick" and "sessile nodule" of the
     polymorphonuclear neutrophil leucocytes.
     1) Obtain a blood sample by puncturing the lower tip of an ear lobe
        with a needle or sharp knife.
     2) Place a small blood drop on a clean glass slide and spread by a
        coverslip.
     3) Immerse slides in 99 % methyl alcohol for 1–2 minutes.
     4) Stain with Wright or Giemsa solution about 20–30 minutes.

THE PROBLEMS AND TECHNIQUES OF UTILIZING IRRADIATION AS A TERATOGENIC TOOL

Robert L. Brent

Professor, Department of Pediatrics and Radiology,
Jefferson Medical College, Philadelphia, U.S.A.

INTRODUCTION

X-ray facilities are available in most hospitals and medical centers through-out the world, providing embryologists with ready access to radiation facilities. Furthermore, embryologists have found many unique advantages of X-irradiation besides accessibility. These include:

1) Ease of quantitation and replication of the dose administered.
2) Ability to deliver experimental doses of irradiation in a short period of time.
3) Ability to irradiate parts of the embryo, the embryonic site, placenta or maternal organism while shielding other structures.
4) Ability to have controls and irradiated embryos in the same litter in polytocous animals.

On the other hand, irradiation as an experimental tool has been abused because the laws of radiation physics have been ignored. There is a certain amount of basic knowledge that is necessary before one can adequately plan a radiation embryology experiment. It is very likely that consultation with a radiation physicist during the planning stages, would avoid all of the mistakes that are frequently made by novice radiation biologists.

The purpose of this laboratory session is to describe the qualitative and quantitative aspects of X-irradiation, the ways of utilizing this information and preventing the mistakes of past investigators.

RADIATION PHYSICS

A. Radiation factors

The X-ray facilities available to most investigators around the world are of two types, a low kilovoltage skin therapy X-ray machine (120 kilovolts) and the usual cancer therapy X-ray machine (250–300 kilovolts). There are some X-ray machines in between the two commonest types and many medical centers have supervoltage Vander Graaf X-ray machines that function in the million volt range. All of the above-mentioned X-ray machines deliver high energy, short wave length, electromagnetic waves that are known as X-rays. These electro-magnetic waves are produced by the bombardment of a metallic target by electrons that have been accelerated by a high electropotential ranging from several thousand to several million volts.

The nature of the X-ray beam produced by these X-ray machines can be described by several physical factors which tell the investigator the ability of the beam to penetrate various materials and the flux or density of the electromagnetic waves.

1. *Kilovoltage*: The kilovoltage at which an X-ray machine is run determines the "hardness" or penetrability of an X-ray beam. The kilovoltage is the voltage potential utilized to accelerate the electrons and therefore indicates the theoretical kinetic energy that the bombarding electrons can attain. The energy of electromagnetic waves that are produced by an X-ray machine will never be greater than the kilovoltage at which the machine is run and the peak energy of the spectrum of X-rays will be somewhat less than the theoretical maximum energy. In fact, the spectrum of energies produced by a 300 KVP X-ray machine will resemble a skewed distribution curve with the peak at about 60–70 % of the maximum voltage and the tails covering the entire 300 KVP range. The higher the peak kilovoltage of an X-ray beam, the more penetrating that beam. It is up to the radiation physicist and embryologist to determine the nature of the X-ray beam which is most suitable for the experiment being planned.

2. *Amperes*: The amperage on an X-ray machine determines the flux or density of the X-ray beam. Most therapy machines can be run at 5, 10 or 15 milliamperes. The dose absorbed at a particular distance, will double if the amperage is doubled. Thus there is a direct relationship between the flux or density of electromagnetic waves from an X-ray machine and the current (amperes) reading on that machine. The limiting factor of the output of an X-ray machine is related to the maximum current tolerated by the machine. This relates to heat production and the limit of the present methods to cool the components of the X-ray machine. It may be confusing to some readers, who know that some diagnostic X-ray machines draw as high as 200 milliamperes, but these machines operate for fractions of a second and therefore do not encounter overheating problems.

3. *Filtration*: The quality of an X-ray beam can be changed considerably by interposing metal filters between the source of the beam and the object being irradiated. Conventional filters consist of one millimeter sheets of aluminum, copper, lead or a combination of these and other metals. The use of filters decreases or eliminates the low energy photons from reaching the dosimeter or object being irradiated. Thus filters increase the average energy of the irradiating photons, but decrease the density or flux of the X-ray beam. The greater the density of the filters being utilized, the greater will be the average energy or penetrability of the transmitted photons and the lower the dose rate of the absorbed beam. A radiation physicist or a radiation biologist should decide on the nature of the X-ray beam to be utilized for various experimental procedures.

4. *Half-Value Layer* (H.V.L.): A very useful descriptive characteristic of an X-ray beam is its half-value layer. It refers to the amount of material that will reduce the electromagnetic flux to fifty percent. As an example, if an X-ray machine produces a beam with an absorbed dose of 100 R/min. at 50 cm. from the tube and two millimeters of copper interposed between the beam reduces the absorbed dose at 50 cm./min. to 50 R, then the half value layer for that

beam is two millimeters of copper.   There are tissue equivalents for half-value layers, so that any radiation physicist or radiation biologist can refer the investigator to tables, for estimating how much tissue or bone will absorb fifty percent of the entering beam.   The less dense the H.V.L. the less penetrating the beam. Thus a beam whose H.V.L. is one millimeter of aluminum would be much less penetrating than a beam whose H.V.L. is three millimeters of copper.   The H.V.L. of a beam tells one nothing about the dose of irradiation being absorbed, only the penetration ability of a particular beam.   Thus an X-ray beam with a H.V.L. of one millimeter of aluminum might not be able to uniformly irradiate a mouse because the exit dose would be considerably less than the entering dose. This might be overcome by slowly rotating the mouse in the beam in order to obtain a uniform exposure.   On the other hand, the beam with a H.V.L. of three millimeters of copper might provide a uniform dose of irradiation to a rat. Yet this latter beam might be quite unacceptable for local irradiation of small structures like the embryonic site or the placenta, because of the penetrating ability of this beam and the difficulty in shielding this beam from structures which were not supposed to be irradiated.

5. *Dose Rate*: The dose rate of a particular X-ray beam is measured by conventional dosimeters (ionization chambers, crystals) at a particular distance from the X-ray tube.   The primary variables that determined the absorbed dose from an X-ray machine are the milliamperage and the distance from the X-ray tube.   Increased filtration will lower the dose rate, by eliminating the lower energy photons.   While the absorbed dose is directly and linearly related to the milliamperage, the target object distance is related inversely as to the square of the distance, since electromagnetic waves follow the "square root" law of emitting sources.

In some instances, discrepancies between two experiments have been explained purely on the basis of a difference in dose rates.   Since recovery phenomena are an important aspect of radiation damage, it is easy to see how variation in dose rates may be meaningful.

6. *Target-Object Distance* (T.O.D.): This parameter is extremely important because it is a variable that can markedly alter dose rate and field size.   Furthermore, lack of attention to the T.O.D. can cause significant errors in the dose absorbed by the experimental animal.   Because X-ray, like all electromagnetic waves, follows, the inverse square law of diminishing flux, the absorbed dose of an irradiated organism will decrease as to the square of the distance from the source of the X-ray beam.   Thus a rat that absorbs 64 R/min. at ten centimeters will absorb 8 R/min. when placed twenty centimeters from that X-ray source. The inverse square law explains why a one centimeter error in placing the dosimeter or animal is equivalent to a seventeen percent error in absorbed dose at ten centimeters and only a six percent error in absorbed dose at thirty centimeters from the X-ray source.

$$\frac{(10 \text{ cm.})^2}{(11 \text{ cm.})^2} = \frac{X_2}{X_1} = \frac{100}{121} = 82.6 \%$$

An increase in the T.O.D. by one centimeter (from 10 to 11) reduces the absorbed dose to 82.6 percent of the dose absorbed at ten centimeters T.O.D.

$$\frac{(30 \text{ cm.})^2}{(31 \text{ cm.})^2} = \frac{X_2}{X_1} = \frac{900}{961} = 94 \%$$

An increase in the T.O.D. by one centimeter (from 30 to 31) reduces the absorbed dose to 94 percent of the dose absorbed at thirty centimeters T.O.D. It is easy to see how a one centimeter error in positioning is much more significant at ten centimeters than thirty centimeters from the source.   Therefore, if an animal is too close to the X-ray source, there will be significant differences in the dose absorbed by the animal at the top and bottom of the animal, purely on the basis of the inverse square law.

Typical examples of X-ray beams for irradiating animals are as follows:

1. Whole-body irradiation of a rat
    250 K.V.P.
    10 M.A.
    2 Millimeters Copper Filtration
    25 Centimeters T.O.D.
    30 R/min. Dose Rate
    2.6 Millimeters Copper H.V.L.

2. Irradiation of an embryonic site in a pregnant rat without intent to irradiate the mother
    100 K.V.P.
    10 M.A.
    1 Millimeter Aluminum Filtration
    20 Centimeters T.O.D.
    40 R/min. Dose Rate
    1.2 Millimeters Aluminum H.V.L.

B.   Dosimetry: Methods and errors

Once an investigator has chosen the radiation factors for his experiments, he must measure the dose of irradiation that will be absorbed.   The most commonly utilized instrument for this purpose is the ionization chamber.   These chambers come in all sizes, even as small as five millimeters in length.   The chambers can be placed in the same position as the animal to be irradiated. The accumulated charge of the standardized chambers can then be easily converted to absorbed dose in Roentgens.   Somewhat newer dosimeters are available in the form of Li F crystals which can be placed within the body cavities of irradiated mammals to accurately measure the absorbed dose.

Dosimetry errors in radiation embryology.

1. Measuring the absorbed dose with the dosimeter in *air* at a specified distance from the X-ray source, *but* placing the animal to be irradiated on an operative board.   This may increase the dose to the animal, because of backscatter.   This error can be avoided by performing the dosimetry measurements under exactly the same circumstances as the actual irradiation.

2. Utilization of a very small T.O.D. in order to obtain a high dose rate. As indicated in the previous section, small changes in position make for large dosage errors when the T.O.D. is small.   Therefore, one has to compromise between a high dose rate and large T.O.D.   As a general rule, the T.O.D. should be greater than twenty centimeters even for small animal irradiation.

A short T.O.D. will also provide a smaller field than with a long T.O.D.

Thus, if a large animal is irradiated twenty centimeters from the X-ray beam source, there is a good chance that the extremities will receive a much lower dose than the trunk. The investigator should know the uniform field size at various T.O.D.

3. The newcomer to radiation biology frequently assumes that shielding parts of an organism with lead shields is relatively simple. It is not infrequently assumed that a lead shield acts like an umbrella to the sun's rays, producing a sharp cutoff between irradiated and non-irradiated tissue. This may not be the case and, in fact, if the K.V.P. is high and the lead shield is thin, a significant dose of irradiation can be absorbed by tissue underneath a lead shield. The "shielded" tissues may be irradiated by lateral scatter or shield penetration. Therefore, every shielding experiment, no matter how simple or crude, should have radiation measurements performed in order to determine the magnitude of the leakage and scatter radiation.

COMBINING X-IRRADIATION AND OPERATIVE PROCEDURES

A. Resistance of the rat embryo to shielding techniques

1. During the laboratory procedures, a movie is shown demonstrating some operative techniques in the pregnant rat. This movie is primarily shown to demonstrate the great tolerance of the pregnant rat and her litter to operative manipulations.

B. X-Irradiation combined with special shielding techniques

The following *operative-irradiation-shielding* procedures are demonstrated on anesthetized pregnant rats in the laboratory session. The surgical, anesthetic and associated techniques are also discussed:

1. Maternal irradiation while shielding the embryos.
2. Embryonic irradiation while shielding the mother.
3. Placental irradiation while shielding the embryo and mother.
4. Uterine irradiation while shielding the oviduct, ovary and mother.
5. Ovarian irradiation while shielding the oviduct, uterus and mother.
6. Oviduct irradiation while shielding the ovary, uterus and mother.
7. Combined X-irradiation and uterine vascular clamping.

Since all these procedures are demonstrated in the laboratory session and all the procedures have been published, it seems appropriate to refer the reader to the specific references which describe the techniques in detail[1-8].

ACKNOWLEDGEMENT

The original works of the author cited were made possible by a grant from the Atomic Energy Commission NYO 2071–45.

REFERENCES

1. Brent, R.L.: Uterine vascular clamping and other surgical techniques in experimental mammalian embryology. In: Teratology: Principles and Techniques, Edited by J.G. Wilson and J. Warkany. Ch. 9. University of Chicago Press, 1965.

2. BRENT, R.L. and McLAUGHLIN, M.: The indirect effect of irradiation on embryonic development. I. Irradiation of the mother while shielding the embryonic site. A.M.A. J. Dis. Child. 100: 94–102, 1960.

3. BRENT, R.L.: The indirect effect of irradiation on embryonic development. II. Irradiation of the placenta. A.M.A. J. Dis. Child. 100: 103–108, 1960.

4. BRENT, R.L. and BOLDEN, B.T.: The indirect effect of irradiation on embryonic development. III. The contribution of ovarian irradiation, uterine irradiation, oviduct irradiation, and zygote irradiation to fetal mortality and growth retardation in the rat. Rad. Res. 30: 759–773, 1967.

5. BRENT, R.L. and BODLEN, B.T.: Indirect effect of irradiation on embryonic development. IV. Lethal effects of maternal irradiation on first day of gestation in the rat. Proc. Soc. Exper. Biol. Med. 125: 709–712, 1967.

6. BRENT, R.L. and BOLDEN, B.T.: Indirect effect of X-irradiation on embryonic development. V. Utilization of high doses of maternal irradiation on the first day of gestation. (abstract) AEC–43 Teratology, 1: 212, 1968.

7. BRENT, R.L., FRANKLIN, J.B. and BOLDEN, B.T.: Modifications of irradiation effects on rat embryos by uterine vascular clamping. Rad. Res. 118: 58–64, 1968.

8. GEORGE, E.F., FRANKLIN, J.B. and BRENT, R.L.: Altered embryonic effects of uterine vascular clamping in the pregnant rat by uterine temperature control. Proc. Soc. Exper. Biol. Med. 124: 257–260, 1967.

THE INCORPORATION OF RADIOACTIVE TERATOGENS BY MAMMALIAN EMBRYOS

C.P. Dagg, *Professor,* and M.K. Dagg

Department of Biology and The School of Dentistry,
University of Alabama, Birmingham, U.S.A.

The purposes and methods of using radioactive drugs in studying teratogenesis are much the same as those for pharmacologic experiments in which the metabolic fates of drugs are investigated. The results of the experiments might provide information on (a) the biochemical pathways by which the teratogen is detoxified or converted to a metabolically active form, (b) whether the injected substance or a metabolic by-product is the active teratogen, (c) the amount of teratogen or metabolic products eliminated through the urine, feces or by other routes, (d) the levels of teratogen or by-products circulating in the maternal blood or present in maternal and embryonic tissues at various time intervals after injection, (e) the localization of teratogen or by-products in specific embryonic tissues, (f) the correlation of the above information with genetic differences in response to the teratogen and, (g) the correlation of the above information with the action of the protecting or potentiating effects of other treatments.

In some instances methods are available for determining at least a part of the fate of the teratogen without using a radioactive form. Examples of such methods have been provided by EVERETT[3] and by WILSON, BEAUDOIN and FREE[7] who injected the teratogenic dye, trypan blue, into pregnant rats and found that the dye, identified by its blue color, was incorporated by cells of the yolk sac epithelium. WILSON, BEAUDOIN and FREE also observed that a relatively high concentraion of the dye remained in the serum for several days after injection. BEVELANDER and COHLAN[1] used the fluorescent properties of tetracycline to demonstrate that it was deposited throughout the skeleton of fetal rats from injected mothers.

The use of isotopically labelled teratogens is justified when the chemical procedures available for determining the metabolic fate of the non-radioactive form or its by-products are not sufficiently sensitive or when they are prohibitive in terms of cost or time. One of the most complete series of investigations with a radioactive teratogen has been published by FABRO, SCHUMACHER, SMITH and WILLIAMS[4], and FABRO, SMITH and WILLIAMS[5]. These investigators reported that thalidomide labelled with ^{14}C was found in rabbit blastocysts after administration to the pregnant doe. Furthermore, four hydrolysis products of thalidomide did penetrate into the embryo. It was concluded that since the hydrolysis products were found in the embryo and since the hydrolysis products were not teratogenic, the active teratogenic agent is thalidomide itself. In another investigation, HAGUE, FABRO and SMITH[4] showed that thalidomide does pass into the hamster embryo and concluded that the failure of thalidomide to be teratogenic in this animal is not due to its inability to reach the embryo.

DAGG, DOERR and OFFUTT[2] injected 5-fluorouracil-2-C[14] into pregnant mice and demonstrated that fluorouracil was incorporated by the embryos when given at teratogenic doses. By increasing the dose of fluorouracil, a higher percentage of embryos were malformed and the amount of teratogen incorporated by them was correspondingly greater. The amount of fluorouracil found in the embryos varied between different inbred strains and hybrids. Most of the fluorouracil in the embryos was found in the RNA fraction, with lesser but appreciable amounts in the acid-soluble fraction.

PROCEDURES

These procedures were devised for the mouse embryo, but with appropriate modifications they are applicable to other mammals. To accomplish all of the procedures described in this demonstration would require three or more days. For that reason, some of the preliminary operations have been completed beforehand. Specimens are available for observation and for use by the students. The mice have been mated and injected with a radioactive compound which has been incorporated by maternal and embryonal tissues. Pregnant females of this sort will be available for dissection by the participants. Other radioactive embryos, placentae and yolk sacs were prepared for scintillation counting. The participants may wish to measure the radioactivity in these specimens and to calculate the amount of injected material retained by the embryos and other tissues.

1. Females, 13-weeks-old and older, were mated and then kept singly in pens until the 10th day of gestation. A saline solution of radioactive teratogen was injected introperitoneally through a 27 gauge needle. The volume of injected solution was 0.20 to 0.50 ml, which was carefully delivered from a microliter syringe. A second group of females, treated as described above, was used as a saline-injected control.

2. At varying periods after injection, from 1 to 24 hours, a small number of females were killed by cervical dislocation. The time between injection and killing of the female is critically important, and therefore, the number of animals that can be satisfactorily processed depends on the number and skill of the operators. To avoid contamination of the bench surface with radioactive materials, the working area is covered with a layer of absorbent paper backed with a waterproof layer of either paper or plastic. Most mice will urinate and defecate when they are killed. These waste products may be radioactive and so care must be taken not to contaminate the equipment or the operator's hands.

3. The uterus was transferred to a chilled petri dish containing a 4–6 mm layer of paraffin wax. The ovarian and vaginal ends of the uterus were pinned to the wax. A slight stretching of the uterus made removal of the embryos easier. If the embryos were to be removed at a later date, the petri dish was immediately placed in a freezer, but if the embryos were to be removed immediately they were covered with cold saline.

4. The uterine wall was torn open, using two fine-toothed, curved forceps, and the conceptuses were exposed one at a time. The frozen uterus was allowed

to thaw in cold saline before attempting the dissection. The decidua and yolk sac were torn open, and the embryo was transferred to another petri dish containing cold saline (without a paraffin layer). The amnion was usually left surrounding the embryo but could be easily removed. The yolk sac was separated from placental and decidual tissue by pulling gently with the forceps. The rest of the conceptus was freed from the uterine wall by gentle scraping with the forceps and placed in the second petri dish. When the wall of the conceptus was torn open and when the extraembryonic blood vessels were severed, there was an unavoidable loss of varying amounts of embryonic blood, except when the uterus had been frozen previously.

5. It was convenient to have another person examine the embryos at this time. Records of the stage of development according to external features were kept for each embryo. The crown-rump length was measured with an optical micrometer to give an estimate of the effect of treatment on body growth.

6. When the embryos and extraembryonic tissues were analyzed chemically for the teratogen or its metabolic products the dissections were done immediately after removal of the uterus. The uterus was not frozen and stored. For the chemical analysis all of the embryos of a litter were combined and the analysis was started immediately, or else they were frozen and stored overnight.

When the total radioactivity in whole individual embryos and extraembryonic tissues was to be measured, they were rinsed once in cold distilled water and placed separately in vials used for scintillation counting. In some cases the vials had been tared, so that the embryos could be weighed after removing the excess fluid on strips of filter paper.

7. When the embryos and extraembryonic tissues are to be analyzed chemically, the methods will depend, of course, on the nature of the teratogen and its metabolic products. In a study by DAGG, DOERR and OFFUTT[2], the distribution of the teratogen, 5 fluorouracil-2-C^{14}, in the acid soluble, RNA and DNA fractions was determined after separation of these fractions by a modified Schmidt-Thannhauser procedure.

When the total radioactivity in whole, individual embryos and extraembryonic tissues was measured, the samples were dissolved by adding 2 ml or less of a suitable solubilizer such as NCS Reagent (Nuclear-Chicago) or Hydroxide of Hyamine (Packard Instrument Co.). The vial was tightly capped and allowed to stand at room temperature overnight or longer. Other tissue solubilizers are available. They should dissolve the tissue sample without becoming discolored and must be miscible with the other solvents used in the scintillation vial. These solubilizers are dangerous and should be transferred only by a hand-operated pipet filler. The vials may be incubated in order to dissolve the tissues more rapidly, but elevated temperatures tend to cause discoloration of the solution which interferes with scintillation counting.

Using a hand-operated pipet filler, 15 ml of the scintillation mixture was added. The scintillation solution used in this demonstration contained 0.5 % 2,5 diphenyloxazole and 0.03 % 2,2-p-phenylenebis (5-phenyloxazole) in toluene.

8. The embryos from the saline-injected control females were prepared for scintillation counting in the same manner as the radioactive embryos. These embryos were used to determine the background radiation.

9. Scintillation counters vary in the efficiency with which they are able to detect disintegrations in the counting vials. It is necessary to determine the efficiency of the counting system and to know the specific activity of the injected teratogen in order to calculate the absolute amounts of teratogen present in the samples. The appropriate method for determining the counting efficiency, whether by internal or external standardization in which a known amount of radioactivity is introduced into the sample vial, will depend upon the type of scintillation counter. The methods are usually described in the instruction manuals accompanying the equipment.

10. Since the urine and feces of the treated females may be radioactive, the bedding should be disposed of, and the pens should be cleaned or disposed of according to the local regulations for handling radioactive materials. In those cases in which one of the metabolic products of the teratogen is $^{14}CO_2$, it may be desirable to keep the treated female in a ventilated container with a CO_2 trap on the air outlet. The mouse carcass and other tissues, the absorbent paper cover for the work surface, and any other disposable radioactively contaminated material, including the rinsing solutions, should also be disposed of according to local regulations. The instruments should be thoroughly cleaned before reuse.

REFERENCES

1. BEVELANDER, G. and COHLAN, S.G.: The effect on the rat fetus of transplacentally acquired tetracycline. Biol. Neonat. 4: 365–370, 1962.
2. DAGG, C.P., DOERR. A. and OFFUTT, C.: Incorporation of 5-fluorouracil-2-C^{14} by mouse embryos. Biol. Neonat. 10: 32–46, 1966.
3. EVERETT, J.W.: Morphological and physiological studies of the placenta in the albino rat. J. Exp. Zool. 70: 243–386, 1935.
4. FABRO, S., SCHUMACHER, H., SMITH, R.L. and WILLIAMS, R.T.: Identification of thalidomide in rabbit blastocysts. Nature 201: 1125–1126, 1964.
5. FABRO, S., SMITH, R.L. and WILLIAMS, R.T.: The fate of the hydrolysis products of thalidomide in the pregnant rabbit. Biochem. J. 104: 570–574, 1967.
6. HAGUE, D.E., FABRO, S. and SMITH, R.L.: The fate of [^{14}C] thalidomide in the pregnant hamster. J. Pharm. Pharmacol. 19: 603–607, 1967.
7. WILSON, J.G., BEAUDOIN, A.R. and FREE, H.J.: Studies on the mechanism of teratogenic action of trypan blue. Anat. Rec. 133: 115–128, 1959.

A SEARCH FOR AN ASSOCIATION OF WILMS' TUMOR
WITH SPECIFIC CONGENITAL DEFECTS

Robert W. Miller

Chief, Epidemiology Branch, National Cancer Institute,
National Institutes of Health, Bethesda

The link between mongolism and leukemia, established by epidemiologic research, has contributed to the understanding of the etiology of leukemia. To afford a similar opportunity in the study of WILMS' tumor, the medical charts of 440 children with this neoplasm diagnosed at six hospitals were reviewed in a search for an excessive occurrence of specific congenital malformations. The diagnoses of malformations were abstracted from all available past histories; from physical, X-ray, and pathological examinations; and from discharge summaries. Two hundred and twenty-three of the cases were boys. Comparison will be made with the malformations described at autopsy of 203 leukemic children, 124 of whom were boys.

The raw data are contained on the pages which follow. Cut along the lines which have been drawn so that for each patient with a congenital defect, you will have one slip of paper. The notation in the upper left hand corner of each slip of paper indicates whether the patient had WILMS' tumor (WT) or leukemia (L). Arrange the slips of paper in a logical order so an evaluation can be made of anomalies which may exceed in number the normal expectation. Do not tabulate the material in detail, but summarize your findings in a paragraph and attempt to interpret them.

WT	WT
Pigmented nevi large, right shoulder and anterior chest wall; Hemangioma of back; Double urinary meatus	Hypospadias with no other defects
WT	WT
Duplication of right ureter and kidney	Cerebral hypotonia, general; Severe mental retardation; Bone age <3 mos. at 6 years of age; Cryptorchidism, bilateral; Small penis; Cytogenetic abnormality not yet fully defined
WT	WT
Hemihypertrophy of left side of face, moderate, and tongue, marked (WILMS' tumor on right)	Congenital nystagmus
WT	WT
Pectus excavatum	Left clubfoot, corrected
WT	WT
3 spider angiomata, right hand and wrist	Pigmented nevi, multiple, hairy, encasing entire back and shoulder to buttocks
WT	WT
Hypospadias with inguinal and umbilical herniorraphies	Mental retardation with frontal bossing

WT Aniridia, congenital, bilateral with cataracts; Thyroid-treated floppiness and retarded bone age	WT Bifid left renal pelvis and double ureter
WT Double right kidney	WT Aortic stenosis
WT Meckel's diverticulum ruptured at 6 days of age	WT 2×3 cms. slightly raised hemangioma above umbilicus
WT Semibifid right renal pelvis; Hypoplastic left first rib	WT Bilobed left kidney with hydronephrosis
WT Aniridia, congenital, bilateral with left cataract; Bilateral dislocation of the lens; Mental retardation; Upper left pinna recurved over itself	WT Horseshoe kidney
WT Hypospadias with bilateral cryptorchidism; Cafe au lait spots	WT Thyroglossal cyst excised at 4 yrs.

WT	WT
Stricture of urethral meatus surgically treated	Hemangioma, right forearm, radiotherapy
WT Tetralogy of Fallot with patent foramen ovale	**WT** Intracranial vascular anomaly causing bruit over vertex, and prominent diploic veins
WT Spasticity since newborn, following icterus and convulsions at 2 days of age, not due to erythroblastosis fetalis; Patent foramen ovale at autopsy at 17 mos.	**WT** Small urethral orifice dilated at 3 mos. of age
WT Pigmented nevi multiple	**WT** Aplastic right kidney and ureter
WT Undescended testes: 5 cases unilateral, 3 cases bilateral on PE, and 1 case bilaterally absent at autopsy	**WT** Aniridia, congenital, bilateral with microcephaly (head circumference 43 cms. at 2 yrs.) and mental retardation and cataracts; Dwarfism
WT Hypospadias with left hydrocele and varicocele	**WT** Hemihypertrophy of *left* arm and leg (2 cms. longer than right) and *right* face and tongue; Omphalocele repaired at birth; (WILMS' tumor on right)

WT	WT
Hypospadias with chordee	Aniridia, congenital, bilateral with head circumference 44.5 cms. at 15 mos. with mental retardation and cataracts
WT Two left renal arteries	**WT** Bilateral small fibrous ovaries
WT Mental retardation; Fusion defects and midline clefts of 11th and 12th thoracic vertebrae; Polycythemia	**WT** Right calf 2 cms. less in circumference than left; limp and flapping gait, cause unknown
WT Multiple neurofibromatosis with compression of spinal nerve at $9\frac{1}{2}$ years of age—6 years after diagnosis of WILMS' tumor	**WT** Horseshoe kidney
WT Congenital dislocation of hip	**WT** Juvenile fibrolipoma, left thigh
WT Congenital spherocytic anemia, as in father and all sibs, 7 of whom had splenectomies; Absent cartilage upper pinnae; 2 first-cousins (brothers) died of WILMS' tumor	**WT** Precocious breast development, moderate on left, beginning at 18 mos.

WT Hemihypertrophy of left breast, marked; left leg 2 cms. longer and left flank fuller than right; left hemipelvis larger than right; Osteochondroma of left ilium; Bilateral partial nerve deafness—all recorded at 12 years of age; (WILMS' tumor on right)	WT Clubfoot, corrected
WT Right metatarsus varus	WT Aniridia, congenital, bilateral; Hypoplastic left kidney having no normal nephrons; (WILMS' tumor on right)
WT Duplication of right ureter and renal pedicles covered with numerous dilated blood vessels	WT Horseshoe kidney
WT Duplication of right ureter and renal pelvis; Focal angiomatous malformations of liver	WT Microcephaly; Rhabdomyosarcoma primary at anal sphincter Bilateral congenital deafness; Bilateral internal tibial torsion; Congenital deformity of right thumb; Capillary-cavernous hemangioma beside 4th ventricle
WT Aniridia, congenital, with bilateral glaucoma and head circumference 45 cms. at 14 mos.; Upper left pinna recurved over itself	WT Pigmented nevi multiple; Horseshoe kidney
WT Hemangiomata of scalp and abdomen removed by family doctor	

L
Cryptorchidism

L
Anomaly of larynx, not further specified

L
Mongol—tetralogy of Fallot

L
Meckel's diverticulum

L
Patent ductus, admits probe

L
Renal cyst

L
Meckel's diverticulum

L
Multiple cysts of kidney;
Rhabdomyomata of heart

L
Hypospadias

L
Abnormal lobulation of liver

L
Eosinophilic adenoma—pituitary (microscopic)

L
Meckel's diverticulum

L Colloid cyst of pituitary; Multiple cysts of ovaries	L Patent ductus (ligated—age 5 yrs.)
L Hemangioma—4 × 5 cms. on leg	L Meckel's diverticulum

EXPLANATION OF EPIDEMIOLOGIC EXERCISE
CONCERNING WILMS' TUMOR

Purpose: To experience a simple procedure with etiologic value in teratology (and oncology).

Results: Should be listed by organ-system subclassified into specific congenital defects. If not subclassified, the excessive occurrence of certain defects may be diluted and go unrecognized; for example, 3 cases of hemihypertrophy would be lost in the total for miscellaneous defects.

Aniridia: There were 6 cases. The usual frequency is 1:50,000 (Michigan), the frequency with WILMS' tumor is $6/440 = 1:73$. This association was never described previously. Aniridia did not occur among the leukemic patients ("controls"), nor among those with any other neoplasm (review of literature). A new syndrome has been defined through epidemiology: WILMS' tumor, aniridia, secondary cataracts (4 cases), small head circumference with mental retardation (3 or 4 cases), urinary-tract anomalies (1 case here, others found in later series) and upper auditory pinna anomaly (2 cases).

Aniridia is usually due to the action of an autosomal dominant gene; on the average 2 or 3 aniridic children will have an aniridic parent. In the WILMS' tumor-aniridia syndrome the parents usually do *not* have eye defects. Hence, the syndrome is either due to mutation or is a phenocopy.

Hemihypertrophy: There were 3 cases. Due to the rarity of the disorder, its usual frequency is not known. The association with WILMS' tumor has been previously described (13 cases in previous literature). The total now published is 27. Hemihypertrophy occurs excessively also with primary liver cancer (6 cases to date) and adrenocortical neoplasia (6 cases to date). There is no overlap between hemihypertrophy and aniridia—the 2 defects have not yet been described in the same person. Thus each is independently associated with WILMS' tumor.

The etiology of hemihypertrophy is unknown. It occasionally runs in families; in one family with 2 affected children, one also had WILMS' tumor. Among other children with WILMS' tumor, one also had primary liver neoplasia and another had had a functioning adrenal cortical adenoma. Thus, the 3 neoplasms associated with hemihypertrophy have occurred as double primaries with one another.

Hamartomas: There were 4 cases with large or widely scattered pigmented nevi, 4 with noteworthy hemangiomas of the skin, and 4 with internal hemangiomas: 1 case with juvenile fibrolipoma and 1 with multiple neurofibromatosis. These defects are hamartomas; i.e., errors of tissue development in which there is an excess of one cellular element in an anatomic area. Hemihypertrophy, in the absence of WILMS' tumor, is associated with pigmented or vascular nevi and with the visceral cytomegaly syndrome. The visceral cytomegaly syndrome affects particularly the adrenal cortex, liver and kidney—the 3 organs in which cancer has occurred in association with hemihypertrophy. Thus, there appears to be a relationship among 4 forms of growth excess: hemihypertrophy, hamartomas, visceral cytomegaly and certain childhood neoplasms. From relatively simple research, associations have now been defined among diseases previously thought to be unrelated to one another.

Genitourinary defects: Among 223 boys 5 had hypospadias as compared with 0.6 cases expected, and 11 had undescended testes (6 bilateral) as compared with 3.3 cases expected. One girl had bilateral small fibrous ovaries. Four children had horseshoe kidneys as compared with an expectation of near zero. A wide array of other urinary-tract defects also was observed. No such anomalies occurred with leukemia in the present control series or excessively with other childhood cancer studied to date, except adrenocortical neoplasia. Hemihypertrophy and aniridia, though not associated with one another, are individually associated with urinary-tract anomalies. Thus maldevelopment of this organ system under some circumstances is followed by development of adrenocortical neoplasia or WILMS' tumor.

Summary: At very little cost, new insight into the genesis of a variety of related disorders, including certain congenital defects, has been obtained.

REFERENCE

MILLER, R.W., FRAUMENI, J.F. JR. and MANNING, M.D.: Association of WILMS' tumor with aniridia, hemihypertrophy and other congenital malformations. New Eng. J. Med. 270: 922–927, 1964.

PART III. EXHIBITIONS

INTRODUCTION

During the Workshop a series of exhibits were on display. These covered a variety of topics of significance to students of teratology. Some extended material presented in lectures while others dealt with topics not discussed elsewhere in the Workshop. It would be difficult and serve no worthwhile purpose to publish all of the material presented in exhibits and the following section contains only a sampling to illustrate the subjects presented and the methods of their presentation. In addition a list of some books and review articles in embryology and teratology is presented. Most of these were on display at the Workshop.

CULTURE OF HUMAN AND MOUSE LIMB-BUDS AS A TOOL FOR TESTING THE EMBRYOTOXICITY OF DRUGS

Hideo Nishimura, *Professor*, and Yoshiko Yasuda, *Graduate Student*

Department of Anatomy, Faculty of Medicine, Kyoto University, Kyoto, Japan.

There is a definite need to investigate the potential toxicity of new as well as old drugs for human embryos. Because of ethical considerations, gynecologists will not consider "testing new drugs" on pregnant women. However, abortuses from healthy mothers at the 2nd to 3rd month of pregnancy can be used legally for experimental studies and we have been performing parallel *in vitro* studies on human and mouse limb-buds in an attempt to compare their sensitivity to drugs by means of Wolff's agar medium method.

We obtained the following results which have important implications regarding the feasibility of drug testing by this method.

1. Similar histological differentiation was shown by human limb-buds at the developmental horizon (Streeter) 15 and mouse limb-buds at the corresponding stage (day 11 of gestation), cultured for 96 hours or 24 hours respectively. No fundamental difference was found in either species with respect to such differentiation *in vitro* and the histogenesis of the limb *in vivo*.

2. When ethylurethane, a mitotic poison, was mixed with the medium at the concentration of 10–50µg/ml, the specimens of both species showed occasional abnormal proliferation of the mesenchymal cells and there was suggestion of a dose-effect response. In several of mouse limb-buds but not in the human material we observed ectopic chondrification and abnormal local protrusion of the surface of the hand plate similar to that observed in polydactyly.

3. Similar experiments with thalidomide and seven of its derivatives also revealed some difference in toxicity between the species. Exposure to thalidomide at the concentration of 1µg/ml caused inhibition of differentiation and growth of the mesenchymal tissues in most of the human limbs, while no remarkable disturbance of development was shown in the similarly treated mouse limbs. In case of the derivatives given at the concentration of 1µg/ml, five compounds induced disturbed development of mesenchymal tissues in the human limbs in a few cases, while all compounds were almost ineffective in the mouse limbs.

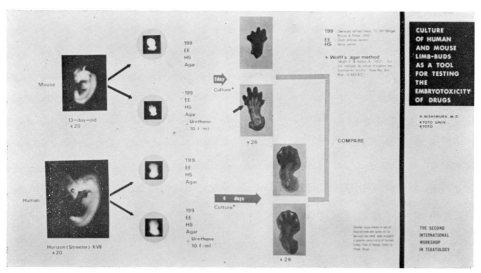

Fig. 1 Photograph of exhibit to demonstrate general setup. Original size: 94 × 185 cm.

PRODUCTION OF MICE IN THE LABORATORY

TATSUJI NOMURA

Director, Central Institute for Experimental Animals, Tokyo, Japan.

The following topics are explained by means of slides and recorded commentary.
1. Reproductive characteristics of mice
2. Programming for production
3. Facilities and equipment for production
4. Handling and feeding
5. Important points concerning mating, pregnancy, parturition and nursing
6. Care of weanling mice
7. Genetical control for production
8. Diseases control for production
9. Environmental control during production

HEREDITARY METABOLIC VARIATIONS IN MICE

Hiroshi Matsushita

Professor, Department of Physiology, Wakayama Medical College
Wakayama, Japan.

The subject matter shown in this exhibition concerns the uses of inherited metabolic variants of mice in medical studies and special genetic techniques used in maintaining stocks of mutant mice. Mutant mice with diseases resembling human ones may play an especially important role in understanding the diseases in man and in carrying out experiments which can not be done with human patients. Among many genetic diseases of the mouse, the two genes that have been most extensively studied are dystrophia muscularis, *dy,* and obese, *ob*. Many of the most interesting mutants used in certain fields of medical research are so pathological in their effects that they interfere with reproduction, and so special methods must be adopted to maintain stocks and to produce sufficiently large numbers for experimental use. Ovarian transplantation and the artificial insemination are employed for this purpose.

HUMAN INBORN METABOLIC ERRORS

Tsuneo Arakawa

Professor, Department of Pediatrics, Faculty of Medicine,
Tohoku University, Sendai, Japan.

A number of inborn errors of metabolism have been discovered through the recent advance in biochemical studies of genetic disorders. The defective enzymes in those disorders are illustrated schematically in metabolic pathways of amino acids, carbohydrates or nucleic acids.

PRINCIPLES OF PREVENTION OF CONGENITAL ANOMALIES BASED ON HUMAN GENETICS

EI MATSUNAGA

Head, Department of Human Genetics,
National Institute of Genetics, Mishima, Japan.

1. *Control of mutagenic agents by legislation*

A number of mutagenic agents are now known to exist in our environment, of which irradiation for diagnostic and therapeutic purposes is the most significant source of induced mutations. Therefore, caution should be taken by medical personnel in order that every individual who is expected to bear children can avoid any unnecessary irradiation upon his or her gonads.

2. *Family planning to bear children at younger maternal age*

This can appreciably prevent chromosome aberrations due to non-disjunction (Fig. 1) and, to a lesser degree, a number of congenital anomalies associated

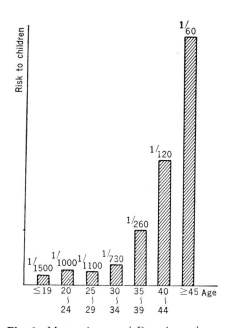

Fig. 1 Maternal age and DOWN's syndrome

The over-all incidence is assumed to be one per 600–births.
The increasing pattern of the risk with maternal age is stereotypical, regardless of racial, geographical and socio-economic differences.

with high maternal age and parity, e.g., Rh-erythroblastosis, cerebral palsy, strabismus, and other congenital malformations of the circulatory and nervous systems and those of sense organs.

3. *Avoidance of consanguineous marriages*

This can prevent not only recessive anomalies with simple genetic mechanism, but also those congenital malformations that are determined by multifactorial inheritance, e.g., club foot, cleft palate, hare lip etc.   However, the extent of the effect is rather small.

4. *Eugenic measures, e.g., contraception and sterilization based upon proper genetic counselling*

This can be applied whenever the genetic risk to the children is reasonably high, i.e., when a parent is affected with dominant anomalies with high penetrance, or when the parents are known to be both carriers of the same harmful gene.

BRITISH COLUMBIA REGISTRY FOR HANDICAPPED CHILDREN AND ADULTS

JAMES R. MILLER

Professor, Division of Medical Genetics, Department of Paediatrics,
University of British Columbia, Vancouver, Canada.
Visiting Research Associate, Department of Anatomy,
Faculty of Medicine, Kyoto University, Kyoto, Japan.

This exhibit demonstrates how the Registry functions and several of the ways it can be useful to those interested in the health problems presented by congenital malformations.

MINAMATA DISEASE OF HUMAN FETUSES

TADAO TAKEUCHI, *Professor*, and HIDEYO MATSUMOTO, *Associate Professor*

Department of Pathology, Kumamoto University School of Medicine,
Kumamoto, Japan.

Minamata disease is a new neurological disease of poisoning which was first described by TAKEUCHI et al. This disease was caused by the consumption of fish and shellfish contaminated by the effluent containing alkylmercury compound (methyl mercury) from a new industrial plant producing vinyl-chloride and acetaldehyde. When the outbreak of this disease occurred from 1954 to 1960 in the specific area of Minamata City, 89 patients (59 adults and 30 children) were observed (Fig. 1). In addition, 22 cases of congenital cerebral palsy (about 6 % in the total new-borns) were found in the infants in the same area during the same period. It was suspected that there might be a close relationship between cerebral palsy in infants and Minamata disease (Fig. 2), but the hypothesis was not convincing because of the following reasons: 1) The affected infants had not eaten contaminated fish and shellfish. 2) Their mother had no typical neurological manifestations showing three main signs such as concentric constriction of visual fields, ataxia and dysarthria. 3) Their clinical symptoms were more difficult to elicit and were more varied in comparison with postnatal infantile and adult cases of Minamata disease.

In autopsy of two cerebral palsy patients who had died in May, 1961 and in September, 1962, it was possible to decide that they were cases of Minamata disease which had obviously been acquired during the prenatal period. TAKEUCHI, therefore, stated that such cerebral palsy cases should be called "fetal Minamata disease" which has a few characteristics different from the adult and postnatal infantile Minamata disease.

Pathologically, it is presumed that the essential changes in Minamata disease must be expressions of a toxic encephalopathy in which the nerve cells in the cerebral and cerebellar cortex are selectively involved irrespectively of age or sex. The toxic agent gives rise to the cortical disturbance, which may occur throughout the whole cortex of the cerebrum and cerebellum, but preferentially is localized in the calcarine and precentral regions of the cerebrum and in the granular layer of the cerebellum. The distribution of the lesions is believed to be related to the intensity and amount of the toxic agent taken and to age and individual condition of the patient.

Particularly in the fetus the neurons throughout the whole cortex of the brain tend to be involved by this toxin. The cortical lesions of the brain are distributed more widely and more severely in the fetal form of Minamata disease than in the infantile one. In addition, the hypoplastic and dysplastic findings in the central nervous systems are represented in the fetal Minamata disease, i.e., resting matrix cells, abnormal cytoarchitecture, columnar grouping of nerve cells, hypoplastic corpus callosum and cerebellum, and poor myelination.

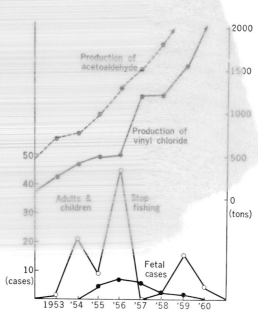

Fig. 1 Yearly incidence of Minamata disease (1953–1960) and its relationship to industrial products.

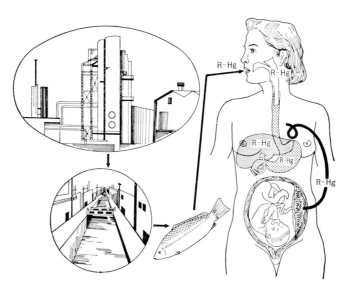

Fig. 2 Etiology of fetal Minamata disease

Both underdevelopment and regressive change of the brain in fetal Minamata disease produce a specific microcephalia with a granular cell type of cerebellar atrophy in which the weight of brain is reduced by one third or even one-half when compared with normal brains of the same age. In spite of severe under-development, no malformations were found in extremities and other parts of the body, except for abnormal dentition. From the familial history and episodes as well as from the pathological findings, it was considered that these prenatally affected patients were presumably damaged in the sixth and eighth month of fetal life.

CARTILAGE SPECIMENS OF RAT
AND MOUSE FETUSES

YOSHIRO KAMEYAMA

Associate Professor, Department Pathology and Embryology, The Research Institute of Environmental Medicine, Nagoya University, Nagoya, Japan

Although not so commonly used in experimental teratology, cartilage-stained specimens are recognized as useful as a means of detecting skeletal anomalies of the fetuses in laboratory animals. Cartilage-stained specimens are also necessary complements of bone-stained specimens in the study and demonstration of the development of the skeleton, since the ossification of the cartilagenous skeleton is far from completion in the mouse and rat fetuses.

Among the procedures used to make cartilage specimens, the Noback modification (Anat. Rec. 11: 292–294, 1916) of the van Wijhe method seems to be the most serviceable one and is recommended for the mouse and rat fetuses. By this method, skeletal abnormalities can be distinctly detected in the early stages of development, because in addition to mature cartilage, precartilage tissue, which differentiates from the mesenchyme on day 13 in the mouse fetus and on day 15 in the rat fetus, is stained with methylene-blue. Another advantage of this method is that microscopic sections can be made and stained with

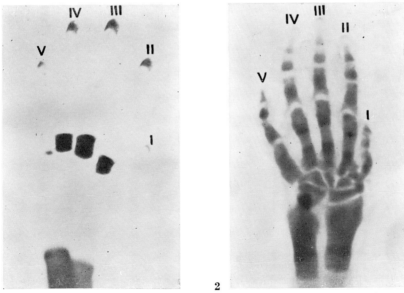

1   **2**

Fig. 1–2 Normal digits of the left forelimb in the Wistar rat fetus on day 20 of gestation
1. Bone specimen (Dawson's method).   **2.** Cartilage specimen (Noback's method).

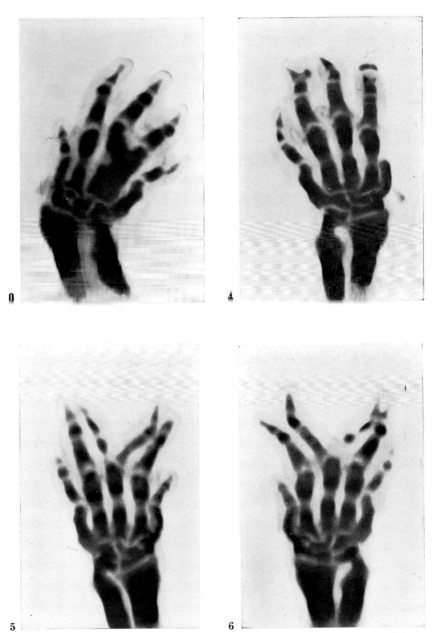

Fig. 3-6 Cartilage specimens of the malformed digits of the forelimbs in the Wistar rat fetuses on day 20 of gestation. The malformations were produced by single administrations of 40 mg/kg of myleran to the mother animals on day 11 of pregnancy.

3. Fusion of the metacarpi III–IV. **4**. Duplication of the distal phalanges II and IV. **5 & 6**. Complete duplication of the phalanges III.

hematoxylin-eosin after gross observation.

The cartilage specimens demonstrated in this exhibition are of the normal fetuses, and of the malformed ones produced by hypervitaminosis-A, X-radiation and myleran (busulfan) in the mouse and rat.   Various states of maldevelopment of the skeletons, which can be hardly detected in the bone-stained specimens, are clearly demonstrated in the cartilage specimens.

HEART ANOMALIES IN MAN

Naomasa Okamoto

Professor, Department of Genetico-pathology, Research Institute for Nuclear Medicine and Biology, Hiroshima University, Hiroshima, Japan.

Congenital cardiovascular anomalies may be classified into the following two groups: (1) isolated individual abnormalities and (2) pathologic complexes. The present exhibition deals mainly with the transposition complexes, congenital abnormalities of the heart involving the relationship of the great arterial vessels to each other and to the ventricles. Lev classified these complexes from pathological anatomical point of view in the following way:

I. Riding aorta (dextroposition of the aorta): The aorta straddles the muscular ventricular septum over a defect in the septum, thus emanating to a varying degree from both ventricles.

    (a) With aneurysm of the *pars membranacea*

    (b) With pulmonary hypoplasia (Tetralogy of Fallot)

        (1) With pulmonary hypoplasia

            (i) With right aortic arch (Corvisart's complex)

        (2) With pulmonary atresia (extreme type of tetralogy of Fallot)

    (c) With aortic hypoplasia (Eisenmenger's complex)

    (d) With common truncus

II. Partial transposition (simple transposition, extreme transposition, double outlet right ventricle, lateral position of the aorta, origin of the both great vessels from the right ventricle): The aorta comes completely from the right ventricle, and no vessel emerges from the left ventricle.

    (a) With pulmonary hypoplasia (Fallot type)

        (1) With hypoplasia

        (2) With atresia

    (b) With aortic hypoplasia (or equal sized aorta and pulmonary artery) (Eisenmenger type)

        (1) With mitral atresia

        (2) Without mitral atresia

    (c) With common truncus

III. Riding pulmonary artery (Taussig-Bing heart, Taussig's syndrome, incomplete transposition of the great vessels with biventricular origin of the pulmonary artery, partial transposition of the great vessels with overriding artery): The aorta emerges from the right and the pulmonary artery comes from the both ventricles.

    (a) Right-sided type

    (b) Left-sided type

    (c) Intermediate type

IV. Complete transposition (crossed transposition): The aorta and the

pulmonary artery emerge from the wrong ventricles.
- (a) With normal A-V orifice
  - (1) With normal architecture
    - (i) Without VSD
    - (ii) With VSD
    - (iii) With pulmonary stenosis
  - (2) With common ventricle
  - (3) With single ventricle and small outlet chamber
- (b) With abnormal A-V orifice
  - (1) With tricuspid stenosis or atresia
  - (2) With mitral stenosis or atresia
  - (3) With common A-V orifice
- (c) With pseudo-truncus
- V. Mixed levocardia:
  - (a) Type IA, Atria normal, ventricles inverted; with complete inverted transposition
  - (b) Type IB, With ventricular inversion and complete (non-inverted) transposition of the arterial trunks
  - (c) Type II, With atrial inversion
  - (d) Type III, With atria and ventricles in almost normal position but wrongly connected

PATHOLOGY OF THE KIDNEY IN
HUMAN NEWBORNS

Shigeru Mitani

Professor, Depatment of Obstetrics and Gynecology, Nippon Medical College, and Director, Japan Red Cross Maternity Hospital, Tokyo, Japan.

Although kidney anomalies developing during the fetal and neonatal period are not very large in number, they are regarded as important, because many of them exert direct influences upon life. Some examples of kidney anomalies found in newborns at our clinic are exhibited.

Bilateral agenesis: This is a rare anomaly which results inevitably in death. Four cases were found among 2,600 autopsy cases.

Unilateral agenesis: Absence of a single kidney is rarer than absence of both kidneys. Only two cases were observed in our series of autopsies.

Hypoplasia: Hypoplasia is reported to be less common than complete agenesis. It is difficult to set a good standard for kidney size.

Large kidney: No definite borderline can be drawn between this condition and the normal size. A male infant with 2,235g body weight had a left kidney weighing 23g and a right one 23.5g. These are the largest in our series.

Ectopia: Although various degrees of dislocation are present, the pelvic kidney is quite rare and seen in only 1 of our 2,600 cases.

Excess number of kidneys: More than three completely independent kidneys are never present in an individual other than the double monster. In some cases of the fused kidney, several separate kidneys are occasionally connected with a single renal pelvis.

Congenital abnormal shape of the kidney: Abnormalities in the shape of an individual kidney and those with fusion of both kidneys are distinguished. The latter are further classified into symmetrical fusion abnormality and asymmetrical fusion abnormality. The horseshoe kidney is most common among these and 14 cases were found among 2,600 infants autopsied.

Hemorrhagic renal infarction in the neonatal period: This condition is rarely seen following operative handling of the newborn. A relationship between the infarction and cerebral hypoxia is suspected, but the hypothesis is not convincing.

Congenital polycystic kidney: This is also called sack kidney or polycystic degeneration. This was found in 17 of 2,600 cases of stillbirth and neonatal death. The cause is unknown. Types of congenital cystic kidney are classified as follows:

(1) Strawberry-type polycystic kidney: Miliary sized cysts are localized in part of the kidney.

(2) Cystic kidney resembling hydatidiform mole: The kidney is formed by many cysts of miliary to rice grain size, which appear like cystic moles.

(3) Cystic kidney resembling multilocular ovarian cyst: About 10 to 20 large cysts exceeding pigeon's egg size assemble to form a kidney resembling ovarian cyst.

(4) Cystic kidney of type IV: This is probably due to some disturbance in flow of urine through the urinary tract. The shape of the kidney is quite irregular and no cortico-medullary borderline is seen. Pronounced inflammatory changes with round cell infiltration are seen. Cartilage tissue is distinctly observed.

(5) Cystic kidney of type V: This condition is unilateral. One kidney is completely normal and cysts are formed on the other.

MALFORMATION OF THE TEETH

Mikio Shirasu, *Professor*, Kuhei Furuhashi, *Associate Professor*,
Kiyoaki Kawabata, *Instructor*, and Takeshi Sato, *Graduate Student*

Department of Oral Anatomy, Osaka Dental College, Osaka, Japan.

There are various types of anomalies of the human tooth. They are roughly classified into three groups, i.e., anomalies (I) in the number, (II) of the shape, (III) of the site. The first group consists of (1) reductive anomalies and (2) supernumerary ones. The second group, malformations of the tooth, are further divided into deformities (1) in the size, (2) of the tuberculum, and (3) of the root.

Some types of tooth anomalies can be induced in experimental animals by prenatal administration of such teratogens as ethylurethane and cortisone. By using mice, we are studying the morphogenesis of tooth malformations. Comparison between malformations of the tooth in human beings and those induced in experimental animals is shown in the present exhibition.

A numerical anomaly of the tooth was observed in 17 day mouse fetuses whose mother had been given ethylurethane at day 7 of gestation. Histological examinations revealed no tooth germ other than that of $\underline{M_1}$. Its enamel organ showed a very poor development; the tissue components were markedly hypoplastic; no dental papilla was formed. Those fetuses were likely to develop a tooth defect. Division or proliferation of the tooth germ, which indicates development of a supernumeraly anomaly, could not be induced by the above mentioned treatment.

Deformities of the tooth could also be induced by prenatal treatments with ethylurethane or cortisone. Microscopic examinations showed, not rarely, a tumor-like appearance of the tooth germ due to a severe local maldevelopment. The most common type of gross malformations was microdont, while macrodont could not be produced experimentally. The degree of maldevelopment depended upon the period of the treatment. Prenatal administration of cortisone resulted in the formation of a cone-shaped microdont in the $\overline{I|I}$ of young mice of 14 days of age. The teeth were tinged with a pearl color. Anaplasia of the ectodermal cells in the tooth germ is considered as a cause of the cone-shape malformation both in human beings and in experimental animals.

In fetuses treated with ethylurethane or cortisone, a partial defect of the young enamel organ due to hypoplasia of the enamel epithelia was observed histologically, together with inactive proliferation of odontoblasts and cells in the dental papilla. This condition leads to the hypoplastic teeth which appeared in the mice prenatally treated with the teratogen.

In man hypoplasia of the whole teeth is a rare anomaly. We observed a 6-year-old boy with this condition. Two-thirds of the crown was covered with a thin enamel layer, the remaining one-third showing exposed dentine; the enamel of the deciduous canine and the first and second deciduous molars was underdeveloped. The hypoplastic state closely resembled to that observed in the above mentioned experimental animals. This case may have had some prenatal disturbances in the formation of the enamel organ, as were seen in the teratogen treated-animals.

SOME BOOKS AND REVIEW ARTICLES
IN EMBRYOLOGY AND TERATOLOGY

I. EMBRYOLOGY AND RELATED SCIENCES

A. Human embryology

1. Hamilton, W.J., Boyd, J.D., and Mossman, H.W.: Human Embryology. W. Heffer & Sons Ltd., Cambridge, 1962.
2. Arey, L.B.: Developmental Anatomy. W.B. Saunders Co., Philadelphia, 1965.
3. Patten, B.M.: Human Embryology. Blakiston Co., Philadelphia, 1958.
4. Kraus, B.S., Kitamura, H., and Latham, R.A.: Atlas of Developmental Anatomy of the Face. Hoeber Medical Division: Harper & Row Publishers, New York, 1966.
5. Valdés-Dapena, M.A.: An Atlas of Fetal and Neonatal Histology. J.B. Lippincott Co., Philadelphia, 1957.
6. Lind, J., Stern, L., and Wegelius, C.: Human Eoetal and Neonatal Circulation. Charles C. Thomas Publisher, Springfield, 1964.
7. Falkner, F.: Human Development. W.B. Saunders Co., Philadelphia, 1966.
8. Tuchmann-Duplessis, H.: Embryologie. Fascicule premier, 1965; Fascicule deux, 1967. Masson & Cie, Editeurs, Paris.
9. Starck, D.: Embryologie. Georg Thieme Verlag, Stuttgart, 1965.
10.* Fischel, A.: Grundriss der Entwicklung des Menschen. Verlag von Julius Springer, Berlin, 1937.
11.* Keibel, F.. und Elze, C.: Normentafel zur Entwicklungsgeschichte des Menschen. In: Normentafeln zur Entwicklungsgeschichte der Wirbeltiere, herausgegeben von F. Keibel, achtes Heft. Verlag von Gustav Fischer, Jena, 1908.
12. Van Wagenen, G., and Simpson, M.E.: Embryology of the Ovary and Testis; *Homo sapiens* and *Macaca muratta*. Yale University Press, New Haven, 1965.
13. Shettles, L. B.: Ovum Humanum. Verlag von Urban & Schwarzenberg, München, 1960.

B. Embryology of experimental animals

14. Austin, C.R.: The Mammalian Egg. Blackwell Scientific Publications, Oxford, 1961.
15. Rugh, R.: Vertebrate Embryology. Harcourt, Brace & World, Inc., New York, 1964.
16.* Hertwig, O.: Handbuch der Vergleichenden und Experimentellen Entwicklungslehre der Wirbeltiere. Verlag von Gustav Fischer, Jena, 1906.
17. Hofer, H., Schultz, A.H., und Starck, D.: Primatologia. Vol. 1: Systematik— Phylogenie—Ontogenie. S. Karger AG, Basel, 1958.
18. Patten, B.M.: The Embryology of the Pig. The Blakiston Co., Philadelphia, 1946.

---

* Out of print

19.* Keibel, F.: Normentafel zur Entwicklungsgeschichte des Schweines (*Sus sucrofa domesticus*). In: Normentafeln zur Entwicklungsgeschichte der Wirbeltiere, herausgegeben von F. Keibel, I. Verlag von Gustav Fischer, Jena, 1897.

20.* Minot, C., and Taylor, E.: Normal Plate of the Development of the Rabbit (*Lepus cuniculus L.*). In: Normentafeln zur Entwicklungsgeschichte der Wirbeltiere, herausgegeben von F. Keibel, fünftes Heft. Verlag von Gustav Fischer, Jena, 1905.

21.* Bischoff, T.L.W.: Entwicklungsgeschichte des Meerschweinchens. J. Ricker'sche Buchhandlung, Giessen, 1852.

22.* Donaldson, H.H.: The Rat. The Wistar Institute of Biology and Anatomy, Philadelphia, 1924.

23. Farris, E.J. and Griffith, J.Q.: The Rat in Laboratory Investigation. Hafner Publishing Co., New York, 1963.

24. Walker, D.G., and Wirtschafter, Z.T.: The Genesis of the Rat Skeleton; A Laboratory Atlas. Charles C. Thomas Publisher, Springfield, 1959.

25.* Henneberg, B.: Normentafel zur Entwicklungsgeschichte der Wanderratte (*Rattus norvegicus erxleben*). In: Normentafeln zur Entwicklungsgeschichte der Wirbeltiere, begründet von F. Keibel, fünzehntes (Ergänzungs-) Heft. Verlag von Gustav Fischer, Jena, 1937.

26. Rugh, R.: The Mouse, its Reproduction and Development. Burgess Publishing Co., Minneapolis, 1967.

27. Green, E.L.: Biology of the Laboratory Mouse. The Blakiston Division, McGraw-Hill Book Co., New York, 1966.

28. Wirtschafter, Z. T.: The Genesis of the Mouse Skeleton; A Laboratory Atlas. Charles C. Thomas Publisher, Springfield, 1960.

29. Patten, B.M.: The Early Embryology of the Chick. The Blakiston Co., Philadelphia, 1948.

30.* Lillie, F.R.: The Development of the Chick. Henry Holt & Co., New York, 1919.

31. New, D.A.T.: The Culture of Vertebrate Embryos. Logos Press Ltd., London, 1966.

C. Developmental physiology

32. Willier, B.H., Weiss, P.A., and Hamburger, V.: Analysis of Development. W.B. Saunders Co., Philadelphia, 1956.

33. Wolstenhorme, G.E.W. and O'Connor, M.: Ciba Foundation Symposium: Preimplantation Stages of Pregnancy. J. & A. Churchill, Ltd., London, 1965.

34. DeHaan, R.L., and Ursprung, H.: Organogenesis. Holt, Rinehart and Winston, New York, 1965.

35. Wolff, E.: New Methods in Embryology; Detection of Molecules Through Immunochemical Methods. Hermann, Paris, 1965.

36. Dawes, G.: Foetal and Neonatal Physiology. Year Book Medical Publishers, Chicago, 1968.

37. Parkes, A.S.: Marshall's Physiology of Reproduction, vol. 1. part 1. 1962, part 2. 1960; vol. 2. 1961; vol. 3. 1966. Longmans, Green & Co., London.

II. TERATOLOGY (IN A BROAD SENSE)

A. Teratology in general

38. Fishbein, M.: Birth Defects. J.B. Lippincott Co., Philadelphia, 1963.
39. Montagu, M.F.A.: Prenatal Influences. Charles C. Thomas Publisher, Springfield, 1962.
40. Minz, B.: Environmental Influences on Prenatal Development. The University of Chicago Press, Chicago, 1958.
41. Gordon, G.C.: Congenital Deformities. E. & S. Livingstone Ltd., Edinburgh, 1961.
42. Willis, R.A.: The Borderland of Embryology and Pathology. Butterworth & Co. Ltd., London, 1958.
43. Woollam, D.H.M.: Advances in Teratology, vol. 1. 1966; vol. 2. 1967. Logos Press Ltd., London.
44. Stoll, R., et. Maraud, R.: Introduction a L'étude des Malformations. Gauthier-Villars, Paris, 1965.
45. Smithells, R.W.: Early Diagnosis of Congenital Abnormalities. Cassell & Co. Ltd., London, 1963.
46. Rubin, A.: Handbook of Congenital Malformations. W. B. Saunders Co., Philadelphia, 1967.
47. Schaffer, A.J., Markowitz, M., and Finberg, L.: Diseases of the Newborn. W.B. Saunders Co., Philadelphia, 1966.
48. Norman, A.P.: Congenital Abnormalities in Infancy. Blackwell Scientific Publications, Oxford, 1963.
49. Potter, E.L.: Pathology of the Fetus and Infant. Year Book Medical Publishers Inc., Chicago, 1961.
50. Macgregor, A.R.: Pathology of Infancy and Childhood. E. & S. Livingstone Ltd., Edinburgh, 1960.
51. Mayer, D.M. and Swanker, W.A.: Anomalies of Infants and Children. McGraw-Hill Book Co., Inc., New York, 1958.
52. Wilson, J.G., and Warkany, J.: Teratology; Principles and Techniques. The University of Chicago Press, Chicago, 1965.
53. Barnes, A.C., Brewer, J.I., and Taylor, H.C.: Symposium on congenital defect. Amer. J. Obstet. Gynec. 90: 983–1250, 1964.
54. Park, W.W.: The Early Conceptus, Normal and Abnormal; Papers and Discussions Presented at a Symposium. D.C. Thomson & Co., Ltd., Dundee; E. & S. Livingstone Ltd., Edinburgh, 1965.
55. Holt, L.E., Ingalls, T.H., and Hellman, L.B.: Prematurity, Congenital Malformation and Birth Injury (Proceedings of a conference). Association for the Aid of Crippled Children, New York, 1953.
56. Warkany, J.: Congenital malformations; papers presented at a conference on teratology. Pediatrics, 19: 719–792, 1957.
57. Rivers, T. M., Warkany, J., Fraser, F. C., Wilson, J. G., Matson, D. D., and McIntosh, R.: Conference on congenital malformations. J. Chron. Dis. 10: 83–151, 1959.
58. Wolstenholme, G.E.W. and O'Connor, C.M.: Ciba Foundation Symposium on Congenital Malformations. J. & A. Churchill Ltd., London, 1960.

59. National Cancer Institute Monograph No. 2: Symposium on Normal and Abnormal Differentiation and Development. 1960.

60. The International Medical Congress: Congenital malformations; papers and discussions presented at the first international conference. J.B. Lippincott Co., Philadelphia, 1961.

61. The International Medical Congress: Congenital defects; papers and discussions presented at the first Inter-American conference. J.B. Lippincott Co., Philadelphia, 1963.

62. The International Medical Congress: Congenital malformations, papers and discussions presented at the second international conference. The International Medical Congress, Ltd., New York, 1964.

63. Giroud, A., et Tuchmann-Duplessis, H.: Malformations congénitales. Role des facteurs exogenes. Pathologie-Biologie 10: 119–151, 1962.

64. Fave, A.: Les embryopathies provoquées chez les mammiféres. Thérapie XIX: 43–164, 1964.

65. Löffler, W.: Teratogenesis; Symposium der Schweizerischen Akademie der Medizinischen Wissenschaften. Schwabe & Co., Verlag, Basel, 1964.

66.* Schwalbe, E.: Die Morphologie der Missbildungen des Menschen und der Tiere, I. Teil: Allgemeine Missbildungslehre (Teratologie), 1906; II. Teil: Die Doppelbildungen, 1907. Verlag von Gustav Fischer, Jena.

67. Büchner, F.: Handbuch der allgemeinen Pathologie. VI. Band, I. Teil: Entwicklung, Wachstum I. Springer-Verlag, Göttingen, 1955.

68. Dyban, A.P.: Grundriss der pathologischen Embryologie des Menschen. Veb Gustav Fischer Verlag, Jena, 1962.

69. Thalhammer, O.: Pränatale Erkrankungen des Menschen. Georg Thieme Verlag, Stuttgart, 1967.

70. Cohrs, P., Jaffé, R., und Meessen, H.: Pathologie der Laboratoriumstiere. Band I. und II. Springer-Verlag, Berlin, 1958.

71. Nishimura, H.: Chemistry and Prevention of Congenital Anomalies. Charles C. Thomas Publisher, Springfield, 1964.

72. Millen, J.W.: The Nutritional Basis of Reproduction. Charles C. Thomas Publisher, Springfield, 1962.

73. Kalter, H. and Warkany, J.: Experimental production of congenital malformations in mammals by metabolic procedure. Physiol. Rev. 39: 69–115, 1959.

74. Dagg, C.P.: Teratogenesis. In: Biology of the Laboratory Mouse, edited by E.L. Green. pp. 309–328. The Blackiston Division, McGraw-Hill, New York, 1966.

75. Palludan, B.: A-avitaminosis in Swine; a Study on the Importance of Vitamin A for Reproduction. Munksgaard, Copenhaggen, 1966.

76. Robson, J.M.: A Symposium on Embryopathic Activity of Drugs. J. & A. Churchill Ltd., London, 1965.

77. Baker, J.B.E.: The effects of drugs on the foetus. Pharmacol. Rev. 12: 37–90, 1960.

78. Sandberg, D.H.: Drugs in pregnancy; their effects on the foetus and newborn. Calif. Med. 94: 287–291, 1961.

79. Black, J.A.: Current therapeutics CLXXV. Effects on the foetus and newborn of drugs given during pregnancy. The practitioner 189: 99–106, 1962.

80. Karnofsky, D.A.: Drugs as teratogens in animals and man. Annual review of

pharmacology 5: 447–472, 1965.

81. Cahen, R.L.: Evaluation of the teratogenicity of drugs. Clin. Pharmacol. Therap. 5:481–514, 1964.

82. Koller, T., und Erb, H.: Medikamentöse Pathogenese fetaler Missbildungen. S. Karger, Basel, 1964.

83. Excerpta Medica Foundation: Proceedings of the European Society for the Study of Drug Toxicity, vol. 1: Effects of drugs on the foetus; vol.2: viewpoints on the study of drug toxicity. Excerpta Medica, Amsterdam, 1963.

84. WHO Scientific Group: Principles for the testing of drugs for teratogenicity (WHO technical report series No. 364). World Health Organization, Geneva, 1967.

85. Weingärtner, L., and Sommer, K.-H.: Arzneimittelwirkungen in der Schwangerschaft und der Säuglingsperiode. Wissenschaftliche Beiträge der Martin-Luther-Universität Halle-Wittenberg, Halle (Saale), 1966.

86. Töndury, G.: Embryopathien über die Wirkungsweise (Infektionsweg und Pathogenese) von Viren auf den menschlichen Keimling. In: Pathologie und Klinik in Einzeldarstellungen, herausgegeben von R. Hegglin, F. Leuthardt, R. Schoen, H. Schwiegk und H.U. Zollinger, Band XI. Springer-Verlag, Berlin, 1962.

87. Thalhammer, O.: Die Toxoplasmose bei Mensch und Tier. Verlag für medizinische Wissenschaften Wilhelm Maudrich, Wien, 1957.

88. Paul, J.: Frühgeburt und Toxoplasmose. Urban & Schwarzenberg, München, 1962.

89. Gross, R.E.: The Surgery of Infancy and Childhood. W.B. Saunders Co., Philadelphia, 1964.

90. Benson, C.D., Mustard, W.T., Ravitch, M.M., Snyder, W.H., and Welch, K.J.: Pediatric Surgery, vol. 1 & 2. Year Book Medical Publishers, Inc., Chicago, 1962.

91. Haring, O.M., and Lewis, F.J.: The etiology of congenital developmental anomalies. Collective review. Surgery, Gynecology and Obstetrics, International Abstracts of Surgery 113: 1–18, 1961.

92. Müller, C., und Stucki, D.: Richtlinien zur medizinischen Indikation der Schwangerschaftsunterbrechung. Springer-Verlag, Berlin, 1964.

93. Kennedy, W.P.: Epidemiologic aspects of the problem of congenital malformations. Birth Defects Original Article Series, vol. 3. No. 2, 1–18, 1967.

94. Stevenson, A.C., Johnston, H.A., Stewart, M.I.P., and Golding, D.R.: Congenital Malformations. World Health Organization, Geneva, 1966.

95. Tünte, W.: Vergleichende Untersuchungen über die Häufigkeit angeborener Menschlicher Missbildungen. Gustav Fischer Verlag, Stuttgart, 1965.

B. Teratology pertaining special organ-systems

96. Kalter, H.: Teratology of the Central Nervous System. University of Chicago Press, Chicago, 1968.

97. Mann, I.: Developmental Abnormalities of the Eye. J.B. Lippincott Co., Philadelphia, 1958.

98. Duke-Elder, S.: System of Ophthalmology, vol. III. Part 2: Congenital deformities. Henry Kimpton, London, 1964.

99. Pruzansky, S.: Congenital Anomalies of the Face and Associated Structures. Charles C. Thomas Publisher, Springfield, 1961.

100. Bremer, J.L.: Congenital Anomalies of the Viscera; Their Embryological Basis.

Harvard University Press, Cambridge, 1957.

101. Thoma, K.H., and Goldman, H.N.: Oral Pathology. C.V. Mosby, St. Louis, 1960.

102. Louw, J. H. : Congenital Abnormalities of the Rectum and Anus. In: Current problems in surgery; a series of monthly clinical monographs, edited by M.M. Ravitch, E.H. Ellison, O.C. Julian, A.P. Thal, and O.H. Wangensteen. Year Book Medical Publishers, Inc., Chicago, 1966.

103. Gould, S.E.: Pathology of the Heart. Charles C. Thomas Publisher, Springfield, 1960.

104. Taussig, H.B.: Congenital Malformation of the Heart. Commonwealth Fund, Cambridge, 1960.

105. Goerttler, K.: Normale und pathologische Entwicklung des menschlichen Herzens. In: Zwanglose Abhandlungen aus dem Gebiet der normalen und pathologischen Anatomie, herausgegeben von W. Bargmann und W. Doerr, Heft 3. Georg Thieme Verlag, Stuttgart, 1958.

106. Stewart, J. R., Kincard, O.W., and Edwards, J. E.: An Atlas of Vascular Rings and Related Malformations of the Aortic Arch System. Charles C. Thomas Publisher, Springfield, 1964.

107. Young, W.C.: Sex and Internal Secretion, vol. 1 & 2. Williams & Wilkins, Baltimore, 1961.

108. Grüneberg, H.: The Pathology of Development; A Study of Inherited Skeletal Disorders in Animals. Blackwell Scientific Publications, Oxford, 1963.

109. LeNoir, J.L., III.: Congenital Idiopathic Talipes. Charles C. Thomas Publisher, Springfield, 1966.

110. Allan, J.D., and Holt, K.S.: Biochemical Approaches to Mental Handicap in Children. E. & S. Livingstone Ltd., Edinburgh, 1965.

111.* Schwalbe, E.: Die Morphologie der Missbildungen des Menschen und der Tiere, III. Teil: Die Einzelmissbildungen. Verlag von Gustav Fischer, Jena, 1909.

112. Lubarsh, O., Henke, F., Rössle, R., und Uehlinger, E.: Handbuch der speziellen pathologischen Anatomie und Histologie. In 13 Bänden. Springer-Verlag, Berlin, 1925–1961.

C. Inborn errors of metabolism

113. Hsia, D.Y.: Inborn Errors of Metabolism. The Year Book Publishers, Chicago, 1959.

114. Levine, R., and Luft, R.: Advances in Metabolic Disorders, vol. 1. 1964; vol. 2. 1965. Academic Press Inc., New York.

115. Holt, K.S., and Raine, D.N.: Basic Concepts of Inborn Errors and Defects of Steroid Biosynthesis. E. & S. Livingstone Ltd., Edinburgh, 1966.

116. Holt, K.S., and Milner, J.: Neurometabolic Disorders in Childhood. E. & S. Livingstone Ltd., Edinburgh, 1964.

D. Cytogenetic abnormalities

117. Court Brown, W.M., Buckton, K.E., Jacobs, P.A., Tough, I.M., Kuenssberg, E.V., and Knox, J.D.E.: Chromosome studies on Adults. Eugenics Laboratory Memoirs, XLII. Cambridge University Press, London, 1966.

118. Eggen, R.R.: Chromosome Diagnostics in Clinical Medicine. Charles C. Thomas Publisher, Springfield, 1965.

119. Valentine, G.H.: Chromosome Disorders; an Introduction for Clinicians. J.B. Lippincott Co., Philadelphia, 1966.
120. Ohno, S.: Sex Chromosomes and Sex-linked Genes. Springer-Verlag, New York, 1967.
121. Moore, K.L.: The Sex Chromatin. W.B. Saunders Co., Philadelphia, 1966.
122. Yunis, J.J.: Human Chromosome Methodology. Academic Press Inc., New York, 1965.

E. Miscellaneous

123.* Gates, R.: Humangenetics. 2 vols. Macmillan, New York, 1946.
124. Becker, P.E.: Humangenetik. Bd. I-V. Georg Thieme Verlag, Stuttgart, 1964.
125. Steinberg, A.G., and Bearn, A.G.: Progress in Medical Genetics, vol. 1. 1961; vol. 2. 1962; vol. 3. 1964; vol. 4. 1965. Grune & Stratton, New York.
126. Reed, S.C.: Counseling in Medical Genetics. W.B. Saunders Co., Philadelphia, 1963.
127. Gedda, L.: Twins in History and Science. Charles C. Thomas Publisher, Springfield, 1961.
128. Von Verschuer, O.F.: Wirksame Faktoren im Leben des Menschen. Franz Steiner Verlag GMBH, Wiesbaden., 1954.
129. Hadorn, E.: Developmental Genetics and Lethal Factors. Methuen & Co., Ltd., London; John Wiley & Sons, Inc., New York, 1961.
130. Grüneberg, H.: The Genetics of the Mouse. Martinus Nijhoff, the Hague, 1952.
131. Benirschke, K., and Driscoll, S.G.: Pathology of the Human Placenta. (Reprint from Handbuch der speziellen pathologischen Anatomie und Histologie, Vol. VII/5). Springer-Verlag, Berlin, 1967.
132. Chipman, S.S., Lilienfeld, A.M., Greenberg, B.G., and Donnelly, J.F.: Research Methodology and Needs in Perinatal Studies. Charles C. Thomas Publisher, Springfield, 1966.

Addendum: some periodicals on congenital malformations

1. Excerpta Medica, Developmental Biology and Teratology, Section 21. Excerpta Medica, Amsterdam.
2. Birth defects–Abstracts of Selected Articles. The National Foundation, New York.
3. Teratology–The official organ of the Teratology Society. The Wistar Institute of Biology and Anatomy, Philadelphia.
4. The Cleft Palate Journal. The American Cleft Palate Association, Baltimore.
5. Birth Defects–Reprint Series. The National Foundation, New York.
6. Proceedings of the Congenital Anomalies Research Association of Japan (Abstracts of presentations at the Annual Meeting). Congenital Anomalies Research Association of Japan, Kyoto.

INDEX